FUSION METHODS IN CHEMICAL MICROSCOPY

FUSION METHODS
IN CHEMICAL MICROSCOPY

Walter C. McCrone, Jr.
Chicago, Illinois

INTERSCIENCE PUBLISHERS, INC., NEW YORK
INTERSCIENCE PUBLISHERS LTD. LONDON

To OTTO LEHMANN
who, in 1891, first suggested
the use of fusion methods

INTERSCIENCE PUBLISHERS, INC.
250 Fifth Avenue, New York 1, N. Y.
For Great Britain and Northern Ireland:
INTERSCIENCE PUBLISHERS LTD.
88/90 Chancery Lane, London W. C. 2

PRINTED IN THE UNITED STATES OF AMERICA BY
MACK PRINTING COMPANY, EASTON, PENNSYLVANIA

PREFACE

Microanalytical methods involving the combination of microscope and temperature control have been termed fusion methods since most of the techniques involve the operation of melting in some way. The methods apply to any fusible compounds, organic or inorganic, although the usual test conditions lie between $-100°$ and $+350°C$. Temperatures between $-200°$ and $+2500°C$ are, however, within practical limits.

This book has an introduction which, in a sense, is an annotated table of contents; the scope and limitations of fusion methods are described in detail in this section. Part II describes most of the commercially available equipment, such as hot stages, cold stages, and hot bars. Part III covers the general techniques for calibration and use of hot and cold stages and hot bars, for characterization and identification of organic compounds, estimation of purity, methods of purification, analysis of mixtures, determination of composition diagrams, and study of polymorphism.

Part IV concludes the text with some research applications of fusion methods, such as the study of pour-point depressants, thermal stability of decomposable compounds, kinetics of crystal growth, recrystallization, and grain growth.

Part V contains tables for the identification of organic compounds based on the measurement of melting points and refractive indices of the melt.

The methods should be very useful to the organic chemist both for analysis and in research. The physical chemist should be interested in the methods for studying composition diagrams, polymorphism, and kinetics of crystal growth. The possibility of using these techniques as an aid in teaching metallography and in understanding many metals systems should not be overlooked by the metallurgist.

The author is heavily indebted to colleagues on both sides of the Atlantic in drawing on published material to fill in a complete study of fusion methods. The three Koflers: Ludwig, Adelheid, and Walter, along with Marie Brandstätter, are noted for their tremendous volume of work in this field and for the ingenuity of their methods. Many chemists now, or in the past, at the Armour Research Founda-

tion deserve a great deal of credit for the contributions from that
Laboratory: O. W. Adams, Mrs. Dorothy Baranski, P. T. Cheng,
V. Gilpin, Mrs. Helen Grant, D. G. Grabar, K. Hattori, R. Hinch,
R. Hites, J. Krc, Jr., D. E. Laskowski, Mrs. Sylvia O'Bradovic, and
Mrs. Annette Underwood. Others who deserve special note are:
H. K. Alber, J. H. Andreen, C. J. Arceneaux, W. M. D. Bryant, N.
Goetz-Luthy, W. J. Hacker, E. E. Jelley, C. W. Mason, J. Mitchell,
Jr., S. M. Tsang, and P. W. West.

Much of the credit for this effort is due to Prof. John R. Johnson
of Cornell University who encouraged the author to stray from the
classical confines of organic chemical research to help develop fusion
methods as a tool of general use to all organic chemists. The author
is also grateful to A. T. Blomquist of Cornell University and R. A.
Connor of Rohm and Haas who, at that time with NDRC, encouraged
the author to develop and apply fusion methods to the study of ordnance problems. Others in the ordnance departments of the Army
and Navy, especially Dr. L. R. Littleton, have helped considerably
in the development of these methods by encouraging (financially)
their application to the study of explosives systems.

The generous assistance of Dr. Edwin E. Jelley of the Eastman
Kodak Co. in the planning and preparation of the color plates is
gratefully acknowledged.

Mrs. Loretta Nacker did much of the work in preparing the tables
for Part V. The drafting ability of Alfred Spenney was of invaluable
aid in preparing many of the figures. The final manuscript and the
earlier drafts were typed by Miss Ruth Hutchinson. Finally, what is
hoped will be a minimum of errors is due to the careful proofreading
of several of the author's colleagues, especially O. W. Adams, who
found this task to be yet another "requirement for the advanced
degree."

W. C. McCrone, Jr.

Chicago, Illinois
September, 1956

CONTENTS

CHAPTER I

INTRODUCTION

A. GENERAL METHODS OF MICROSCOPICAL ANALYSIS

The analytical uses of the microscope have been pretty much restricted in the past to the study of metals (metallography) and of minerals (petrography), with some application to inorganic compounds. The application to organic compounds has, until recently, been limited.

The microscope was first applied to analysis in 1833 by Raspail,[1] who suggested observation of crystal habit as a means of identifying chemical compounds. His ideas were developed by Wormley[2] and others (Behrens, Kley, Emich, and Chamot) to form a definite method of analysis. This method of analysis involves the addition of a definite quantity of the reagent to a test drop, and the comparison of the resulting precipitate with a description (or better, a drawing or photograph) of the precipitate obtained under identical conditions with known compounds. This procedure was applied to inorganic anions and cations, and to selected small groups of organic compounds such as the alkaloids,[3] and the common carboxylic acids.[4] It has not, as yet, received wide use in organic chemistry.

As the use of optical crystallography became more widespread, a second type of analysis came into use. This involves the preparation of tables of the optical crystallographic properties of each compound so that an analyst can check the properties of his unknown against the tabulated properties to establish identity. Tables of this type have been prepared for all the minerals, most of the common inorganic compounds,[5] and certain small groups of organic compounds (e.g.,

---

[1] F. V. Raspail, *Nouveau Système de Chimie Organique Fondé sur des Méthodes Nouvelles d'Observation,* Paris, 1833.

[2] T. G. Wormley, *Microchemistry of Poisons,* William Wood, New York, **1869.**

[3] L. Rosenthaler, *Mikrochemie* **1,** 90 (1923).

[4] E. M. Chamot, unpublished work.

[5] A. N. Winchell, *Microscopic Character of Artificial Minerals,* John **Wiley and** Sons, New York, 1931.

1

sugars,[6] amino acids,[7] and many aromatic nitrogen compounds[8]). Winchell[9] has also tabulated crystallographic data for organic compounds. This method of analysis is limited by the length of time required for complete studies and the relatively small number of qualified optical crystallographers.

Basis for a third general method of analysis was laid by Lehmann in 1891,[10] when he pointed out that crystallization of an organic compound from its own melt is very characteristic. He listed a number of properties that could be determined on crystals from the melt, and discussed the value of this technique in studying the phase diagrams of systems of one and two components. Kofler[11] has refined these methods for the study of binary systems and also for the characterization and identification of organic compounds. It is this third general method which has been referred to as fusion methods that is the subject of this book.

B. FUSION METHODS

1. Scope

The term "fusion methods" will be used to include the methods and procedures useful in research and analysis, which involve heating a compound or mixture of compounds on a microscope slide. It includes all observations made during heating of the preparation (decrepitation, sublimation, decomposition, melting, etc.) on the melt itself (refractive index, boiling point, critical solution temperature, etc.), solidification of the melt (crystal angles, birefringence, rate of growth, etc.), and cooling (polymorphic transformations, orthoscopic and conoscopic observations, composition diagrams, etc.). Data obtained from observations on binary, or even ternary, systems and accessory operations of analysis, purification, etc., are also included.

[6] J. Wherry, *J. Am. Chem. Soc.* **40,** 1852 (1918).

[7] G. L. Keenan, *J. Biol Chem.* **62,** 163 (1924).

[8] W. M. D Bryant, *J. Am. Chem. Soc.* **65,** 130 (1943).

[9] A. N. Winchell, *Optical Properties of Organic Compounds*, Academic Press, Inc., New York, 1954.

[10] O. Lehmann, *Die Krystallanalyse*, Wilhelm Engelmann, Leipzig, 1891.

[11] L. Kofler and A. Kofler, *Thermo-Mikro-Methoden zur Kennzeichnung Organisher Stoffe and Stoffgemisch*, Wagner, Innsbruck, 1954.

2. Applications

The identification of fusible compounds by fusion methods is very rapid, consumes only small quantities of material, and requires relatively little specialized training or equipment. Whereas, a complete optical crystallographic description of a given compound may require from a few hours to several days, complete characterization of a new compound by fusion methods seldom requires more than an hour. Furthermore, an unknown compound in a limited category (e.g., polynitro compounds) usually can be identified in less than five minutes, if that compound has once been studied by fusion methods. There are so many characteristic properties that can be observed on crystals from the melt that one or two easily recognized and typical properties can be remembered for each compound, hence a complete check of all properties is not usually necessary (Section III,B).

The purity of a fusible compound is, in many cases, very quickly determined by fusion methods since impurities usually are visible as high-melting material, as liquid eutectic, or as early melting material during a hot stage melting point determination (Section III,C). A mixed fusion (Section III,B,5,b) gives a rapid and dependable means of determining whether two given samples are the same compound. The mixed fusion can also be used for rapid qualitative determination of composition diagrams of fusible compounds. Complete binary or ternary composition diagrams can be determined usually in a few hours time (Section III,G). In contrast with classical physical chemical techniques, fusion methods permit determination of composition diagrams between unstable polymorphic forms. Binary mixtures may be analyzed quantitatively by several techniques, one of the most general of which is the determination of the refractive index of the melt using standard glass powders of known refractive indices (Section III,B,2,a). Compounds may be identified using hot bar or hot stage techniques based on tabulated melting point and refractive index data (Chapter V). Finally, fusion methods are very useful in supplementary ways for preparation of good crystals for x-ray diffraction or optical crystallography, for separation of mixtures (Section III, D), studies of polymorphism (Section III,F), studies of grain growth and recrystallization (Section IV,D), etc.

Many of these techniques have been in use for a number of years by a number of microscopists (L. Kofler, A. Kofler, M. Brandstätter, C. W. Mason, W. M. D. Bryant, E. E. Jelley, N. Goetz-Luthy, C. J.

Arceneaux, V. Gilpin, D. E. Laskowski, W. C. McCrone, etc.), and their publications form the backbone of this book.

The use of the hot stage microscope and accessory equipment has received a tremendous impetus during the last dozen years largely through the efforts of the Koflers[11] in Austria. Their development of techniques and the application of these techniques to microanalysis is an outstanding contribution, not only to microchemistry but also to more general research methods in organic and physical chemistry.

The study of fusible compounds, usually organic, as a function of temperature under the microscope is called "Thermo-Mikro-Methoden" in the German literature to designate the fields of interest of the Koflers and their co-workers, whereas the term "fusion methods" has been used in the United States to designate the same fields of interest.

Fusion methods were developed in the United States later than the "Thermo-Mikro-Methoden" although apparently independently. Since these two schools of thought developed along different paths with different results, it is interesting to make a systematic comparison. Both groups were familiar almost from the start with the publications of Otto Lehmann, who in 1891[10] described many of these techniques including the mixed fusion (Kontaktmethode) for the qualitative determination of the phase diagram (as a basis for the determination of identity or lack of identity of two compounds).

Although Lehmann's efforts in this field were almost completely ignored for nearly fifty years, they have now been extended to cover many applications in research and analysis. A partial list of these applications follows.

1.0   Determination of purity.
2.0   Analysis of mixtures.
3.0   Characterization and identification of fusible compounds and mixtures.
4.0   Determination of composition diagrams.
    4.1   Two-component systems.
    4.2   Three-component systems.
5.0   Investigations of polymorphism.
6.0   Measurement of physical properties.
    6.1   Molecular weight.
    6.2   Rates of crystal growth.
    6.3   Crystal morphology.
    6.4   Crystal optics.
7.0   Study of boundary migration.
8.0   Study of kinetics of crystal growth.

9.0 Correlation of physical behavior with crystal properties (e.g., thermal stability of decomposable compounds with lowering of melting point, change in refractive index of the melt).

The difference in interests of the two schools of thought is shown readily by listing the items from the above classification which represent the interests of the two groups. The Kofler school has concentrated on 1.0, 2.0, 3.0, 4.0, 5.0, and 6.1, while the microscopists interested in fusion methods in the United States have spent most of their time and effort on 3.0, 4.0, 6.0, 7.0, 8.0, and 9.0. Each group has, however, developed methods and techniques under each of the classifications listed.

Another fundamental difference between the two groups has resulted from the dependence of the Kofler group on the highly precise Kofler hot stage (Section II,B,2). Until relatively recently this instrument was not available commercially in the United States and it was necessary to develop simple techniques applicable with slight technical background and less refined equipment. As a net result the Kofler group, in general, make their observations during heating in the hot stage, and the United States group during spontaneous cooling of the preparation.

Before considering further differences in the two approaches, the following list of properties, determinable during heating and cooling of a microscope preparation, shows the wide range of useful properties that may be obtained by the application of fusion methods (Section III,B).

1.0 During heating.
    1.1 Sublimation.
        1.11 Degree of sublimation.
        1.12 Nature of sublimate.
            1.121 Liquid globules.
            1.122 Liquid plus crystals.
            1.123 Poorly formed crystals.
            1.124 Well-formed crystals of stable form.
                1.1241 Profile angles.
                1.1242 Forms, habit, system.
                    1.12421 Isotropic or anisotropic.
                    1.12422 Uniaxial or biaxial.
                1.1243 Extinction.
                1.1244 Sign of elongation.
                1.1245 Principal refractive index or indices.
                1.1246 Conoscopic observations.

1.12461   Optic axial plane.
1.12462   Optic axial angle.
1.12463   Dispersion.
1.12464   Sign of double refraction.
1.1247   Pleochroism.
1.125   Well-formed crystals of unstable form.
1.1251–1.1257   Same as 1.1241–1.1247.
1.2   Polymorphic transformation.
1.21   Temperature at first discernible transformation.
1.22   Monotropic transformation.
1.23   Enantiotropic transformation.
1.231   Transition temperature.
1.3   Loss of water (or solvent) of crystallization.
1.31   Temperature at first discernible loss.
1.4   Decomposition.
1.41   Temperature at first discernible decomposition.
1.42   Color of decomposition products.
2.0   During melting.
2.1   Melting point.
2.2   Refractive index of the melt.
2.3   Temperature coefficient of refractive index of the melt.
2.4   Dispersion of refractive index of the melt.
3.0   During cooling.
3.1   Supercooling of melt.
3.11   Slight supercooling.
3.12   Readily supercools.
3.121   Mobility of supercooled melt at room temperature.
3.2   Rate of growth of crystals as a function of temperature.
3.3   Form of crystal front.
3.31   Poorly formed crystals.
3.311   Same as 1.1242–1.1247.
3.32   Well-formed crystals.
3.321   Same as 1.1241–1.1247.
3.4   Polymorphic transformation.
3.41   Same as 1.21–1.231.
3.5   Gas bubbles.
3.6   Shrinkage cracks.
3.7   Mechanical twinning.
3.8   Anomalous polarization colors.
3.9   Characterization of unstable polymorphs.
3.91   Same as 1.1241–1.1247, 3.2, 3.3, 3.5–3.8.
4.0   Meltback (leaving some crystalline material unmelted as seed).
4.1   Same as 1.0, 2.0, and 3.0, omitting 1.1, 2.2, 2.3, and 3.1.
5.0   After cooling to room temperature.

On cursory examination, this outline seems to include an abundance of quantitative physical properties which would serve to uniquely characterize any possible compound. Unfortunately, however, too many compounds show only a few or none of these necessary properties. Some, like hexachloroethane, sublime completely before melting; others, like sucrose, decompose completely before or during melting, or crystallize to give poorly formed minute crystals without crystallographic character. Another difficulty is that while one group of compounds may grow well from the melt to give a number of quantitative characteristics, a second group may give an equal number of numerical characteristics but of a different type (e.g., refractive index of the melt, temperature coefficient, and dispersion of the refractive index, as compared with profile angles, extinction angles, and optical axial angles). Obviously, the properties to be chosen for classification purposes must be measurable on all compounds to be included.

The requirements for the ideal physical property to characterize all compounds studied might be listed as follows. Each property should:

1. Be measurable on all compounds under study.
2. Be easily and quickly determined without extraordinary background and training.
3. Be measured with high accuracy and precision and be expressed numerically.
4. Have a wide variation from compound to compound.
5. Be tabulated readily so that an unknown can be identified quickly.

Consideration of the properties determined by fusion methods as listed above shows that few, if any, properties satisfy all these criteria. For example, anomalous polarization colors, dispersion of refractive index, and pleochroism defy ready tabulation; profile angles do not vary greatly from compound to compound; the presence of gas bubbles, shrinkage cracks, etc., cannot be expressed numerically; conoscopic observations cannot be made with rudimentary background and equipment; and none of them can be determined on all fusible compounds.

The Koflers have been especially ingenious in the manner in which they have surmounted these difficulties. A few listings from their identification tables[11] illustrate their approach to this problem (Table I).

In the complete tables, which include about 1200 compounds, the primary tabulating characteristic is the melting point, or the best possible substitute for the melting point for those compounds which decompose or sublime before melting. Then, since most decomposable compounds are stable somewhat below the melting point, the Koflers have introduced the eutectic melting point with two standard compounds. The eutectic melting point is as easy to measure as the melting point of the pure compound and of essentially the same value analytically.

This gives three numerical constants characteristic of each compound; yet the Koflers, in order to make identification even more certain, have developed a very clever technique for measuring the refractive index of the melt (Section III,B,2,a). This involves the use of a set of glass powder standards covering the range from 1.43 to 1.69 in increments of about 0.01. The refractive index measurement is made by determining the temperature at which the glass powder

TABLE I

Excerpt from Kofler's Tables for the Identification of Organic Compounds

Melting point, °C	Substance	Eutectic temp. with Azobenzene	Benzil	Glass powder	Temp., °C	Miscellaneous characteristics
95	Carbon tetrabromide	54	40	1.5898	111–113	Sublimes strongly above 30°C to give plates and rosettes having scalloped edges, above 46°C gives isotropic honeycomb.
95	3-Methyl indole (Skatole)	43	44	1.5700 1.5611	100 121	Odor, sublimes above 50°C. Gives thin rounded plates.
95	4,6-Dichlororesorcinol	50	46	1.5700	95–97	Usually colored brown, above 55°C sublimes giving needles; long needles from the melt.
96	Methyl p-nitrobenzoate	51	63	1.5101 1.5000	111–112 130	Yellow, sublimes above 70°C to give rhombs.

standard has the same index as the melt. This temperature is, of course, quite unique although the compound must be very pure before the determination is made. The Koflers have taken care of this requirement by developing two ingenious methods for the purification of fusible compounds. One, the absorption method, involves heating of a few milligrams of mixture between two half-slides and on a $^1/_2$ inch square of filter paper at successively higher temperatures on a hot bar so that the eutectic melt soaks into the filter paper leaving the pure solid on one slide (Section III,D,2). The second procedure is called by the Koflers "adsorption sublimation" since the mixture is sublimed slowly through a chromatographic column (Section III,D,4).

Occasionally when the compound decomposes it is possible to, at least, bracket the refractive index between two of the glass powder standards (e.g., the melt of phenylthiourea has a refractive index at the melting point between 1.6231 and 1.6353), or, in some cases, to determine the refractive index in the usual manner not on the pure compound but on an accurately weighed 1:1 mixture of that compound and a standard.

Finally, the use of fusion methods for the study of polymorphism (Section III,F) and of two- and three-component phase diagrams

(Section III,G) have been developed to a high degree by the Koflers.[11] They are responsible for showing that most organic compounds possess several polymorphic forms and that the phase diagrams for organic systems are fully as complex as those obtained for metals. Their discovery of quasi-eutectic syncrystallization (Section III,G,5) in which the supercooled melt crystallizes, apparently as eutectic, over a wide range of binary composition was made as a result of microscopic study of crystallization from the melt. The stabilization of lattices, unstable for either pure compound, by forming suitable solid solutions is a curious and important observation difficult, if not impossible, by classical macro methods (Section III,G,1).

To return to fusion methods as used by workers in the United States many of these same problems have been solved, in general, in a similar fashion. There are, as noted above, however, important differences.

The determination of purity (Section III,C) is usually carried out in the United States by the semiquantitative observation of the crystallization process on cooling of the melt. The amount of eutectic melt remaining after crystallization is an indication of the amount of impurity. The absence of eutectic melt is possible only with pure compounds, when the impurity is unmelted and undissolved, when the impurity shows solid-solid solubility, or in the trivial case when the two melts are completely immiscible. Observation of the melt itself before crystallization will detect the latter as well as the presence of higher melting undissolved solid components. The use of melting point depression in known two-component systems (Section III,E,6), the change of optical properties in isomorphous mixtures (Section III,E,3), the refractive index of the melt (Section III,E,7), the use of the refractive index in the differentiation of impurity from the major component (Section III,E,2), the change of crystal habit (Section III,E,4), areal analysis (Section III,E,1), and changes in the rate of crystal growth (Section III,E,5) have all been used to determine purity and most of them can be made quantitative and become useful, then, as methods for the quantitative analysis of mixtures.

The measurement of optical properties on isomorphous crystals as a quantitative method has been applied only to binary mixtures. The method based on rate of crystal growth and on melting point depression is suitable for poly-component mixtures if the same impurities, no matter how many or even whether they are known, are always present in about the same ratio to each other. A given impurity may increase or decrease the rate of growth of the major component and will have a greater or lesser effect on the melting point, hence the method has to be standardized carefully in terms of the nature of the impurity compounds.

The characterization and identification of fusible compounds and their mixtures (Section III,B) has developed quite differently on the two sides of the Atlantic. Most of the value of this means of identification in the United States has resulted in the study of relatively small groups of compounds: substituted aminoquinolines,[12] sterols,[13] waxes,[14] high explosives,[14] hexachlorobenzenes,[15] etc. In these cases, the analyst has worked with each of the compounds almost daily so that the fusion characteristics of each compound become familiar at a glance. Identification is made usually on the basis of some outstanding morphological or optical characteristic, such as anomalous polarization colors, unique shrinkage cracks or gas bubbles, odd crystal habit, and transformation mechanism. Obviously, such characteristics cannot be recorded in tabular fashion and only with difficulty in descriptive terms. The analyst must remember each characteristic perhaps with the help of photomicrographs or a tabulated suggestion as to the proper key property of each. In spite of these limitations there seems to be no difficulty of applying this method to the analysis of groups of compounds up to fifty or more in number. In one research program on high explosives the analyst had no difficulty remembering the key properties of a group of nearly fifty high explosives, boosters, and mixtures thereof. As a result, any one of that group could be recognized unequivocally in one to two minutes including sample preparation. Actual observation time through the microscope probably averaged under ten seconds for conclusive identification and often a glance alone sufficed.

This system has the serious limitation that only those analysts trained in the recognition of each compound can make the analysis, although a second man may learn the distinctive characteristics quickly. Also, the analyst must maintain his ability by frequent examination of compounds in the system; otherwise he may forget the

[12] N. Goetz-Luthy, *J. Chem. Education* **26,** 159 (1949).

[13] V. Gilpin, *Anal. Chem.* **23,** 365 (1951).

[14] W. C. McCrone, J. H. Andreen, and S. M. Tsang, "Microscopic Examination of High Explosives and Boosters," Final Report to Division 8 NDRC of OSRD, August 1, 1944; classification cancelled by order Secretary of the Army August 3, 1950.

[15] C. J. Arceneaux, *Anal. Chem.* **23,** 906 (1951).

key properties.   In spite of these limitations, however, the method has obvious application to research and analysis.   The problem of general analysis of a number of compounds by fusion properties assembled into tables analogous to the Kofler tables also has been considered. Rather than melting points and refractive index of the melt, however, crystallographic properties are utilized as identifying characteristics.

The use of crystallographic properties has the advantage that present tabulations[6–9,14,16] of data can be used directly, but it has the serious disadvantage over the use of descriptive or other fusion properties (Section III,B,7,a) that the analyst must have a more extensive background in crystallography.   It is possible, however, to determine both optical and morphological properties by fusion methods (Section III,B,4 and 5) with another advantage that the unknown usually need not be purified before analysis.   The general method involves successive steps as outlined above in the classification of properties determinable by fusion methods.   The method is suitable for compounds which decompose if the compound is recrystallized on the microscope slide from thymol, nitrobenzene, benzyl alcohol, aroclor, or a similar high-boiling liquid having a high surface tension (Section III,B,6).   This technique is, by the way, an excellent means of obtaining otherwise unobtainable unstable high-temperature polymorphs.   It is for this reason that in the identification scheme the original crystals of the unknown are not usually melted completely so that they remain as seeds during cooling.

A paper[17] by Laskowski characterizes aromatic compounds by tabulating the melting points of all solid phases formed during mixed fusion with 2,4,7-trinitrofluorenone (Section III,B,7,c).   Since each system includes at least one eutectic, an addition compound, a second eutectic or a transition temperature (peritectic reaction), and the compound itself, there are at least three easily determined melting points to use for identification purposes.   This scheme is unique in that the formation of the addition compound characterizes the unknown as one of the group of aromatic compounds that react with 2,4,7-trinitrofluorenone, and the four melting points identify the unknown specifically.   Eventually it is hoped that a group of reagents, including 2,4,7-trinitrofluorenone, will be used to classify and identify organic compounds as part of a general scheme of microscopic organic qualitative analysis.

[16] "Crystallographic Data," *Anal. Chem.*, monthly since March, 1948.

[17] D. E. Laskowski, D. G. Grabar, and W. C. McCrone, *Anal. Chem.* **25,** 1400 (1953).

The microscopists in the United States have little to add to the excellent techniques developed by the Koflers for the determination of composition diagrams (Section III,G). It seems probable, however, that the qualitative technique for determining composition diagrams is used more often in the United States as a means of proving lack of identity or identity of a given pair of compounds. By this test two compounds can be fused and allowed to crystallize in contact across a narrow zone of mixing so that the entire composition diagram is shown in the composition gradient. Lack of any discontinuity during growth (including growth rate) across this gradient indicates identity of the two components. A discontinuity in the rate of growth indicates a difference in purity (1 discontinuity), or solid solution formation (2 discontinuities).

The use of rate of crystal growth in determining the amount of p,p'-DDT in technical DDT[18] (Section III,E,5) has created an interest in learning more about the mechanism of crystal growth by fusion methods (Section IV,A). The results have been published in part[19] although the work is continuing. This work has shown that the rate of crystal growth of a given compound in mixtures is directly related to the viscosity of the mixture. It is hoped also that additional work on the kinetics of crystal growth may result in the calculation of heats of fusion from crystal growth rate data.

Recrystallization on annealing[20] (Section IV,D) is a phenomenon occurring with a few organic compounds which show anisotropy of elasticity permitting them, in a sense, to develop unidirectional stress. As a result, crystals of such compounds show unidirectional growth into and through each other, usually on reheating. This is strictly an orientation effect such that one particular face grows into a different face of another identical crystal in contact with it. This is a most interesting effect which can be observed and studied directly by fusion methods.

The use of fusion methods to measure other physical properties of fusible materials has been studied by microscopists in the United States. For example, the decomposition of organic compounds on heating can be followed quantitatively and the kinetics of decomposition determined by fusion techniques (Section IV,B). Decomposition

[18] W. C. McCrone, A. Smedal, and V. Gilpin, *Anal. Chem.* **18**, 578 (1946).

[19] V. Gilpin, W. C. McCrone, A. Smedal, and H. Grant, *J. Am. Chem. Soc.* **70**, 208 (1948).

[20] W. C. McCrone, *Discussions Faraday Soc.* No. **5**, 158 (1949).

TABLE II

Melting Points of Inorganic Compounds[a]

Melting point, °C	No. of compounds	Per cent
0–100	94	17
100–200	59	11
200–300	60	11
300–400	40	7
400–500	33	6
500–600	23	4
600–700	26	5
700–800	19	4
800–900	33	6
900–1000	21	4
>1000	136	25
Total	544	100

[a] Salts of Ag, Al, As, Ba, Be, Bi, Cd, Co, Cr, Cu, Fe, Hg, K, Li, Mg, Mn, Mo, Na, Nb, NH$_4$, Ni, Pb, Re, Si, Sn, Sr, Ta, Te, Ti, Tl, U, V, and Zn as found in Lange's *Handbook of Chemistry*.

will result in a lowering of the equilibrium melting point and in a change of refractive index of the melt. Either property can be used, depending on the temperature at which the study is to be made and the melting point of the compound under study. The density of cast high explosives is related to the manner in which they crystallize from the melt since gases dissolved in the melt, cavitation and shrinkage cracks contribute to lowering of the density. Microscopic fusion methods are, therefore, a logical means of studying this problem.

Finally, fusion methods have been used at high temperatures and in the study of inorganic systems.[21−24] This is done by the direct application of fusion methods at high temperatures by means of special hot stages and furnaces and with auxiliary lens systems to prevent damage to the microscope optics (Section II,B). It is also done indirectly by fusing low-melting organic reagents, such as 8-hydroxyquinoline, with inorganic salts to give precipitates characteristic of the various inorganic ions.[23]

Table II shows the number of inorganic compounds melting in the various temperature ranges. Nearly one-half melt in the range covered by the usual hot stages and three-quarters can be handled by commercially available hot stages.

[21] H. N. Bauman, Jr., *Am. Ceramic Soc. Bull.* **277**, 267 (1948).
[22] D. G. Grabar and W. C. McCrone, *J. Chem. Education* **27**, 649 (1950).
[23] P. W. West and L. Granatelli, *Anal. Chem.* **24**, 870 (1952).
[24] R. E. Cech, *Rev. Sci. Instr.* **21**, 747 (1950).

CHAPTER II

ACCESSORIES FOR MICROSCOPIC FUSION METHODS

A. INTRODUCTION

The use of fusion methods requires the observation of hot objects on the microscope stage, hence it is necessary to observe certain precautions in order to avoid damage to the microscope. Fortunately, low magnifications (20–100×) are not only sufficient but most useful. Seldom are magnifications higher than 100× required. An objective

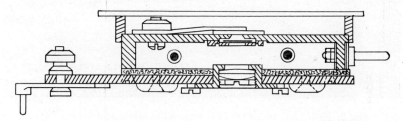

Fig. 1. Cross section through the Kofler 30° to 340°C hot stage.

in the range of 32–48-mm. focal length (3–5×) is, therefore, usually used with either a 10× or 20× eyepiece. During melting point determinations or, in general, when slightly better definition is required a 10× objective may be used, however, it should have as long a working distance as possible. It should also be reserved for this use. Whenever possible, except during direct observation, the objective should be racked up to a position as high as possible above the object. For this same reason the microscope condenser should be removed, or racked as far below the stage as possible. The Kofler hot stage (Figures 1 and 2) has a built-in condensing lens system to eliminate the need for the regular substage condenser.

When these precautions are observed it is possible to examine microscopic preparations heated to 350°C, with no damage to the micro-

15

scope, even those with hard rubber stages.   If insulating supports are used to support the slide, far hotter slides can be examined as they cool; for example, quartz slides heated to 1000°C.   No hot glass slide should be placed directly on the stage of the microscope, not so much because of possible damage to the microscope but because the slide is sure to break.   Such slides can be supported above the stage with the fingers for preliminary observation until they cool sufficiently to be placed on the stage.

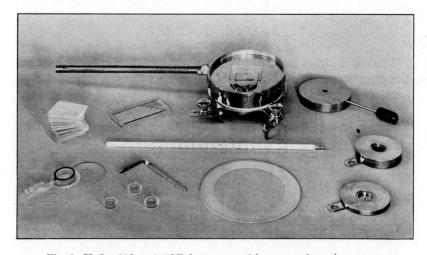

Fig. 2. Kofler 30° to 340°C hot stage with accessories; thermometer, heat baffle, vacuum sublimation cell, glass cover plate, cooling block, and sublimation blocks.   (Courtesy of Arthur H. Thomas Co., Inc.)

Conoscopic observations should never be made until the preparation has cooled to within a few degrees of room temperature in order to avoid inducing strain in the high-power objectives.   Any lens subjected to repeated heating and cooling soon develops strains which are visible between crossed polars, and the birefringence thus induced is superimposed on the field of view.

Almost any microscope stand can be used with most hot stages and cold stages, although a stage of cast iron rather than hard rubber is desirable.   A medical or biological stand may be used since a rotating stage is seldom required.   Crossed polars are often useful but since these can be adapted quickly to any stand, their absence initially is not a handicap.

Since the best scopes for hot stage use are, in general, the most rudimentary models, the prices are uniformly low.   An exception is the use of the 1000°C hot stage of Leitz which requires a stage which can be independently raised and lowered.

B. HOT STAGES

1. General Types

Many hot stages have been designed and built during the past 50 years.   For many purposes it is sufficient to build relatively crude laboratory models for the particular purpose in mind, however, such stages do not usually permit precise temperature measurement.   To

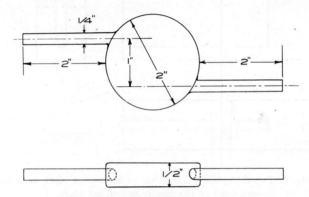

Fig. 3. Circulating liquid (heating or cooling) stage.

obtain a carefully constructed stage capable of high precision, it is better usually to purchase one of the commercially available models. Most of these are based directly on, or influenced by, the Kofler stage, which is capable of reproducible temperature measurements to plus or minus a few tenths of a degree.

Before discussing the stages available commercially in the United States, it might be well to indicate some of the general types of construction since they are simple to construct and often serve very useful purposes.   The simplest is probably the circulating liquid type[1] (Figure 3), which can be used with any laboratory liquid pump and any of the common provisions for heating or cooling liquids.   Actu-

[1] W. C. McCrone, A. Smedal, V. Gilpin, *Anal. Chem.* **18,** 578 (1946).

ally, quite precise temperature measurements are possible with this stage since temperature equilibrium is so rapid. A glass blower usually can fashion the stage itself in less than thirty minutes. The top surface should be as flat as possible except for a shallow groove to accommodate a thermocouple. The preparation, on a half-slide, is sealed to the top plate of the glass stage with several drops of glycerin to improve both light and heat conductivity to the preparation.

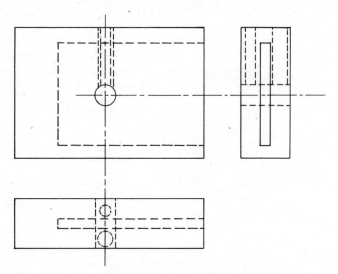

Fig. 4. Details of basic design for an aluminum block used to construct an electrically heated hot stage.

The stage may be insulated if temperatures below zero or above about 100°C are used, but otherwise this is unnecessary. Insulation is necessary only if the operator chooses to manipulate the stage and preparation as a unit with his fingers by sliding both across the microscope stage to change the field of view. The latter usually is advisable at low temperatures, especially those at which the glycerin becomes very viscous and the slide moves only with difficulty.

Another simple type of hot stage is the Nichrome-wrapped aluminum block with a slot for the microscope slide[2] (Figure 4). Such a stage, wrapped with about 30 feet of 21-gauge Nichrome wire, will give temperatures to at least 500°C. Any variable voltage transformer can be used, and the stage itself is wrapped with asbestos to

[2] D. G. Grabar and W. C. McCrone, *J. Chem. Education* **27**, 649 (1950).

insulate it from the microscope stage or other surroundings.   For use at high temperatures it is wise to insulate the hot stage from the microscope very carefully, or to use an auxiliary lens to form a real image of the hot object which can, in turn, be studied with the microscope.   Such an arrangement is also shown in the paper cited.[2] The simplest auxiliary lens is a 32-mm. objective, however, the numerical aperture of such a lens is so low that final microscope magnifications in excess of 100✕ are unsatisfactory.   However, with that limitation, the system works very well.   The use of an auxiliary lens is useful also, of course, in stages that function at higher temperatures.[3]

The easiest way to construct hot stages for temperatures from 500° to 2500°C is by the use of very small but hot ribbon filaments.[4] The current requirements for such heating elements are of the order of 100–300 amp at about 1 volt.   This can be achieved by means of a step-down transformer controlled by a variable voltage transformer; however, the easiest way to accomplish this is to purchase a gun-type soldering unit[5] and either use the heating element supplied, or replace it with a platinum or molybdenum ribbon.   The preparation usually is placed directly on the heating element, and temperature readings above approximately 1000°C are best interpolated from a calibration curve prepared by melting pure standard compounds or metals as a function of voltage.   For more accurate work a platinum-platinum rhodium thermocouple may be used.

Returning briefly to the low-temperature hot stage, the use of electrically coated (Corning Glass Works EC coating) microscope slides (available from A. H. Thomas, Philadelphia) form a simple nucleus for a hot stage.   Such slides can be incorporated in a variety of different designs, and temperatures up to 300°C can be obtained easily with good control using a variable voltage transformer (Section II,C,5).

As mentioned above, however, most homemade stages are relatively crude, and if refined usually cost more than the commercial equivalent.   Most of the hot stages commercially available in the United States are manufactured by Reichert, Leitz, or A. H. Thomas, and most are Kofler designs or adaptations of Kofler designs.   The only exceptions to the latter are some of the Leitz stages and the combination hot-cold stage sold by A. H. Thomas (Section II,C,5).

[3] H. N. Bauman, Jr., *Amer. Ceramic Soc. Bull.* **277**, 267 (1948).
[4] R. E. Cech, *Rev. of Sci. Instr.* **21**, 747 (1950).
[5] Weller Soldering Gun available from Weller Electric Corp., Easton, Pa.

2. Kofler Hot Stage; +30° to 350°C

The basic Kofler hot stage for controlled temperature measurement between room temperature and about 350°C is manufactured by Reichert[6] and A. H. Thomas.[7] The principal advantage of this careful design is the precise and reproducible temperature measurement possible. Melting points accurate to ±0.2°C are possible on a routine basis. This accuracy is achieved through good design; controlled heating rate; careful positioning of thermometer, glass cover bridge and plate; and finally, by very careful calibration of thermometers using standard compounds with known melting points. The care with which this is accomplished, personally or closely supervised by the manufacturers, is one reason for the great success of these stages in the United States.

The stage (Figures 1 and 2) should be described. The electrically heated metal stage, together with the removable metal rim and the glass cover, form the actual heating chamber. The stage is connected through a rheostat to a current supply of 115 volts AC or DC. A glass heat baffle covers the mounted sample to assure more uniform heat distribution. The thermometer is inserted into an opening radially to the central lightwell of the stage. A metal guard protecting the thermometer is screwed onto the guard socket. The metal stage is provided with two extending adjustable arms and pins with set screws. The pins are to be inserted into the holes of the microscope stage—provided for the use of microscope stage clips—in order to fix the stage securely in its position relative to the optical axis of the microscope.

The metal stage itself has a diameter of about 90 mm. A threaded post with a knurled screw on the stage serves for affixing certain pieces of apparatus, such as sublimation blocks or fork. The central lightwell is about 2 mm. wide. It is closed toward the heating chamber by means of a Pyrex glass plate. A condensing lens system is incorporated within the base plate of the stage. Three transite feet extend below the base plate in order to protect the microscope stage from direct heat transfer. The heating element of Nichrome wire is mounted around the optical axis inside the heating chamber.

Two thermometers are supplied by both A. H. Thomas and W. J.

[6] Available from Wm. J. Hacker and Co., Inc., 82 Beaver St., New York 5, N. Y.

[7] Available from A. H. Thomas Co., 230 South 7th St., Philadelphia 5, Pa.

Hacker with each stage—one covering the range from $+30°$ to 230°C; the other from $+60°$ to 350°C. They have been calibrated on the serially numbered stages and are correspondingly marked. In most cases, the approximate melting point of the substance is known from preliminary experiments and the proper thermometer is chosen—the low-range thermometer is best suited for temperatures up to 180°C in order to take advantage of the larger distance between the graduation marks; and the high-range thermometer for temperatures to 150°C and above.

3. Kofler Hot Stage; $+30°$ to 750°C

Hot stages are limited usually to temperatures in the neighborhood of 400°C, thus restricting their use to organic and low-melting inorganic compounds. The reason for this limitation has been the necessity for special optics such as auxiliary lens and long-working distance objectives. Although many stages have been suggested in the literature to cover this range, the Kofler instrument is the first refined hot stage of general applicability to cover the range to 750°C. This hot stage, manufactured by Reichert, is available in the United States from W. J. Hacker in New York.

The Kofler high-temperature stage (Figure 5) can be used with thermometers at temperatures to 750°C and requires no special optics. The stage itself consists of a plate of heat-treated steel with a diameter of 55 mm. This is placed in an aluminum container about 30 mm. high, having a 75 mm. diameter, and supported therein at three points so that an air space of not less than 7 mm. remains between them. This air space acts as an insulator and as an aid in uniform heating of the upper surface of the steel plate. The hot stage is fastened to the microscope stage with two binding screws. An aluminum plate extends across the entire stage about 5.5 mm. above the steel plate. The aluminum plate has a thin glass window in its center.

A low voltage current from a variable transformer supplies the heat. The power consumption is little different from the ordinary hot stage. Two thermometers are used: a Supremax glass thermometer for the range 300–500°C and a quartz thermometer for the range 500–750°C. The stage has a central opening for transmitted light. Observations are made at 80–100× just as with the ordinary hot stage. To avoid overheating of the objective the body-tube is raised at all times except for actual observation.

The use and calibration of this stage is no different in principle from that of the ordinary Kofler hot stage (Section III,A).

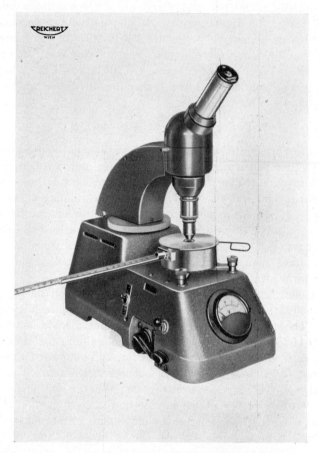

Fig. 5. Kofler 30° to 750°C hot stage.   (Courtesy William J. Hacker and Co., Inc.)

4. Leitz Hot Stage; +30° to 1000°C

For the range above that at which thermometers may be used, Leitz has provided a stage using thermocouples as the temperature measuring element. This stage (Figure 6) can be evacuated and is useful at temperatures slightly in excess of 1000°C using either transmitted or reflected light. It is electrically heated but has a water

jacket for quick cooling. Because of its thickness, approximately
51 mm., it is necessary to use a microscope stand on which the stage
can be raised or lowered. The following types of Leitz stands are
recommended: Panphot, BME (UB stand), MOP, and AMOP.
Any other stand which permits a large working distance would also
be satisfactory.

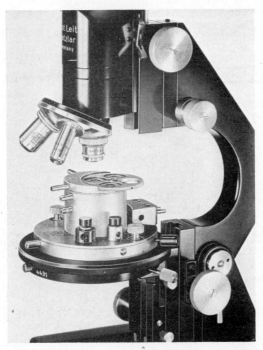

Fig. 6. Leitz 30° to 1000°C hot stage. (Courtesy E. Leitz, Inc.)

The heating of this stage is also controlled by means of a variable
voltage transformer; the stage will carry 18 amp at 13 volts without
damage and can be heated rapidly up to the range of interest. A
platinum-rhodium thermocouple and galvanometer are furnished with
a regulating transformer having a fine adjustment for accurate temperature control. The latter is not, however, necessary if this stage is
calibrated in the same manner as suggested above for the Kofler
stages.

5. Leitz Furnace; to 1800°C

The Leitz micro heating furnace is designed for the study of sintering of fuel ashes, slags, ceramics, glazes, etc., at temperatures up to 1600–1800°C. An image of the object in the furnace is projected by a low-power microscope onto a ground glass for visual observation or onto 35-mm. film. The projected image is only 5× although it can, of course, be enlarged several times photographically if necessary.

6. Kofler "Universal" Hot Stage Microscope; −55° to 1500°C

Figure 7 shows a stage and microscope which can be used over the entire range from −55° to 1500°C. The microscope body-tube

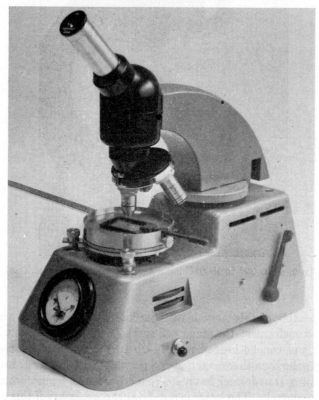

Fig. 7. Reichert "Universal hot stage microscope"; −55° to +1500°C. (Courtesy of Dr. Fritz Gabler of C. Reichert Optische Werke.)

swings to one side when not in active use to avoid overheating, and the entire assembly is planned for ease of use.   Provision has been made for vertical illumination (not shown), for phase contrast, polarized light and crossed polars, dark field and light-filtered illumination.

C. COLD STAGES

1. General Types

All of the cold stages commercially available are combination heating and cooling stages having the following characteristics:

Manufacturer	Distributor	Temperature range	Cooling medium
Reichert	W. J. Hacker	$-55°$, $+340°C$	CO_2
		$-55°$, $+ 80°C$	CO_2
E. Leitz	E. Leitz[a]	$-20°$, $+350°C$	CO_2
		$-20°$, $+ 80°C$	CO_2
A. H. Thomas	A. H. Thomas	$-100°$, $+100°C$	Cooled N_2

[a] Available from W. H. Kessel in Chicago, Ill.

The Reichert and Leitz (350°C) stages are very similar in design and use; the $-20°$ to $+80°C$ Leitz stage is a very compact design (by Eisenberg).   The A. H. Thomas design is unique in that the heating unit is an EC coated microscope slide; the cooling is carried out with dry nitrogen gas cooled by passage through a copper coil immersed in liquid nitrogen or a dry ice-acetone slurry, and the stage is the only one, except for the $-20°$ to $+80°C$ Leitz stage that can be used with the ordinary phase contrast accessories.   The latter is very important for the study of fats, oils, and waxes.   Long focal length condensers and special phase plates are, however, now available for use when a long condenser working distance is required.

The use of carbon dioxide cylinders for direct cooling deserves comment.   This method is simple and cheap and gives rapid cooling to about $-50°C$.   It is, however, limited to temperatures above a minimum of $-60°C$, and it cannot be used with any degree of precision in holding temperatures between $-60°C$ and room temperature because cooling is due to expansion of the carbon dioxide which is difficult to control to give a definite temperature reading.

The A. H. Thomas cooling stage has been designed to use dry cooled nitrogen gas as coolant and this arrangement has several advantages. In the first place, the lower temperature limit depends on the cooling agent through which the nitrogen gas passes, and in the second place the temperature in the cold stage is held readily at any desired temperature to ±1°C for hours at a time by adjusting and holding constant the rate at which cold nitrogen gas enters the stage.

The other commercially available cold stages can also be cooled in this fashion, of course, however, all of them except the −20° to +80°C Leitz stage would probably require excessive amounts of nitrogen gas and coolant to reach and maintain the lower temperatures.

2. Kofler Cold Stages; −55° to 80°C and −55° to 340°C

Basically, these stages are identical in design, appearance, and use with the Kofler hot stage described above (II,B,2), except that an expansion chamber for carbon dioxide gas and a valve to control the rate of release of gas are included.

3. Leitz Cold Stage; −20° to 350°C

This stage (Figure 8) is essentially a hot stage in which provision has been made for cooling with carbon dioxide gas. It is unique in

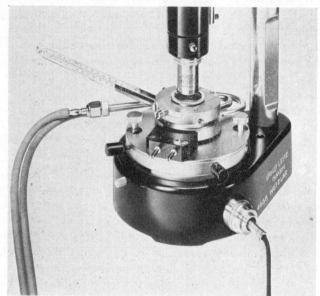

Fig. 8. Leitz −20° to +350°C cold stage. (Courtesy E. Leitz, Inc.)

that the specimen chamber is removable so that different types of specimen holders can be used. Three thermometers, $-20°$ to $120°C$, $+100°$ to $240°C$, and $+220°$ to $360°C$, are furnished. An effort has been made to keep the heat capacity of this stage low so that cooling may be rapid after a heating experiment. Water cooling is also provided to further increase the cooling rate and, of course, carbon dioxide gas can be used to give very rapid cooling.

(a)

(b)

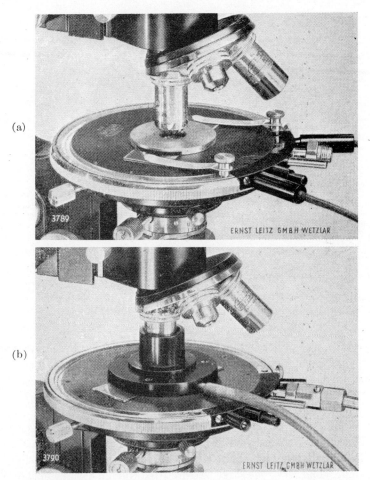

Fig. 9. Leitz $-20°$ to $+80°C$ cold stage: (a) as a hot stage with temperature stabilizing cover, (b) as a cold stage with nitrogen chamber to prevent condensation of moisture on preparation and objective. (Courtesy E. Leitz, Inc.)

4. Leitz Cold Stage; −20° to 80°C

This cold stage is unique in design since it is incorporated apparently into the microscope stage itself (Figure 9). The preparation is placed directly on the top of the stage in the usual way and covered with a small chamber to help equalize the temperature (Figure 9a), and if

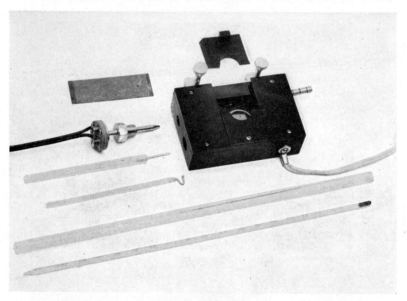

Fig. 10. McCrone −100° to +100°C cold stage.   A resistance thermometer and other accessories are shown.   (Courtesy Arthur H. Thomas Co., Inc.)

necessary, a chamber to contain a dry nitrogen atmosphere to prevent condensation of moisture on the preparation and objective (Figure 9b). This stage is very convenient and may be used with phase accessories.

5. McCrone Cold Stage; −100° to 100°C

This stage[8] was designed primarily as a cold stage in contrast with all the above stages which are essentially hot stages with provision for cooling.   The McCrone stage (Figure 10) although designed primarily as a cold stage, has provision for heating using an EC coated micro-

[8] W. C. McCrone and S. M. O'Bradovic, *Anal. Chem.*, **28**, 1038 (1956).

scope slide as a heating element. The dimensions have been kept small so that phase accessories can be used; in this connection it is worth noting that the American Optical Co. furnishes long working distance condensers and special phase annuli for use with hot stages, etc., where long working distances for the condenser are necessary. The heating slide forms the upper portion of a thin chamber through which the cooling gas passes. The gas then exits into the preparation chamber and out around the objective, which extends into the chamber through an opening in the top. This stage is furnished also with a set of thermometers covering the range of operation.

The cooling arrangement for this stage differs from that recommended for all of the above cold stages. Instead of carbon dioxide gas, a tank of oil pumped nitrogen is used as a gas supply. The supply of nitrogen (and thereby the temperature of the cold stage) is controlled by the needle valve of the tank gauge assembly. The nitrogen is passed through about 10 feet of $^1/_4$-inch copper coil immersed in a 2-liter dewar flask filled with an appropriate cooling medium (liquid nitrogen or dry ice-acetone). The exit end of the copper coil in the dewar passes directly and with a very short insulated lead to the cold stage. By this means any temperature down to $-55°C$ can be maintained using a dry ice bath, and down to $-120°C$ using liquid nitrogen. There is no difficulty with frost condensing on the preparation or objective since both are bathed in the dry cold nitrogen atmosphere.

D. HOT BARS

There have been many melting point bars in the past, however, again the Koflers have refined the design and use of the melting point bar until it can now be used with precision in the determination of melting points ($\pm0.5°C$). The Kofler hot bar is manufactured by Reichert and sold by W. J. Hacker in New York. Three models are available varying in the temperature range covered: 50–260°C, 10–210°C, and 80–180°C.

The 50–260°C hot bar (Figure 11) consists of a stainless steel bar, 38 mm. by 370 mm., heated at one end. The temperature at the hot end is about 260°C and falls at a uniform rate to about 50°C at the opposite end. The bar is constructed so that the gradient is nearly linear. This is accomplished by using two different metals of different conductivities, and by using the proper shapes of each metal. The upper portion of the bar is stainless steel and the under portion is made up of several aluminum strips of different lengths so that they form, as a whole, a wedge. For a short range at the hot end the steel alone conducts the heat, while at the lower end there are several strips of aluminum to conduct the heat. The heating element is contained in a downward extension of one end of the bar.

The heating current is stabilized by a special iron wire resistance bulb developed by Dr. L. Kahovec of Graz and is also available from W. J. Hacker and Company. This bulb fits in a socket behind and beneath the hot bar. The normal variation in room temperature is taken into account by a nomagraph scale, which allows the reading

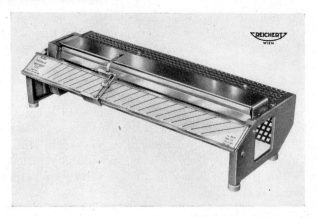

Fig. 11   Kofler 50° to 260°C hot bar.   (Courtesy William J. Hacker and Co., Inc.)

of the hot bar temperature as a function of room temperature from 10° to 30°C.

The 80–180°C hot bar was designed to give greater accuracy in the range of most melting points. The 10–210°C hot bar covers the room temperature region and is much more independent of variations in room temperature than the other two bars.

These hot bars and especially the 50–260°C bar have many other uses not related directly to their use for accurate temperature measurement. Many of these uses will be discussed in more detail in Chapter III on general techniques but may also be summarized here. The bars are used for quick melting of a preparation, or for holding a preparation at a definite temperature to induce crystallization or a. polymorphic transformation, to heat a sublimation block at the best possible constant temperature, or to determine an approximate melting point before use of the hot stage.

E. MICROREFRACTOMETER

The refractive index of liquids and especially of organic melts can be very valuable identifying characteristics.   One of the most flexible microrefractometers is the Jelley design.   Unfortunately, the Fisher

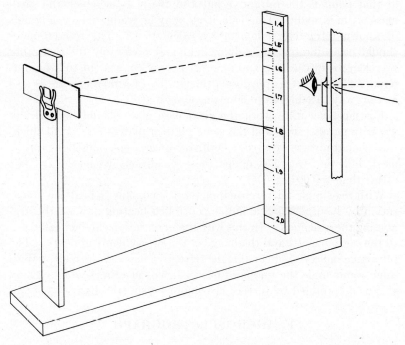

Fig. 12. Jelley microrefractometer; the optical arrangement at the sample end is shown at the right.

modification of Jelley's design looses much of the flexibility needed for microscopy.   Such an instrument is, however, very easily built and calibrated (Figure 12).

An illuminated slit is viewed through a small aperture.   A very small glass plate, about 0.5 mm. thick and 5 mm. square beveled at approximately 45° on one end, is placed small flat side down on a half microscope slide, or better, an optical flat of about the same size, so that a minute liquid prism is formed by touching a micro drop of liquid to the bevel. The small glass plate with the bevel is pressed into close contact with the half-slide, and the whole assembly is then placed over the aperture of the refractometer so that the liquid prism lies over the aperture. Looking through this aperture, the illuminated image of the slit appears superimposed on the printed scale thereby indicating the refractive index of the liquid.

The slit is cut at a point on the scale such that the refractive index at that point is the refractive index of the glass of which the small glass prism is made. The scale, itself, may be graduated using liquids of known refractive index, or by calculation.[9] The refractometer should be calibrated for sodium light and preferably for two other wavelengths in the blue and red. It is very convenient to use interference filters for this purpose although use of a mercury arc is also an easy way to achieve the same purpose.

For most accurate work the glass base plate should be optically flat with parallel sides and the same plate or plates of identical thickness should always be used. Ordinary microscope half-slides can be used, but the accuracy under those conditions would be ±0.002 rather than ±0.001.

With the simple microrefractometer it is possible to heat the preparation by incorporating a simple controlled heating unit on the arm holding the specimen. In this way the preparation can be heated until the sample melts and the image of the slit suddenly appears. The refractive index so indicated is the refractive index of the melt. With some compounds the temperature coefficient of refractive index may also be determined by further heating or by supercooling.

F. MICROSPECTROGRAPH

Dr. Edwin E. Jelley[10-12] has also contributed another ingenious and useful instrument to the study of crystals and one which is very useful in the characterization and identification of fusible compounds by fusion methods. This is the instrument with which the image of any colored object under the microscope with or without polarized light or crossed polaroids, and with either conoscopic or orthoscopic

[9] E. E. Jelley, *J. Roy. Microscop. Soc.* 234–245 (1934).

[10] E. E. Jelley, *Photog. J.* 514 (1934).

[11] E. E. Jelley, *J. Roy. Microscop. Soc.*, 101 (1936).

[12] E. E. Jelley, *Anal. Chem.* **13,** 196 (1941).

illumination, can be focused on a slit of a spectrograph.   This instrument, which is called a microspectrograph, can be used to analyze the colors shown by a pleochroic crystal (Section III,B,4,c), to deter-

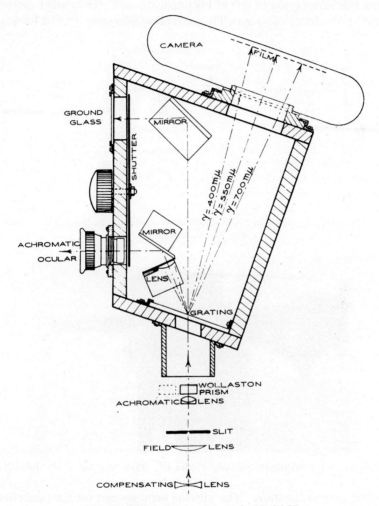

Fig. 13. Jelley microspectrograph, Model II.

mine the birefringence of a given orientation and the dispersion of that birefringence (Section III,B,4,f), and finally, the dispersion of the optic axis or optic axial angle (Section III,B,4,g).

Unfortunately, no commercial model of this instrument is yet avail-able although an acceptable model (Figure 13), not so refined as Dr. Jelley's latest instrument (Figures 14 and 15), can be constructed from the information in one of his publications.[11]   The earlier model built by Dr. Jelley contains a Thorne replica diffraction grating having

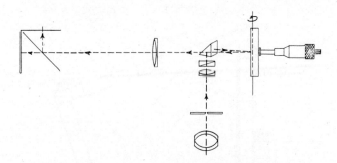

Fig. 14. Schematic diagram for the Jelley microspectrograph, Model IV,   (Cour-tesy Dr. E. E. Jelley.)

Fig. 15. Jelley microspectrograph, Model IV.   (Courtesy Dr. E. E. Jelley.)

14,950 lines to the inch.   The viewing arrangement for the spectrum consists of an achromatic Ramsden eyepiece to which the light is deviated by a lens and a silvered mirror.   The viewing arrangement for the direct image of the slit may consist of a finely ground glass screen, which is examined with a low-power magnifier, or of a cross-hair eyepiece containing a Wratten neutral density filter to cut the light intensity. A density of 1.6 (2.5% transmission) is suitable for this purpose. A silvered deflecting mirror enables this viewing arrangement to be placed directly above the eyepiece used for viewing the spectrum. A metal shutter, actuated by a knob placed between these two light outlets, is provided so that the camera can be made light tight. The camera is a 35-mm. film holder without lens.

The dispersion of the spectrum is such that the distance between the centers of adjacent film perforations is 50.0 mμ. In practice the film with perforations is enlarged and the scale is then drawn to match the perforations.

The design of the slit eyepiece depends, to some extent, on the type of polarizing microscope being used. The slit must, however, be placed at the proper position for which the optical system is corrected or a correction lens must be inserted. Further details regarding the optical arrangement can be found in the second of the two papers[11] referred to.

A more refined model of the microspectrograph, actually Dr. Jelley's fourth instrument, has also been described.[12] This instrument was designed to eliminate the astigmatism evident in the spectra obtained by earlier instruments. The general principle of this new design is shown in Figure 14 and a photograph is shown in Figure 15.

A Steinheil lens is used to focus the microscope image on the slit. The microscope, which is used with an eyepiece not fitted with cross hairs, is focused for an image distance at infinity, so that the Steinheil lens is used at its principal focus from the slit. This lens is provided with centering screws so that the center of rotation of the image can be adjusted onto the center of the slit. The collimating lens is an achromat that collects light from the slit and gives a collimated beam, which is then reflected by a silvered right-angle prism onto a plane grating. A Wollaston prism, which is provided with a fine adjustment to its rotation, may be swung into the beam for studies of dichroism. Over half of the light incident on the grating is diffracted in one of the first order spectra, which is collected by a cemented achromatic camera lens and brought to focus in the image plane of a reflex camera that uses 35-mm. Panatomic film. Further details can be found in the original paper.[12]

G. OTHER ACCESSORIES

There are a number of other accessories useful in the study of fusion methods assumed to be too simple, or too well known to merit description.   These include: sublimation blocks (A. H. Thomas Company has a new and very simple vacuum-sublimation block), refractive index liquids (R. P. Cargille Laboratories, Inc., 117 Liberty St., New York), glass standards for measurement of refractive index of the melt (A. H. Thomas and W. J. Hacker), micro soldering irons for local heating of portions of preparations, cooling blocks and heating rings (for evaporating low-boiling solvents on a slide without spreading), etc.

CHAPTER III

GENERAL TECHNIQUES OF
FUSION METHODS

A. CALIBRATION OF HOT STAGES, COLD STAGES, AND HOT BARS

The Kofler stages and other commercial stages are capable of highly precise and accurate use when carefully calibrated. The necessary calibration requires several hours and is absolutely essential for careful work; the calibration once determined must also be checked every few months.

It is of the greatest importance for proper calibration that standard practice as outlined below be followed point by point.

1. Calibration of the Kofler Hot Stage

The thermometer is inserted through the guard socket into the well at the left side of the apparatus. Rotate the thermometer carefully to overcome the slight resistance exerted by the spring holder within the bore. The thermometer must be maneuvered carefully to the very end of the bore, since it was calibrated in this position and indicates the proper temperature only in this position. Likewise, the metal guard for the thermometer should be in place before use both to protect the thermometer and to duplicate the thermal surroundings used during calibration of the thermometers.

Before the first use the stage should be heated to about 200°C without thermometer or glass cover in order to drive out the moisture which is absorbed by the insulation within the stage. After cooling the stage is ready for calibration using the melting point standards supplied with the stage.

The most important variable is the rate of heating and the first step in calibration of any hot stage, or cold stage for that matter, is to determine the conditions which correspond to heating rates of 2°, 3°, and 4°C/min. This is done with the hot stage in place on the micro-

scope stage and arranged, in every respect, as if a micro melting point
were being taken: hot stage on the microscope stand, thermometer all
the way in, a dummy preparation in place, heat baffle or glass bridge
in place, cover plate on the stage, etc.   The voltage regulator is then
set at a definite low reading, preferably but not necessarily, expressed

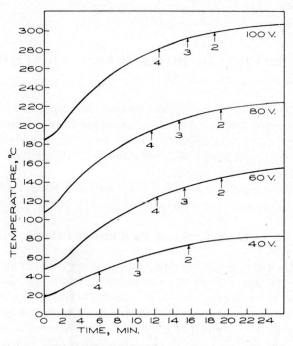

Fig. 16. Heating curves for various voltages showing temperatures at which rate of heating is 2°, 3°, and 4°C/min.

in volts as read on a voltmeter in the hot stage circuit.   As the temperature rises with constant voltage the temperature reading is recorded each minute until the rate of increase has fallen below 2°C/min.
(Figure 16).   From these data the temperature at which the rate of
increase is 2, 3, 4, etc., degrees/min. can be determined for that particular voltage.

The stage is then allowed to cool, the voltage is increased, and the
recording of temperature-time data is repeated.   Several such runs
at voltages of say 40, 60, 80, and 100 volts will give sufficient information to plot a curve relating the temperature at which the rate of

rise will be 2 and 4 degrees/min. to the voltage across the hot stage
(Figure 17).

The next step in the calibration is to determine the melting points
of the available standard compounds by the several standard pro-

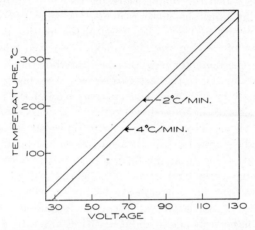

Fig. 17. Temperatures at which heating rate is 2° and
4°C/min. with the corresponding voltage setting.

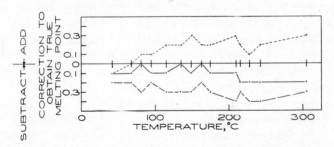

Fig. 18. Error in observed hot stage melting points for different methods of
observing the melting point: dotted line, equilibrium melting point;   dashed
line, crystalline film, 4°C/min.;   full line, few separate crystals, 4°C/min.

cedures (Figure 18).   It is wise, even here, to check the heating rate
1–2°C below the melting point, partly to make certain the rate is
accurately adjusted and because over a 1°C range it is possible to use a
stopwatch rather than the thermometer as the more accurate indication of temperature.   Assume, for example, that melting is due to
occur just above 68°C with a heating rate of 4°C/min.   As the tem-

perature reaches about 65°C the rate of heating should be checked with a stopwatch; by 68°C it will be apparent just how long in seconds it should take for the temperature to rise from 68° to 69°C (it can and should be 15 ± 1 second). If the time is measured from the point at which the temperature passes the accurately observed 68°C marking until the melting point, the time fraction thus obtained will permit accurate estimation of the melting point, without the necessity of moving the eye quickly from the microscope eyepiece to the thermometer magnifier and interpolating a temperature on a scale graduated to the nearest degree. As a matter of fact, the stopwatch may be placed or held near the base of the microscope in the field of view of the unused eye so that it appears superimposed on the field of view. This is not necessary, however, since most stopwatches can be stopped to give the time interval without removing the eye or the attention from the field of view; it is only necessary to start the watch as the mercury column passes the degree mark and to stop the watch as the last crystals disappear. The precise time of disappearance of the last crystals can be estimated easily to ±0.2 second. This corresponds to about ±0.01°C at a rate of temperature rise of 4°C/min. In this manner, melting points are repeated easily to ±0.2°C.

In accurate work of this sort it is necessary to look for temperature variations across the preparation within the field of view of the microscope since it is difficult, if not impossible, to construct a hot stage in which the temperature is uniform during heating, even over the $^{1}/_{16}$-in. opening in the center of the stage. The usual and simplest indication of such lack of uniformity is the observation that on melting of a continuous crystalline film of pure material, complete melting first occurs always on the same side of the field and progresses rapidly across the field as the temperature continues to rise. The difference in temperature is usually only 0.1–0.2°C, and the effect can be eliminated entirely by taking the temperature at which the last crystals in the field disappear, presumably in the coolest portion of the field of view.

It is desirable also to calibrate the hot stage for melting points using two types of preparations: one, a few hundredths of a milligram of finely powdered crystals well dispersed on the slide under a cover slip; and second, a continuous film of crystalline material crystallized from the melt between the slide and cover slip. In the first case, the crystals should be very finely divided; this is best done by crushing with a micro spatula or with a slide or cover slip. In the latter cases, the upper slide or cover slip must be replaced with a fresh clean cover slip before heating, since crystals adhering to the under surface of the cover slip usually melt as much as 1°C higher than the crystals on the slide.

When the preparation sublimes, the sublimed crystals on the under surface of the cover slip will also melt about 1°C too high, hence the melting point should be taken when the last crystals on the slide disappear, or a calibration curve (Figure 18) can be prepared for powdered samples lying on the underside of the cover slip.

The equilibrium melting point (Section III,B,1,d) is determined by very careful manipulation of the variable voltage transformer so that the temperature in the stage changes only a few tenths of a degree up and down over the melting range of the compound under test. The object is to determine the two nearest temperatures at which definite melting and definite freezing can be observed. The stage should also be calibrated at several temperatures by this technique (Figure 18).

One important precaution, however, must be observed in calibrating the hot stage for equilibrium melting points. Nearly every melting point standard is slightly impure and, therefore, melts over a small but definite temperature range. The equilibrium melting point determined with the hot stage will, therefore, vary depending on the percentage of the sample actually melted. If most of the sample is still crystalline the observed equilibrium melting point will be lower than if most of the sample is already melted. The proper point to take is, obviously, the latter; the last crystals to disappear should be held at equilibrium with a large excess of melt.

Occasionally an equilibrium melting point may change with time even with compounds that show no decomposition. This is apparently due to thermal diffusion due, in turn, to the small temperature gradient between the cooler area over the lightwell and the hotter area in contact with the stage itself. The equilibrium melting point may either increase or decrease in these cases and may change by several degrees in a few minutes. Extrapolation back to zero time is one way to eliminate this difficulty. Another and better solution is to use a sample which fills only a part of the field of view.

This interesting behavior can be observed easily with most of the melting point standards furnished with the hot stages, but is especially noticeable with azobenzene. In one series of experiments to determine the effect of per cent solid remaining on the equilibrium melting point, the data shown in Table III were taken in the sequence shown. The entire sequence of experiments required less than 30 minutes, hence thermal diffusion was rapid even with the necessarily very low thermal gradient. As further proof of the thermal diffusion mechanism by which this lowering of melting point occurred, the preparation was moved about $1/8$ inch after experiment 8 and the equilibrium melting point with 90 per cent melted was found to be 68.4°C. The equilibrium melting point on the original sample was only 68.1°C (on a small droplet entirely within the field of view), hence definite purification occurred in the region immediately surrounding the portion of the sample just over the lightwell.

TABLE III

Equilibrium Melting Points for Azobenzene as a Function of Percentage of Solid Remaining and as a Function of Time

Experiment no.	Percentage melted	Equil., m.p. (°C)
1	25	66.0
2	50	66.5
3	75	67.0
4	90	67.3
5	99	67.2

(The preparation was then cooled to 60°C after which some of the same experiments were redone.)

6	25	63.0
7	50	65.0
8	90	66.2

The information so obtained can then be plotted (Figure 18) to show the difference between the observed and true melting points as a function of temperature for each of the different heating rates and for the equilibrium melting point. Since all thermometers change slowly with time the calibration should be rechecked periodically. For precise work during a given set of experiments it is always best to determine the melting points of several standard compounds in the melting range of interest at the same time and under precisely the same conditions as the experimental melting points. The data observed can then be corrected in terms of the melting point corrections for the standard compounds.

The proper designation for melting points taken in this manner is "micro melting point (corrected)," which means that the melting point was observed using a suitable microscope hot stage heated at a standard rate and corrected by observing the melting point of standard compounds under the same conditions. Any variations from standard procedure, such as a variation in heating rate, should be noted.

It is well to form the habit of always using the glass bridge (heat baffle) over the preparation. This bridge helps to distribute the heat uniformly over the preparation and to prevent clouding of the field of view by the sublimate, which otherwise often collects in the center of the upper glass plate.

One final precaution must be observed if accurate results are to be obtained. A small burette-reading magnifier or equivalent must be used to read the thermometer. Its use is partly to magnify the scale but even more important to eliminate parallax. Temperature reading can be in error by as much as $0.5°C$ from parallax alone, and the use of the burette-reading magnifier with its long collimating tube effectively eliminates this error.

Further information on melting point determination, especially on

TABLE IV

Compounds for Use in Calibration of High-Temperature Hot Stages

$NaNO_3$	308	CsCl	646	$BaCl_2$	962
KNO_3	333	Mg	651	K_2CrO_4	975
CdI_2	385	NaI	651	NaF	992
Na_2CrO_4	392	Al	660	Au	1063
$K_2Cr_2O_7$	398	$MgCl_2$	712	Cu	1083
PbI_2	402	PbCl	715	PbS	1120
Zn	419.4	KI	723	SnO_2	1127
AgBr	434	KBr	730	$MgSO_4$	1185
AgCl	455	NaBr	755	CaF_2	1330
$CuCl_2$	498	$CaCl_2$	772	MgF_2	1396
$PbCl_2$	501	KCl	790	Si	1420
CdF_2	520	NiS	797	$NaAlO_2$	1650
KBF_4	529.5	NaCl	800.4	Zr	1700
NaCN	563.7	As	814	SiO_2	1710
B_2O_3	577	$PbCrO_4$	844	Pt	1755
$Ba(NO_3)_2$	592	Na_2CO_3	851	ZnS	1850
LiCl	614	LiF	870	Cr_2O_3	1900
Li_2CO_3	618	KF	880	CeO_2	1950
CsI	621	Na_2SO_4	884	La_2O_3	2000
KCN	634.5	K_2CO_3	891	UO_2	2176
CsBr	636	Ag	960.5	SrO	2430

methods for the determination of melting points for compounds that sublime or decompose, can be found in Section III,B,1,d.

2. Calibration of High-Temperature Hot Stages

The use and calibration of high-temperature hot stages (Section II,B) is no different from that of the 350°C stage (Section III,A,1). Compounds suitable for use in calibrating high-temperature hot stages can be found quickly in any handbook containing melting point tables. Inorganic salts are best since they are usually very stable, easy to purify, and readily available. The following are suggested (Table IV).

3. Calibration of Cold Stages

The calibration of the cold stage is basically the same as for the hot stage. It is, however, more difficult to maintain the proper heating rates, especially with those stages which use carbon dioxide gas for cooling. There is no substitute for experience in this regard, and no way to obtain reliable temperature data without maintaining the proper heating rates. The constant use of a stopwatch is even more essential for precise temperature measurement than with the hot stage.

TABLE V

Melting Points of Recommended Standard Compounds for Calibration of Cold Stages

Compound	m.p., °C	b.p., °C	Compound	m.p., °C	b.p., °C
Ethyl alcohol	−112	78.4	Benzyl alcohol	−15.3	204.7
Acetone	−94.6	56.5	Methyl benzoate	−12.4	198
Methyl ethyl ketone	−85.9	79.6	Acetonyl acetone	−9	194
Ethyl acetate	−82.4	77.1	Aniline	−6.1	184.4
n-Butyl acetate	−76.3	125.1	Water	0.0	100.0
Chloroform	−63.4	61.2	Dimethyl aniline	2.5	193
Bromoacetone	−54	136.5	Benzene	5.5	80.1
Acetoacetic ester	−45	180	Dioxane	11.8	101.1
Diethyl ketone	−39.9	101.7	m-Decylamine	17	216–8
Ethyl benzoate	−34.7	211–2	Ethyl phenyl ketone	21	218
Nitromethane	−28.5	101.5	Isoquinoline	24.6	241
Benzaldehyde	−26	179	Cyclohexanol	25.45	160
Carbon tetrachloride	−22.65	76.8			

The standard compounds to be used are liquids at ordinary temperatures that can be purified readily by distillation and crystallized readily on cooling below their melting points (Table V).

4. Calibration of Hot Bars

The 50–250°C hot bar requires about 40 minutes to come to equilibrium, but it may be left on for long periods of time without damage. Each instrument should be carefully calibrated using the series of standard melting point compounds furnished with each bar. These standards are: azobenzene 68°C, benzil 95°C, acetanilide 115°C, phenacetin 135°C, benzanilide 163°C, salophen 190°C, and saccharin 228°C.

It is usually not possible, however, to calibrate the hot bar with sufficient care so that temperatures accurate to ±1°C can be measured at any later date. In general, room temperature variations, drafts, etc., will cause a temperature variation exceeding 1–2°C. The procedure used to determine precise melting points is based on simultaneous use of the melting point standards. In this way the room temperature effect and all other variables are eliminated automatically and the accuracy is limited to the accuracy by which linear distances can be measured. The melting point is determined as follows: a few crystals of the finely ground test compound are sprinkled along the bar in order to determine the approximate melting point; an additional quantity of finely divided test compound is then sprinkled over the region of melting to give a fine dividing line between the melted and unmelted crystals; next, the two standards whose melting points bracket that of the test substance are sprinkled on the bar in their proper areas. The three melting points are measured carefully (a millimeter scale of graph paper fastened to the coarse scale already present is very useful at this point), and the accurate melting point of the test compound is calculated by interpolation. Melting points accurate to at least ±0.5°C can be measured in this way.

Sprinkling of the sample on the hot bar is best carried out using a small piece of brass sieve 50–100 mesh. The finely divided sample is placed on the sieve and sprinkled over the desired area of the hot bar by lightly tapping the edge of the sieve. The melting of the crystals should be followed by a hand magnifier (at least 5×; preferably 10–15×). The melting point is noted when equilibrium is established.   Under the best conditions this may be after 4–5 seconds, however, if the bar has just been cleaned or touched in any way, equilibrium may take 1–2 min.

For compounds that decompose, the bar should be allowed to equilibrate for several minutes before sprinkling on the sample; the melting point should then be read after 4–5 seconds before significant decomposition has occurred.

An example of the precision possible with the hot bar when the greatest of care is used is shown in Table VI where the melting points of identical samples of azobenzene were determined with the 50–250°C hot bar and the 30–350°C hot stage.   These data were obtained by replacing the scale with a millimeter scale using the hot stage melting point for Sample B and for benzil (m.p. 95°C) as standards for the hot bar.   The melting point of B on the hot bar is, therefore, taken as 68.4, and the other four melting points are taken relative to the melting points of B and benzil.

TABLE VI

Comparison Between Melting Points of Azobenzene Samples by Hot Bar and Hot Stage

| | Melting point, °C | |
Sample	Hot stage	Hot bar
A	68.2	68.3
B	68.4	68.4
C	68.4	68.4
D	67.9	68.1
E	67.6	67.7

There are only minor differences in construction and use of the other two hot bars.   The 10–210°C has an ice-water reservoir at the cold end that reduces the effect of room temperature variations. The 80–180°C bar has a temperature scale approximately twice as long per degree as the other two scales and readily permits measurement of melting points by the above procedure of direct comparison with standards to about ±0.3°C.   Additional compounds for use with this stage are: benzophenol 48.1°C, naphthalene 80.2°C, pyrocatechol 104°C, β-naphthol 122.5°C, cholesterol 148.5°C, and noctol 183.5°C (5-isopropyl-5-[β-bromallyl]-barbituric acid).   β-Naphthyl ethyl ether, 35°C, may be used to calibrate the 10–210°C hot bar.

B. CHARACTERIZATION AND IDENTIFICATION OF FUSIBLE COMPOUNDS

The techniques used for characterization and identification vary from the observation of descriptive properties, such as shrinkage cracks, gas bubbles, and type of crystal front, to the quantitative measurement of melting points and refractive index of the melt. Descriptive properties are useful for the characterization and identification of small groups of compounds that the analyst can remember and recognize almost at a glance. This method of analysis is illustrated by the work of Gilpin on sterols,[1] by similar work at Cornell University[2] on waxes, and on explosives. Identification of any member of one of these groups can be carried out very quickly and simply by relatively untrained personnel, however, such schemes are limited to small groups of compounds. The use of identification schemes based on melting points, refractive indices of the melt, and optical properties are capable of wider application and effectively identify any of a very large number of compounds. The Kofler tables which have been retabulated and incorporated in Chapter V already include nearly 1200 common and important organic compounds. Laskowski[3,4] has been able to develop the use of a specific classification reagent, 2,4,7-trinitrofluorenone, to characterize an unknown as a particular type of aromatic compound. Following this the melting points of the unknown compound, the addition compound, and the two eutectics are then measured in a single heating experiment in the hot stage to identify the particular member of that class of compounds (Section III, B,7,C).

The discussion of all such techniques that may be used for the characterization and identification of fusible compounds are included in the order in which they would normally be carried out: during heating, melting, during and after cooling, reheating, etc.

1. Observations During Heating

A small amount of the compound, approximately 2–5 mg., is

[1] V. Gilpin, *Anal. Chem.*, **23**, 365 (1951).

[2] J. H. Andreen, W. C. McCrone, S. M. Tsang, NDRC Report 3014, "Microscopic Examination of High Explosives and Boosters," Aug. 1, 1944, declassified Aug. 3, 1950.

[3] D. E. Laskowski, D. G. Grabar, and W. C. McCrone, *Anal. Chem.*, **25**, 1400 (1953).

[4] D. E. Laskowski and W. C. McCrone, *Anal. Chem.* **26**, 1497 (1954).

placed on a microscope half-slide, covered with a cover glass, and heated slowly on a melting point bar or over a micro flame. As the preparation becomes warm, the following properties are noted.

A. EASE OF SUBLIMATION

Most organic compounds sublime over a wide range of temperatures below the melting point, although the tendency to sublime varies widely from compound to compound. Many compounds, like hexa-

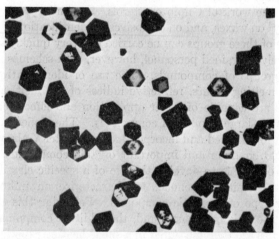

Fig. 19. Sublimed crystals of hexamethylenetetramine obtained by sublimation from one microscope slide to a second warm slide held above it over a microburner.

methylenetetramine (Figure 19), resorcinol, carbazole, hydroquinone, benzoic acid, camphor, p-dichlorobenzene, and 4,6-dinitroresorcinol, give a characteristic crystalline sublimate collecting on the underside of the cover glass. There is, however, no single sublimation temperature; a given substance sublimes only at a faster or slower rate as the temperature rises or falls.

Usually it is possible to determine a number of morphological and optical properties on crystals obtained by sublimation, especially if the sublimation is carried out more slowly and carefully. One of the best methods of obtaining a good sublimate is to spread the material thinly over a portion of a half-slide, cover with a large cover glass, and heat slowly. When the sublimate is well formed, the cover glass is removed to a clean slide for examination. It is also possible to form good crystals by sublimation from one microscope slide to a second held above it (Figure 19). For best results the upper slide should also be heated so that its temperature is only slightly below that of the lower slide.

The best method for sublimation of small quantities of material is by use of the Kofler block (Figure 20a). This simple block, in which perhaps 50 mg., may be sublimed, is covered with a cover glass and

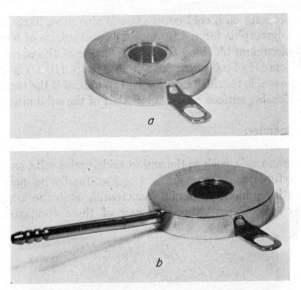

Fig. 20. Kofler sublimation blocks: (a) for sublimation at ordinary pressure, and (b) for vacuum sublimation (modified by McCrone).

heated either on the hot bar or hot stage. A simple modification of this block for vacuum sublimation is also shown in Figure 20b. This block is used in precisely the same manner, except that a half-slide is used to cover the opening and a vacuum is maintained during heating. The top surface of the block is highly polished and no sealing compound is used; the vacuum is sufficient to seal the cell by forcing the half-slide into intimate contact with the upper surface of the block. Both blocks are available through A. H. Thomas in Philadelphia.

The temperature of the condensing surface is the most important variable second to the sublimation temperature itself. A high rate of sublimation is best obtained when the difference between these two temperatures is the highest possible.   On the other hand, the most effective purification and the best and largest single crystals are obtained when the two temperatures are close together.   In using the Kofler block for successive samples, for example, it is desirable to preheat the cover glass or half-slide on the top side of the block before sliding it over the opening in the center if large well-formed crystals are desired.   This is unnecessary if the entire block is being heated from room temperature.

The condensate on a cold cover glass is also more likely to be an unstable polymorphic form.   By placing a wet square of filter paper or a cold aluminum block on the upper surface of the cover slip the unstable form III of p-hydroxybenzoic acid (m.p. 110°C) is obtained, whereas the stable form I (m.p. 126°C) is obtained if the temperature of the condensing surface is just below that of the subliming crystals.

B. DECOMPOSITION

A few compounds, such as the amino acids, amine salts, amides, and many polyfunctional compounds (e.g., sulfosalicylic acid, tetra-hydroxyanthraquinone, saponin, pancreatin, and the sugars) decompose on melting.   Although many of these compounds (e.g.,

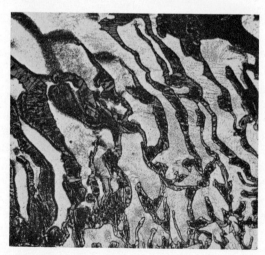

Fig. 21. Crystalline film of hexanitrodiphenylamine obtained on rapid cooling of the decomposing melt.

some of the sugars and specific compounds such as butane-2,3-dicyanohydrin) decompose so completely that no crystals can be obtained on cooling, most compounds decompose only slightly on melting. Even a compound like hexanitrodiphenylamine that decomposes vigorously at the melting point crystallizes on cooling to give very characteristic and easily recognized crystalline films (Figure 21).

Rapid heating characteristic of the use of the hot bar, hot stage, and micro burners helps to eliminate the effects of decomposition. Indications, such as discoloration and gas evolution, should be noted, however.

C. POLYMORPHISM

Occasionally on heating, a phase transformation from one solid crystalline modification to a second occurs before melting, e.g., veronal, sulfathiazole, carbon tetrabromide, ammonium nitrate, and mercuric iodide. In such cases there exists the possibility on continuous heating of measuring one of several possible melting points, or even of observing resolidification of an already melted droplet with subsequent remelting. Several close friendships between organic chemists have been strained because each claimed a different melting point for a given compound and all because, for reasons best known to the compound, the two chemists always obtained different polymorphic forms with different melting points.

The evidence for a polymorphic transformation on heating is a discontinuous change in physical properties, usually most apparent as changes in polarization colors and extinction positions. The change may be rapid or it may be slow. In the latter case, a tiny drop of benzyl alcohol, nitrobenzene, or other liquid which will act as a solvent, added at the edge of the cover slip will usually increase appreciably the transformation rate by adding a solution phase. Additional information on polymorphism is included in Section III, B,3,d and III,F.

D. MELTING

On continued heating, if the sample does not sublime or decompose completely it will usually melt, quickly changing to a pure liquid. If melting occurs gradually over a range of several degrees the sample is obviously impure. The temperature at which the last crystals melt is taken as the melting point.   It can be measured with accuracy and, as such, serves as an excellent identifying characteristic (Figure 22). The technique for the determination of melting points is discussed in

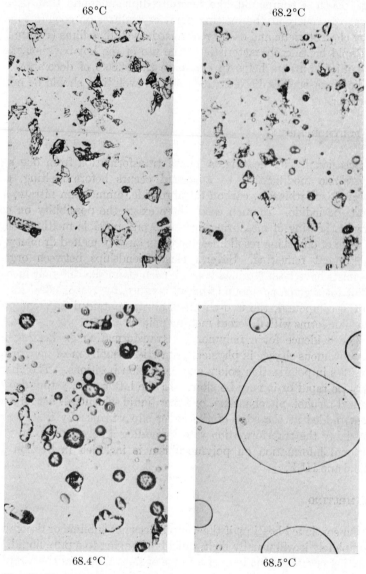

Fig. 22. Photomicrographs taken during melting of very pure azobenzene.

Section III,A,1 (hot stage), in Section III,A,4 (hot bar), and in Section III,A,3 (cold stage). A few points may be added, however, and others emphasized.

In general, the smaller the quantity of material used the more accurate the melting point. The sample should be small and should consist of well separated small crystals. A field whose area is only 10 per cent covered with separate crystals smaller than 325 mesh (44μ) is best. A convenient way to make a suitable preparation is to place a fraction of a milligram of sample on a half-slide, cover it with a clean cover glass, then slide the cover glass under pressure with a rotary movement using a pencil eraser. This simultaneously crushes and disperses the sample. The cover glass *must then be removed*, cleaned, and replaced so that all of the crystals are lying on the slide with none adhering to the underside of the cover glass. Crystals on the slide will melt consistently 1°C lower than crystals on the underside of the cover glass.

The equilibrium melting point determination has not yet been described in detail (see also Section III,A,1). To determine a melting point by this procedure, the hot stage or cold stage is heated and cooled very slowly over a narrow temperature range. To do this a certain amount of skill and practice is required since, in a sense, the temperature changes have to be anticipated. The preparation, a small-sized droplet (preferably about 1 mm. or less in diameter) under the cover glass, is allowed to crystallize and then placed in a hot stage already heated to a point just below the melting point. The stage is slowly (about 1°C/min.) heated until the crystals are partly melted. The stage is then allowed to cool until crystallization begins. Heating is recommenced at the instant, or just before, the crystals begin to grow. In the same way heating is stopped at the instant, or just before, the crystals begin to melt. The equilibrium melting point is given as the midpoint of the range between which growth and melting occur. These two temperatures usually lie about 0.2–0.3°C apart.

Occasionally, it is necessary to observe melting points on complex mixtures, such as waxes, fats, and oils. Such materials melt over a wide range as successively higher melting eutectics become liquid. Subtle polymorphic transformations often also take place. Because the eye is not particularly sensitive to subtle changes taking place slowly over a period of several minutes, it is advisable in many of these cases to replace visual observation with an instrumental means of recording such changes.   A photovoltmeter is very useful for this purpose.   The photocell is clamped above the eyepiece so that all the exit light from the microscope is utilized.   The temperature and the amount of light collected by the photocell is then recorded at appropriate intervals.   Crossed polars, phase contrast, dark field illumination, or ordinary light may be used depending on the

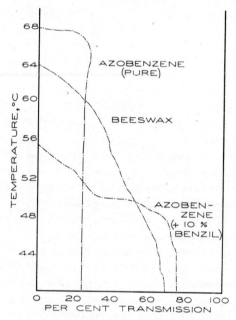

Fig. 23. Photovoltmeter readings during melting of beeswax and two samples of azobenzene, one pure and one impure.

particular system involved and the subtlety of the changes to be observed.   Figure 23 shows several such curves for systems of interest.

It is also important to be able to measure an accurate melting point on crystals that decompose at the melting point.   There are two ways of doing this: one, based on use of the hot bar, and a second, based on the hot stage (Section IV,B).   The use of the hot bar is, of course, quicker and simpler.

Small crystals sprinkled on the hot bar come to temperature equilibrium in about 5 seconds, hence have little opportunity to decompose before melting.   Kofler has compared melting points taken on the hot bar with literature values taken by the capillary method (Table VII).

TABLE VII

Melting Points of Substances Melting with Decomposition

Substance	Melting point, °C	
	Hot bar	Capillary
Chloral hydrate	76	49–53, 52–57
Glucose	150	146
Sucrose	189	170, 180, 185, "about 160"
Lactose	218	201.6
Phloroglucinol	222	217–9, 200–9, 217–9
α-Arginine	260	207
Sulfathiazole	266	252–6, 254–9

The melting points of decomposable compounds can also be followed as a function of time in order to obtain an indication of stability as a function of temperature (Section IV, B).

A special case of decomposition is loss of water, or more generally solvent, of crystallization. Such compounds (e.g., oxalic acid dihydrate) usually lose their water of hydration just below 100°C and change either slowly or abruptly to an opaque, white, powdery pseudomorph of the hydrate. The change may sometimes occur in such a way as to look like a polymorphic transformation. To differentiate between these two phenomena, a second preparation is heated in which the crystals have been immersed completely in a drop of mineral oil before covering with a cover glass. If the crystals contain water of hydration, the droplets of water formed on dehydration will be apparent in the mineral oil. The absence of liquid droplets in the mineral oil after such a change indicates polymorphism, especially if it can be ascertained that some solvent of crystallization soluble in mineral oil is not present. This may be done by replacing the mineral oil with other liquids, such as methyl phenyl silicone.

The heating of hydrates may, depending on the heating rate and access to air, result in dehydration followed by melting of the anhydrous substance or the hydrate directly. In the latter case, the anhydrous substance then gradually becomes dehydrated and may resolidify as solid anhydrous crystals, which melt on further heating. All these types of behavior are shown by oxalic acid dihydrate.

When good crystals from the melt are desired, it is necessary to minimize decomposition by cooling the melted preparation very quickly by placing the slide top-side down on a cold metal block for a few seconds. In some cases, however, this means of lessening the amount of decomposition may lead to the crystallization of a metastable polymorphic form.

Decomposition often has other peculiar effects. For example, hexanitrodiphenylamine crystallizes from fusion in a characteristic manner because solidification of a few crystals liberates heat (heat of crystallization) locally and decomposes some of the surrounding melt. The gases produced push the melt ahead of the crystal front a short distance, where more melt crystallizes and the procedure continues. This results in a "terrace structure" (Figure 21) of alternate gas bubbles and crystals characteristic of compounds that decompose on melting.

The quantitative study of thermal stability, i.e., decomposition of fusible compounds, and melting of decomposable compounds, is discussed in further detail in Section IV,B.

Occasionally, the sample for melting point determination may sublime so strongly that it coats the heat baffle and glass cover for the stage and may completely sublime before melting. Hexamethylenetetramine, borneol, p-bromobenzoic acid, and hexachloroethane are offenders in this respect. The simplest remedy is a large cover glass and plenty of sample. Other means of preventing loss of sample due to sublimation are to seal the edges of the cover glass with a suitable cement, or to use a sealed capillary. Silicone cement (stopcock grease) is an excellent sealing material for general use, although a nitrocellulose lacquer (duPont Duco cement) may be used if time is taken for drying. The preparation should, in spite of these precautions, be placed in the hot stage only 5–10°C below the melting point. It must be remembered, as pointed out earlier, however, that the melting point of sublimed crystals on the underside of the cover glass is about 1°C higher than that of crystals in contact with the slide. In some cases, it is an advantage to use a fused salt as cement (55 per cent KNO_3—45 per cent $NaNO_2$ melts at 141°C).

If a sealed capillary is used to eliminate the effects of sublimation there are the usual problems of reflection and refraction at the rounded surfaces. This is taken care of partly by the immersion of the entire capillary in silicone grease, or other cement, covered with a cover glass. However, this solves only half of the problem since the inside walls of the capillary still reflect and refract light.

Fischer[5] has proposed the use of a microbulb which is essentially a flattened capillary. This is made with a 2 mm. inside diameter glass tube about 6 cm. long by flattening a portion at one end to form a chamber about 1 mm. thick and 3 mm. wide. The flattened end is then sealed and cooled; the sample is introduced and the opposite end is sealed. A final length of about 30 mm. is best so that the preparation can lie flat on the hot stage. It is important to remember again, but for the last time, that with such a preparation the melting point of the sublimate onto the top of the chamber will be higher by several degrees than the true melting point, and that only the crystals on the bottom of the chamber constitute the sample so far as the melting point is concerned.

This bulb is useful also for molecular weight determination by the Rast method (Section III,B,2,c), for measurement of critical solution temperatures (Section III,B,2,b), and for refractive index measurement of volatile liquids by the glass powder method (Section III,B, 2,a).

2. Observations on the Melt

After the compound has melted, the properties to determine include the refractive index of the melt and, in some cases, the boiling point, molecular weight, and critical solution temperature.

A. REFRACTIVE INDEX OF THE MELT

The refractive index of the melt may be used for characterization of pure compounds, or for the analysis of binary mixtures. Ordinarily, such refractive indices would have to be determined using a refractometer capable of operation at high and controlled temperatures. However, Kofler[6] has suggested a novel method based on the use of a standard set of glass powders of accurately known refractive indices. This technique is just the reverse of the Emmons variation technique for determining the refractive indices of crystals. Emmons varies the temperature in order to change the refractive index of the liquid in which the crystal is mounted for study. The index of the liquid is then determined at the temperature at which the crystal disappears.

[5] R. Fischer, *Mikrochemie* 28, 173 (1940).
[6] L. Kofler, *Mikrochemie* 22, 241 (1937).

The Kofler technique, on the other hand, uses isotopic solids of known refractive index mixed with the solid substance whose refractive index is desired.   On heating the solid substance to its melt-

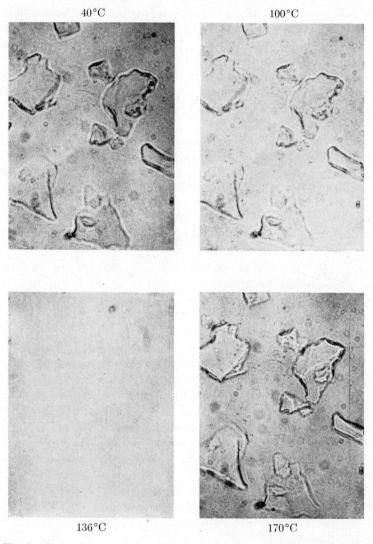

Fig. 24. Determination of the refractive index of acetanilide melt using glass standard 1.5203; the position of the body-tube is slightly above best focus in order to show the becke line.

ing point the particles of glass appear immersed in the melt, and the
becke line technique is used to distinguish the phase having the higher
refractive index (Figure 24). By this test a given glass particle
illuminated with axial light will show a bright line outlining the particle. This line will move toward the phase having the higher refractive index as the body-tube is focused higher. The reverse will
occur on focusing downward. If the two refractive indices are identical the glass particles will, of course, be invisible. A red filter is
used usually to eliminate the effects of dispersion, and the data in the
tables (Chapter V) were, in general, determined with the red filter.
It should be remembered, however, that the indices of the glass powder standards were measured with sodium light. This is unimportant
analytically because each glass standard will always have the same
index at the same temperature even though that index is not precisely known.

The temperature coefficients of refractive index of glass are of the
order of $0.000001/°C$, whereas the coefficients for most organic compounds lie between 0.0002 and 0.0009; hence, the refractive index of
the glass particles can be assumed, for practical purposes, to be constant over the range from about $50-250°C$. The organic melts, on
the other hand, will vary considerably $(0.04-0.18°C)$ over the same
range. If, now, a given melt is observed to have a refractive index
only slightly greater than a known glass particle immersed therein, a
temperature may be reached on further heating at which the particle
disappears. At this temperature and wavelength the melt and the
glass particle have identical refractive indices taken for simplicity
as the refractive index of that glass particle at room temperature
and as measured with sodium light.

If a second glass particle of slightly lower refractive index is mixed
with the same compound and melted it may be possible to determine a
second temperature, higher than the first, at which the two have
identical indices. This gives a second quantitative characteristic, as
well as data from which the temperature coefficient of refractive
index may be easily calculated.

The temperature coefficient varies as indicated above from about
0.002 for relatively simple unconjugated molecules to about 0.009
for complex highly conjugated molecules, or molecules with several
halogen or nitrogen containing functional groups.

Some compounds decompose or sublime so strongly above the
melting point that it is difficult to determine the refractive index of the

melt by this technique.   It may, in these cases, be possible to supercool the melt using glass standards of higher refractive index thus
reaching a temperature at which the supercooled melt has the same
index.   Supercooling of any melt is much easier the smaller the
amount of melt present, hence very small droplets should be used.
As the stage cools the index of the glass particle is checked; if crystallization occurs the preparation is removed and remelted on the hot
bar, then replaced in the hot stage for continued observation.   This
procedure may have to be repeated several times, but if the droplet is
small enough there should be no difficulty in supercooling most compounds even to room temperature.

The test set of glass powder standards is available either through
A. H. Thomas or W. J. Hacker and consists of 24 glass powders with
the following refractive indices (Table VIII).

TABLE VIII

Refractive Indices (n_D) of Standard Glass Particles for Use in Measuring the
Refractive Index of Organic Melts

1.3400	1.5204 (1.5203)	1.6011 (1.6010)
1.4339	1.5299 (1.5301)	1.6126 (1.6128)
1.4584	1.5403 (1.5400)	1.6231 (1.6229)
1.4683	1.5502	1.6353 (1.6346)
1.4842 (1.4840)	1.5611 (1.5609)	1.6483 (1.6482)
1.4936 (1.4937)	1.5700	1.6598 (1.6593)
1.5000	1.5795 (1.5794)	1.6715 (1.6718)
1.5101	1.5897 (1.5898)	1.6877

These values are specified by the manufacturer (Jena Glasworks).
The indices, using the red filter that is always used by the Koflers
and for most, if not all, of the data in the tables in Part V, are close
to but not identical with the above values which were determined with
sodium light.   The powder n_D = 1.3400 is cryolite, 1.4339 fluorite,
1.4584 vitreous silica; all the others are optical glass.

Since a second batch of optical glass almost never exactly matches
the first in refractive index, large supplies of the original glasses were
ordered.   However, this supply was destroyed during World War II
and a new supply had to be obtained.   The refractive index values
for the second set are given in Table VIII with the corresponding
earlier values in parentheses for the first set where differences occurred.   The differences are, in all cases except two (1.6353–1.6346
and 1.6598–1.6593), very small and amount to temperature differences

of less than 1°C. An average correction can be easily calculated, in any case, assuming an average temperature coefficient of 0.0005/°C. The error involved in such a procedure is well within the accuracy of the method since small amounts of impurity may change the temperature of refractive index match by several degrees.

In the preceding section (Section III,B,1,d), the use of melting point determination as a function of time of heating is suggested as a means of quantitatively following the decomposition of a given sample. In a similar manner, the rate of decomposition of a sample can be measured by the rate at which the refractive index of the melt changes. These two functions, rate of change of melting point and rate of change in refractive index, are most useful in measuring the relative stabilities of two different samples of the same substance. Such problems are important, especially in the explosives industry and the pharmaceutical industry where the thermal stability of certain high explosives and certain drugs is very important. Progress in the search for stabilizing agents for such compounds is measured quickly by either of these two techniques.

The measurement of refractive index of the melt is also very useful in the analysis of binary mixtures (Section III,E,7).

B. CRITICAL SOLUTION TEMPERATURE

This simple constant is easily determined using the hot stage and requires very small amounts of sample (1–2 mg. of each component).

TABLE IX

Test Substances for Use in Determination of Critical Solution Temperatures

Test substance	Use
Aliphatic hydrocarbons	Aniline, benzyl alcohol, or tricresyl phosphate
Lower fluorinated aliphatics	Performic acid
Naphthenes	Aniline or methanol
Lower aliphatic alcohols	Paraffin oil
Intermediate aliphatic alcohols	Water
Aliphatic aldehydes	Glycerin
Aliphatic ketones	Glycerin
Fatty acids	Paraffin oil
Benzene and homologues	Glycol or ethylenecyanide
Phenols	Water
Essential oils	Glycerin
Aqueous inorganic salt solutions	Phenol, or butanol

The two components are sealed in a glass capillary 30 mm. long and 0.7–0.8-mm. inside diameter, and placed on the hot stage so that the liquid meniscus can be observed during heating. The meniscus usually appears and disappears at a single reproducible temperature. The following test substances are recommended by Fischer (Table IX).[7,8]

Binary systems of miscible organic compounds can be analyzed quantitatively as illustrated in Figure 25, which shows Fischer's data for the analysis of phenol-cyclohexanol and phenol-aniline mixtures by determining the critical solution temperature of these mixtures with water as test substance.

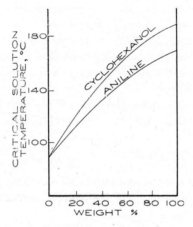

Fig. 25. Critical solution temperatures in the systems: phenol-cyclohexanol and phenol-aniline using water as reagent.

The usefulness of this technique in the identification of compounds and in the quantitative analysis of mixtures is limited only by the lack of analytical tables and the fact that, in general, the method can be applied only to liquids or low-melting solids.

C. MOLECULAR WEIGHT DETERMINATION

Molecular weight may be determined by the Rast method using the hot stage. A simple cover glass preparation is used if the components

[7] F. Fisher and G. Karesek, *Mikrochemie* **33**, 310 (1947).
[8] F. Fischer and E. Neupauer, *ibid.* **34**, 319 (1949).

are not too volatile, and a capillary if either of the components is too volatile. However, even when a cover glass preparation is apparently justified, it is desirable to use a cement to seal the mixture under the cover glass and to measure the melting point at the center of the preparation. Camphor requires a capillary, however, bornyl chloride may be used with a sealed cover glass. The compounds that may be used include those listed in Table X.

TABLE X

Solvents for Use in the Microscopic Determination of Molecular Weight

Compound	m.p., °C	Compound	m.p., °C
Perylene	276	Tetrabromoethane	93
Borneol	204	2,4,6-Trinitrotoluene	81
Hexachloroethane	186	Cyclopentadecanone	65
Camphor	178	Camphene	49.5
Bornyl chloride	130		

The determination of molecular weight using a microscope slide and cover glass is carried out in the following way. A carefully weighed mixture of the solvent and the test substance are mixed with a small mortar and pestle in the approximate weight ratio of 10:1. The mixture (100–200 mg.) should be wetted with a few drops of pure ether during grinding and mixing. A small portion of this mixture (5–10 mg.) is placed on a microscope half-slide, covered with a cover glass, and melted on the hot bar at 150°C, or a hot stage preset at about 150°C. As soon as the mixture is completely melted, the preparation is removed and crystallized rapidly by placing the slide cover glass side down on a metal cooling block. The cover glass is then cemented all around the periphery using a nitrocellulose lacquer, such as duPont Duco Cement, and the preparation is allowed to dry at a temperature not exceeding 50°C on the hot bar. Several identical preparations should be made up at the same time; the initial melting operation should be as rapid as possible to minimize sublimation of either component.

The preparation, after the cement has completely hardened, is placed in the hot stage preheated to a temperature 10–20°C lower than the expected melting point and with the stage set approximately for a temperature rise of 4°C/min. at the expected melting point. The center of the preparation is observed as heating continues; if the solvent is isotropic, crossed polars cannot be used, however, visibility is improved by using axial illumination. After the melting point is known within a degree from the first determination, the variable voltage is set for succeeding determinations to give more precisely a 4°C rise per minute at that temperature. The precise melting point is then determined using the stopwatch as described in the section on calibration of the hot stage (Section III,A,1). The point at which the last crystals of solvent disappear is taken as the melting point. The melting point should be measured several times on each of several identical preparations. The melted preparation should be chilled, cover glass side down, on a cold metal block after each determination to ensure fine crystals and a well-mixed preparation for the next determination.

The melting point of the solvent and the molar depression constant must be determined for each new sample of solvent since both properties depend on purity. The molar depression constant is, of course, determined by measuring the depression of melting point as described above using a substance of known molecular weight. No suitable solvent has been found that can be used above 130°C (bornyl chloride) in cover glass preparations, and, in general, only substances melting below about 130°C will be soluble enough in bornyl chloride to give good melting point depression.

It is, therefore, necessary to use capillary tube preparations at temperatures above 130°C. The capillary should be about 1.5–2.0 mm. inside diameter and about 30 mm. long. To prevent the solvent from subliming into a cooler portion of the capillary it is enclosed completely in a flat metal block having a small opening, about 3 mm. in diameter, through which the lower end of the capillary may be observed. The opening for the capillary is about 2.5 mm. in diameter, 35 mm. long, and slants downward at a very slight angle (about 5°). Before placing the capillary in the block, the mixture should be quickly melted and cooled in a water bath to give an intimate mixture of very fine crystals.

The temperature of last melting is determined as with the cover glass preparation, although heating should be at a slower rate (2°C/-min.) in order to maintain equilibrium conditions during melting. Although the stage is not calibrated to give corrected melting points under these conditions, the error involved is not important as long as the melting point of camphor, or other solvent, as well as its molar depression are determined in an identical fashion.

In order to avoid errors due to supercooling, the temperatures determined should, in every case, be melting points rather than freezing points. The use of a given solvent depends on the extent to which the test substance will dissolve. In most cases, it is wise to check each combination before taking time to weigh out precise amounts and mix them. The extent of solubility can be quickly estimated by a mixed fusion (Section III,B,5,b) between the solvent and the test substance.

D. BOILING POINT

The boiling point of liquids is easily determined using the same capillary heating block as described above for the determination of molecular weight. The only requirement is a short length of liquid in the bottom of the capillary, in or below which is a small bubble of air (the smaller the better). As the temperature increases the air bubble expands until it is approximately twice its original size. At about this point the bubble will suddenly expand many times its volume and expel most of the liquid from the capillary. This is the temperature at which the vapor pressure of the liquid is equal to the atmospheric pressure, i.e., the boiling point.

The major problem is to form a small air bubble in the liquid near the bottom of the capillary so that the meniscus will be in the field of view during heating. This is best done under a Greenough binocular microscope using a long drawn-out, capillary-tip eyedropper to introduce the liquid into the boiling point tube or capillary. With a little practice the liquid can be introduced close to the bottom so that a small bubble of air is trapped. The eyedropper capillary can also be used when empty to introduce an air bubble into the liquid droplet in the boiling point tube, or to change the size of one already present.

This boiling point block should be calibrated using several pure liquids of known boiling point. Suitable standards can be found in Table V, Section III,A,3, on the calibration of the cold stage.

3. Observations on Cooling

A. TENDENCY TO SUPERCOOL

Most organic compounds crystallize easily and quickly on cooling. However, some, like thymol, must be seeded or physically shocked to induce crystallization. Nearly all organic melts solidify to a glass if strongly supercooled in liquid air, or even a dry ice-cooling mixture. A few, like luminal, sulfamic acid, quinine, and n-butylamine hydrochloride, solidify to a glass even at room temperature. As a general rule, compounds crystallizing in flat plate-like habit (e.g., anthracene, naphthalene, fatty acids, diphenyl, and β-naphthol) seem to supercool less readily than compounds that crystallize as rods or needles.

A few compounds show intermediate tendencies. For example, thymol must usually be seeded or shocked to induce crystallization, while 2,4,6-trinitrotoluene, 2,4-dinitrophenol, and 1,3,5-trinitrobenzene supercool easily but always crystallize without seeding. The higher the temperature to which the melt is heated above the melting point, the longer the time at that temperature, and the smaller the sample, the greater the tendency for any compound to supercool.

B. CRYSTALLIZATION VELOCITY

The crystallization velocity appears to bear little or no direct relation to the inherent tendency of a compound to form a supercooled melt. It is generally true, however, that the rate of crystallization plotted against temperature passes through a maximum. As the temperature falls below the freezing point, the rate of crystallization passes through a maximum and then decreases on further cooling. The maximum in the rate of crystallization may occur between room temperature and the melting point (e.g., DDT, tetryl, and quinine). In many cases, however, the maximum lies below room temperature and the rate of crystallization becomes more rapid as the preparation cools (e.g., trinitrotoluene).

C. FORM OF THE CRYSTAL FRONT

As the melt cools, crystallization progresses from one or more nuclei or seeds and definite, characteristically shaped crystals grow through the melt (Figure 26). There are three general types of crystal fronts. One type rather rare, is shown by acetylsalicylic acid, p-azoxyanisole, naphthalene, and anthranilic acid. The crystal fronts for these compounds are almost formless, insofar as crystal forms are concerned. In general, the front is smooth, is made up of large areas of uniform orientation, has few crystal markings, and grows rapidly.

A second, and very common type of crystal front, is shown by thymol, sulfur, acetanilide, 2,4,6-trinitrotoluene (Figure 26), sulfonal, benzamide, and picric acid. These compounds form discrete crystals whose habit may be described as rod-like, plate-like, etc.

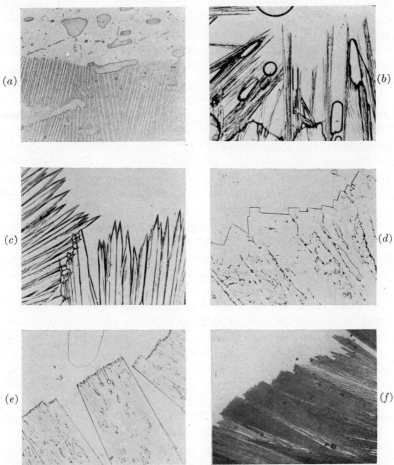

Fig. 26. Variation in habit of the growing crystal front: (*a*) ammonium nitrate V, (*b*) pentaerythritol tetranitrate II, (*c*) 2,4-dinitrotoluene I, (*d*) bis-(β-nitroxyethyl)nitramine II, (*e*) 2,4,6-trinitrotoluene I (pure), (*f*) 2,4,6-trinitrotoluene I (impure).

Many of them show definite profile angles and extinction (e.g., thymol, sulfur, and salol) that can be correlated with the corresponding conoscopic observations.

The third type of crystal front is shown by p,p'-DDT (Figure 27) and tetryl at low temperatures, quinine, 2,4,7-trinitrofluorenone, and cholesteryl acetate.   These compounds all grow as spherulites starting from a number of separate nuclei.   The spherulites are, in most cases, made up of thousands of fine needles, although occasionally the crystal units (e.g., tetryl at 50–60°C) may be fairly broad rods.

The form of the crystal front of a given compound depends on several variables; polymorphic form, purity, and temperature.   Each of the above cases refers to the polymorph stable at room temperature. Crystal growth from an impure melt is usually slower, but the crystals may be either larger or smaller than crystals grown from a pure melt.   In general, the crystals will become better formed the more slowly the crystal front grows.   Thus, it may be possible to measure profile angles on impure samples even though it may have been impossible with crystals from the pure melt.   On the other hand, some compounds, e.g., 2,4,6-trinitrotoluene, are less well-formed and harder to identify in the impure state.

Temperature exerts a strong influence on appearance of the crystal front of most compounds (Figure 27).   This is due to the effect of temperature on rate of growth, and the fact that crystals grown slowly just below the melting point are larger and better formed than crystals grown rapidly.

In some cases, the form of the crystal front varies from point to point in the preparation, owing to different crystal orientations. Fortunately, however, most crystals always show nearly the same orientation.   For example, 2,4,6-trinitrotoluene and picric acid almost always show a bisectrix view.   On the other hand, 2,4-dinitroresorcinol shows a flash or an obtuse bisectrix figure, or more often, a position intermediate between these two principal views.   For this reason, it is necessary in all cases to correlate crystal angles, extinction, etc., with conoscopic observations.

There are other properties that may be determined on the crystal front.   A more or less complete list, except for conoscopic observations, is as follows:

Profile angles, correlated with extinction angle and/or interference figure.
Habit of the crystal front.
Refractive indices relative to the melt.
Birefringence and dispersion.
Sign of elongation.

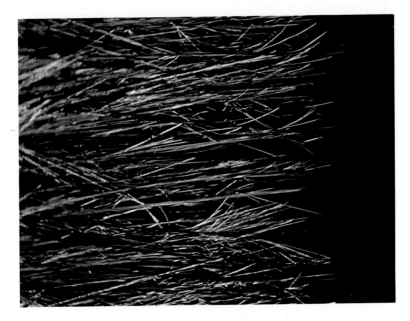

80 °C

60 °C

Fig. 27. Effect of temperature on the habit of the growing crystal front of

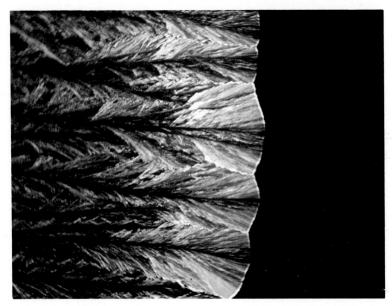

45°C

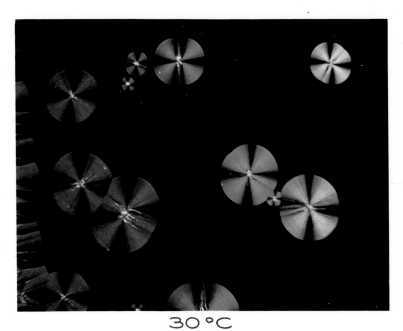

30°C

1,1,1-trichloro-2,2-bis(*p*-chlorophenyl)ethane (DDT).

There are several ways in which these determinations can be made easier. This is desirable because the crystal front often grows rapidly and repeated fusions are necessary to measure all the properties. The "meltback" (Section III,B,5,a) and "mixed fusion" (Section III,B, 5,b) have been developed as methods of stabilizing the crystal front so that crystal angles and other properties can be measured.

D. POLYMORPHIC TRANSFORMATIONS

A second growth of crystals indicating a polymorphic transformation is sometimes observed after the usual crystallization of the melt. This may occur spontaneously (e.g., mercuric iodide, vanillin, cholesteryl acetate, ammonium nitrate, carbon tetrabromide, β-naphthol, dibenzyl), or it may require seeding (e.g., monochloroacetic acid, resorcinol, and hydroquinone).

Some systems, e.g., cholesteryl acetate and p-azoxyanisole, have a liquid crystalline modification as the high-temperature "solid" phase. This phenomenon is quite easily recognized as the first anisotropic crystals tend to flow like a liquid, and since they can be deformed readily by local pressure on the cover glass. The liquid crystal phase usually transforms spontaneously on cooling to a stable, solid polymorphic form. The characteristic appearance of the liquid crystals often aids considerably in identifying these compounds since there are relatively few common compounds that exhibit this phenomenon.[9]

In general, however, polymorphic transformations do not afford a dependable observation for establishing the identity of a compound. Only a few compounds (e.g., mercuric iodide, vanillin, cholesteryl acetate, ammonium nitrate, and carbon tetrabromide) show a dependable solid-solid transformation which always occurs as the preparation cools. Other compounds may crystallize directly in the stable form, or in a high-temperature modification that could supercool to room temperature without transforming to the stable form. In a few cases, it is possible to obtain any one of several different polymorphic forms depending on conditions of size of sample, temperature, seeding, and shock. Kofler[10] has published a careful fusion study of 1,3,5-trinitrobenzene covering the methods used to obtain any one of three possible polymorphic forms. Spontaneous crystallization of a com-

[9] H. W. Foote, *International Critical Tables*, Vol. I, 1926, pp. 314–320.
[10] L. Kofler, *Z. physik. Chem.* **A188**, 201 (1941).

pletely fused very small sample of some compounds often gives an unstable polymorph not ordinarily obtained (e.g., acetanilide, 2,4,6-trinitrotoluene, and 1,3,5-trinitrobenzene).

Kofler has also suggested a method for crystallizing unstable polymorphic forms by seeding with a stable isomorphous phase. He illustrates this with the picric acid-trinitrobenzene (TNB) system in which picric acid has a highly unstable polymorphic form, which has been obtained only by seeding with the stable form of TNB. This is carried out in a mixed fusion (Section III,B,5,b) between TNB and picric acid in which only a very small area under the cover glass is occupied by picric acid. The picric acid can be supercooled below the melting point of the unstable phase (75°C), and the stable form of TNB will seed the isomorphous solid solution between stable TNB and unstable picric acid (Figure 85).

Polymorphic transformations make fusion analysis more complex, but increase the number of properties that may be determined for each compound. The mechanism of the transformation and the optical properties of the new crystalline phase are as characteristic of the compound as the properties of the first crystalline phase, and their use often make identification more certain. It is often difficult, however, to control conditions so that a desired polymorph is obtained. The transition temperature and reversibility of a given transformation (monotropic, irreversible; or enantiotropic, reversible) are also characteristic properties, but usually they are so difficult to determine they have little value in routine analytical work.

E. BOUNDARY MIGRATION

Occasionally on cooling, an already completely crystallized preparation may show further recrystallization in the solid state. This may happen spontaneously on cooling, e.g., bis(β-nitroxyethyl) nitramine (DINA), and vitamin K, or more often on reheating to a point just below the melting point, e.g., 2,4,6-trinitrotoluene, p,p'-DDT, and octachloropropane. There are two types of boundary migration: one, grain growth, characteristic of metals and many organic or inorganic compounds whose molecules are approximately spherical, e.g., octachloropropane, camphor, pinene hydrochloride, ice, fluorite, and periclase, and second, recrystallization characteristic of a few anisotropic organic compounds whose lattices show anisotropy of elasticity, e.g., TNT, p,p'-DDT, vitamin K, and DINA.

Such compounds show characteristic unidirectional boundary migration. For a more thorough discussion of this phenomenon with figures see Section IV,D.

4. Observation after Cooling

A. VOLUME CHANGES

Volume changes on cooling often lead to very characteristic shrinkage cracks, e.g., ammonium nitrate, PETN, 2,4,6-trinitroresorcinol, and tetrachlorohydroquinone (Figure 28). The pattern of the shrinkage cracks often make it easier to recognize a given compound. Different orientations or, especially, different polymorphs of a given compound can often be more easily recognized by typical shrinkage cracks.

B. SOLUBILITY OF AIR IN THE MELT

Some compounds, such as thymol, 1,3,8-trinitronaphthalene (Figure 28), o-nitrobiphenyl, 2,4,6-trinitrotoluene and acetanilide, dissolve air or other gases in the molten condition but reject them on crystallization. This causes the crystallized preparation to be more or less filled with gas bubbles. The shape and number of these gas bubbles is often useful in the characterization of fusible compounds. The arrangement of these bubbles is often a function of the crystallization temperature, e.g., 1,3,8-trinitronaphthalene.

C. COLOR AND PLEOCHROISM

A colorless or an isotropic colored compound will not show pleochroism. On the other hand, probably all colored anisotropic crystals show pleochroism, although in many cases the different absorption of light in different directions may not be discernible to the eye. Most of the polynitro compounds, such as ammonium picrate (especially the red variety) and hexanitrodiphenylamine, show strong pleochroism. It is possible to obtain a spectrographic record of the pleochroism of a given compound by use of the Jelley microspectrograph.[11] This reference also includes an excellent general discussion of pleochroism.

[11] E. E. Jelley, in A. Weissberger, ed., *Physical Methods of Organic Chemistry*, Vol. I, Interscience, New York, 1949, page 847.

Qualitatively, pleochroism can be observed easily by rotating the crystal on the microscope stage using either the analyzer or polarizer. A color change on rotation indicates pleochroism.   Nakamoto gives a

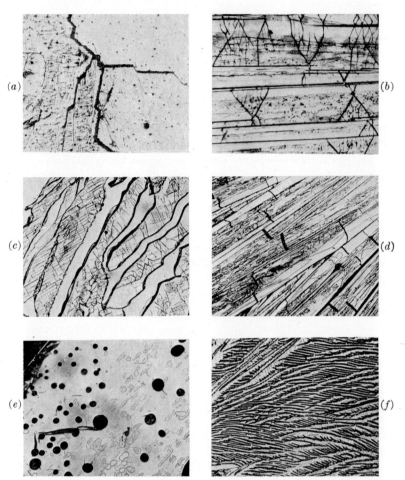

Fig. 28. Shrinkage cracks for: (*a*) ammonium nitrate II, (*b*) tetrachloro-hydroquinone, (*c*) 4,6-dinitroresorcinol, (*d*) pentaerythritol tetranitrate;   gas bubbles for: (*e*) ethylenediamine dinitrate, and (*f*) 1,3,8-trinitronaphthalene

good account and discussion of pleochroism in hexamethylbenzene and hexabromomethylbenzene.[12]

[12] K. Nakamoto, *J. Amer. Chem. Soc.* **74,** 390 (1952).

The quantitative study of pleochroism as described by Dr. Jelley
is far more refined than the usual operation of illuminating the crystal

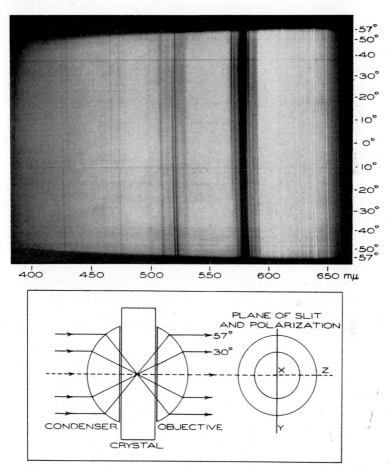

Fig. 29. Experimental arrangement and absorption curve for neodymium
sulfate octahydrate obtained by Dr. E. E. Jelley using Model IV of his microspectrograph.

with axial polarized light and noting the color in each of the
different principal orientations. The steps taken by Dr. Jelley include: (1) confining the area of illumination to that of the crystal
under study, (2) aluminizing the substage mirror to prevent double
reflections, (3) substituting an achromatic condenser or a 4-mm.

achromatic objective for the usual condenser, (*4*) focusing the image of a distant arc or ribbon-filament lamp on the crystal being studied, and (*5*) using the analyzer but never the polarizer for visual observations.   The microspectrograph (Section II,F) has a Wollaston prism that produces two adjacent spectra corresponding to the two vibration directions in the crystal.   The use of the Jelley microspectrograph is also illustrated by its application to the study of pleochroism of rare earth salts.[13]   Figure 29 shows one of the absorption curves obtained by Dr. Jelley with neodymium sulfate octahydrate.

D. TWINNING

Occasionally crystals grown from fusion show twinning.   This is evident under crossed polars as an abrupt change in extinction position in one part of what seems to be a single well-formed crystal or crystal grain.   One portion, or portions, of the crystal will show extinction in one position, while other portions of the same crystal show extinction in a different position.   The polarization colors may be different in the two twinned portions, but are not necessarily so.

It is sometimes possible with certain compounds, e.g., *p*-dichlorobenzene (Figure 47) and *p,p'*-dicaproyldiphenyl, to cause mechanical twinning by exerting pressure on the cover glass after the melt has solidified.   The lamellar twin-bands which develop in these two compounds are due to slipping along specific lattice planes.   A few compounds develop this same type of lamellar twinning spontaneously during cooling.   A good example of this is the unstable beta polymorph of 2,6-dinitrotoluene, which is often obtained on spontaneous solidification of the melt.

E. BIREFRINGENCE

The birefringence of a given crystal can be estimated as high, low, or moderate, however, almost every microscopist has his own ideas as to the proper levels for these three designations.   It is of some use to refer the birefringence to that of some common compound, such as picric acid, since all preparations of thin crystalline films have about the same thickness (20–30 μ usually).   Picric acid under these con-

[13] E. E. Jelley, *Nature* **136**, 335 (1935).

ditions shows colors averaging around a first-order red or slightly lower.

Determination of the birefringence can also be carried out by direct comparison with the known birefringence of picric acid, or by measurement of the thickness of the preparation indirectly by measuring the diameter of a glass rod in the preparation. The first method is carried out by preparing a mixed fusion (see Section III,B,5,b) with picric acid; the thickness of the preparation is determined from the polarization color and known birefringence (0.043) of picric acid. The thickness, determined in this way with the polarization color of the unknown, gives the birefringence of the unknown compound. The relationship between these properties is given by the equation:

$$n_2 - n_1 = \frac{\text{birefringence}}{1000 \times \text{thickness}}$$

The thickness is measured in microns and the birefringence in millimicrons. It is necessary, of course, to obtain the customary bisectrix view of picric acid, and one of the principal views of the unknown compound.

It is usually more accurate to use a fine glass fiber obtained from commercial fine glass wool. Fiberglas No. 85, made by Owens-Corning Fiberglas Corporation, is made up of fibers that are remarkably uniform and usually about 20–25 microns in diameter. The preparation is made by fusing the compound under a cover glass with one or two of these rods in the preparation. The cover glass is held down as the melt solidifies, so that the distance between the slide and the cover glass is the same as the diameter of the rod. The diameter of the rod is measured and the birefringence is then determined from the above relationship. The largest source of error is in the estimation of the polarization color. This requires some practice and a polarization color chart or the use of a compensator, preferably the Berek type.

The determination of birefringence is often a shortcut in the determination of crystal optics, since it enables quick measurement of the difference between two of the principal refractive indices.

F. ANOMALOUS VARIATION OF POLARIZATION COLORS WITH THICKNESS

All crystals have optical properties whose values vary with the wavelength at which they are measured. This is true of isotropic as well as anisotropic, uniaxial as well as biaxial, crystals.   An anisotropic crystal whose refractive indices do not vary appreciably with wavelength will show, when examined between crossed polaroids, interference or polarization colors apparently identical with Newton's series of thin film interference colors.   This series is shown in the photomicrograph of the "lens crystal" of thymol (see the Frontispiece; upper left).

The polarization colors of a crystal arise through interference between two components of plane polarized white light that travel through the crystal at different velocities (different refractive indices), and with vibration directions normal to each other.   Since one component travels more rapidly, it will emerge from the crystal a certain distance ahead of the slow component (dependent on the velocities of the two components and the thickness of the crystal).   The distance (designated as the retardation) between the fast and slow component when they emerge from the crystal determines the polarization color in the same way that the distance between the top and bottom surface of a thin film determines the interference color obtained from that film.   Only when the retardation is nearly constant for all wavelengths will the polarization color be indistinguishable from the corresponding color in Newton's color series.

The retardation will, in general, vary with the wavelength, because the refractive indices are not constant at all wavelengths.   Hence the polarization colors will vary, more or less, from the standard (Newton's series).   Usually the variation is so slight that a normal eyesight cannot detect a difference.   With certain compounds, however, the anomaly is very strong and can be used as an aid in identifying that compound.

Since anomalous polarization colors are due to variation with wavelength of the refractive indices, which, in turn, cause variations in the birefringence, the phenomenon is usually designated as "dispersion of birefringence."   Many compounds (usually highly conjugated compounds, or molecules containing highly refractive groups, such as bromo, iodo, nitro, and conjugated double bonds, e.g., picric acid, benzil, ammonium picrate, tetranitroaniline, and hexanitrodiphenylamine) show anomalous polarization colors.   These colors are very characteristic for such compounds and aid in identification.   Unfortunately, very few compounds show sufficiently anomalous colors for this property to be of general use.

The variation in polarization colors with thickness is obtained by crystallizing the compound from fusion in such a way that a thickness gradient is obtained. This can be done qualitatively and quickly by depressing a part of the cover glass during crystallization. Depression of an edge of the cover glass gives a wedge-shaped preparation with a wide variation in thickness, especially good for low birefringent materials. Depression near the center of the cover glass, on the other hand, gives polarization colors increasing radially from the point of depression. There is a better chance, in this way, of obtaining different orientations with different birefringence and polarization colors.

Jelley, who is responsible for the refinement of this technique, proposes two methods[11] for the preparation of wedge-shaped crystalline films suitable for quantitative study. The first of these requires a small plano-convex lens for use as a "cover glass." The preparation filling the space between the slide and the convex lens will form a plano concave lens of crystalline material; hence the name "lens crystal."

The color photomicrographs (Frontispiece) show examples of normal and anomalous polarization colors. The lens crystal of thymol shows very nearly ideal polarization colors. The next two, picric acid and HND (hexanitrodiphenylamine) are good examples of strong dispersion of birefringence. Comparison of the polarization colors of these two with the colors shown by thymol will show strong differences. The colors of picric acid corresponding to the first order yellow and orange, are tan and reddish-brown, respectively. The colors of HND are very different in the low first order colors: indigo for black; purple for gray; and blue for white. These variations from the ideal Newton's series are easy to remember, and quite sufficient for the identification of these two compounds by anyone trained in recognizing variations in polarization colors.

The Jelley microspectrograph can be used to determine quantitatively the dispersion of birefringence of any compound for the orientation shown. Two models of this instrument have been described in Section II,F.

The determination of dispersion of birefringence using the wedge preparation can be carried out in two ways: one, in the absence of information regarding the actual wedge angle the dispersion of birefringence is determined in terms of the birefringence at 5893 A taken as 1; and two, when the wedge angle is known the actual birefringence at any wavelength can be calculated. In both of these the image of the wedge is focused on the slit of the microspectrograph with the bands of polarization colors oriented perpendicular to the length of the slit. The spectrogram is then photographed using 35-mm. Pana-tomic-X film. Two parallel lines are now ruled across the spectro-gram corresponding to the thick and thin ends of the wedge, and the bands of polarization colors are numbered by order as in Figure 30. A wavelength scale is then attached to the spectrogram, and the wavelengths λ_n, λ_{n+1}, λ_{n+2}, ..., at which the nth, $(n+1)$th, $(n+2)$ ..., interference bands cross the upper ruled line are recorded.

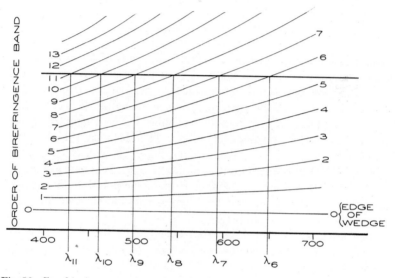

Fig. 30. Graphical computation of birefringence at different wavelengths (courtesy of Dr. E. E. Jelley).

The value of the retardation for any wavelength, λ_n, at which an interference band of the nth order intersects the upper ruled line is $n\lambda_n$, and the corresponding birefringence is $n\lambda_n/t$, where t is the thick-ness of the wedge at that point. The value of the retardation at 5893 A is then obtained by graphical interpolation, and the values of retardation for any other wavelength are calculated relative to the retardation at 5893 A taken as unity. In this way it is unnecessary to know the thickness of the wedge.

If the thickness, and hence the slope of the wedge are known, the birefringence at any wavelength can, of course, be calculated. If the slope is taken as θ and the distance between two bands measured using the eyepiece micrometer is d for a wavelength λ, the birefringence for that view is $\lambda/d \tan\theta$.

The lens crystal may also be used to determine the birefringence at any wavelength (Figure 31). Such a lens, which should be plano-convex and preferably of fused quartz, can be calibrated by photographing Newton's rings in sodium light with the slit of the microspectrograph wide open, or by photographing the interference bands using a compound of known birefringence which will always crystallize in a definite known orientation. Such a standard compound is picric acid with a birefringence of 0.043 at 5893 A for the usual view showing a centered obtuse bisectrix interference figure.

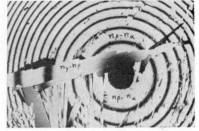

Fig. 31. Birefringence rings on lens crystals of 1-nitronaphthalene (left) and piperonal (right) (courtesy of Dr. E. E. Jelley).

If the lens and microscope are calibrated using Newton's rings by transmitted light, the two surfaces involved must be half-silvered or coated with a highly reflective dye, such as 1,1'-diethyl-2,2'-cyanine chloride. This dye is applied as a 1 per cent solution in 9 parts of methanol to 1 part of water. When a drop of this solution is applied to each surface, it spreads and evaporates leaving a film of dye having a very sharp absorption band at 5780 A and, therefore, a high reflectivity for sodium light. The Newton's rings obtained from surfaces treated in this way are quite as good as those from half-silvered surfaces.

To prepare a lens crystal, a plano-convex lens is placed convex side down on the object slide and touching a little of the substance under study. The slide is then heated so that the substance melts and flows in a continuous film into the space between the slide and the lens. The slide is then cooled and seeded, if necessary, to induce crystallization. It is usually desirable to melt back the crystals leaving a small portion as seeds so that the crystal front grows slowly to give large well-formed crystals. When such a preparation is examined between crossed polars in monochromatic light, a series of dark rings are observed, corresponding to retardations of λ, 2λ, 3λ, etc., whose radii are proportional to 1, $\sqrt{2}$, $\sqrt{3}$, etc. When several different orientations are present, each orientation will show a ring diameter that corresponds to the birefringence for that orientation. Birefringence spectrograms (Figure 32) are obtained by projecting the image of the lens crystal onto the slit of the microspectrograph so that the slit passes through the center of the lens. From a comparison

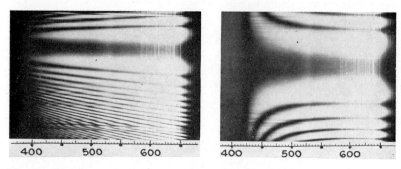

Fig. 32. Birefringence spectrograms for *p*-nitrophenol (left) and benzil (right) (courtesy of Dr. E. E. Jelley).

of Newton's rings using air and the interference spectrogram, the birefringence of the substance can be determined at all wavelengths for which sensitive film is available.

In the absence of a microspectrograph a monochromator or even good filters, especially those of the interference type, may be used with equally accurate results. The microspectrograph, however, increases greatly the ease of making the necessary measurements.

G. CONOSCOPIC OBSERVATIONS

The interference figure of a crystal is a most important identifying characteristic. It allows determination of the optic axial angle, sign of double refraction, as well as the dispersion. It is sometimes difficult, however, to obtain an interference figure, and in a few cases almost impossible to obtain the acute bisectrix or optic axis figure by fusion methods. Most crystals that tend to crystallize as needles, such as 1-nitronaphthalene, are in this latter class.   In these cases, other properties must be used in place of those usually obtained conoscopically.

On the other hand, it is often possible to obtain good interference figures (acute bisectrix or optic axis figures) by use of one of the following or similar techniques.

If separate crystals, approximately 20–50 μ on edge, are available these may be mounted in a viscous medium, such as Canada balsam, Aroclor, Aquaresin (a glyceroborate furnished by Glyco Products Company), methyl phenyl silicone, or thick Karo syrup.   By sliding the cover glass horizontally using a needle the suspended crystals, if not too large, will roll so that any desired orientation can be obtained.   Any master of this technique will have no need for a Universal Stage.

All of the following techniques involve methods of seeding the melt which will give random orientations with the attendant possibility of obtaining the desired interference figure.   For example, the melt may be seeded by touching with a needle around the edge of the cover glass, or an uncovered melted preparation may be seeded in the following way.   Very fine crystals are sprinkled on a clean cover glass which is then pressed into the melted preparation.   Another method involves heating the unfused sample under one side of the cover glass so that when fusion occurs the melt will spread quickly into the cooler region under the far side of the cover glass.   Here the melt cools rapidly and crystallizes at once to give many randomly oriented crystal grains.   These methods are designed to give crystal orientations that would not be obtained by spontaneous crystallization.

A study of normal biaxial interference figures shows that the birefringence is zero at the points of emergence of the optic axes, increases toward the position of the acute bisectrix, and continues to increase along the normal to the optic axial plane.   The birefringence in a uniaxial figure increases radially from the point of emergence of the optic axis.   Dispersion of birefringence observed on the interference figure is not the same as that observed on a lens crystal, since the latter depends on changes in thickness, and the former principally on changes in orientation.   As a matter of fact, it should be emphasized that, in general, an anomalous series of polarization colors is characteristic only for that particular orientation of that compound.   Other orientations usually give a different series.   The reason that the series of colors shown in the Frontispiece for picric acid and HND are so characteristic is because these two compounds always solidify in the same orientations, so that they always show the same series of colors.

Strictly speaking, therefore, observation of anomalous polarization colors on an interference figure should always be carried out on crystals of the same thickness, to ensure that the same components of the refractive indices always produce a given polarization color. Practically, however, crystals of all normal thicknesses will show identical series of colors so far as the average eye can tell. This method is often one of the best for a given compound. RDX gives excellent results by this method, as can be seen in the photomicrograph of the interference figure in the Frontispiece (lower right). The dispersion of the optic axes of a biaxial crystal is also worthy of study, since many compounds can be characterized uniquely by these data alone.

The optic axial angle of a biaxial crystal is dependent upon, and can be calculated from, the refractive indices. The relationship is as follows:

$$\sin^2 V_\alpha = \frac{\alpha^2(\gamma^2 - \beta^2)}{\beta^2(\gamma^2 - \alpha^2)}$$

where V_α is one-half the optic axial angle for negative crystals, and 90° minus one-half the optic axial angle for positive crystals. α, β, and γ are the three principal refractive indices. It is obvious that dispersion of birefringence ($\gamma - \beta$ and $\gamma - \alpha$) will cause a variation in, or dispersion of, the optic axial angle. This variation in the optic axial angle with wavelength is usually designated as dispersion of the optic axes.

Dispersion of the optic axes can be studied best through observation of the interference figure. If a crystal shows no dispersion of the optic axes, the isogyres (black brushes) will show no colored fringes in the vicinity of the eye of the brush. However, almost all organic compounds show at least slight dispersion of the optic axes, even though dispersion of the birefringence may be too weak to detect.

In general, dispersion of the optic axes can be expressed as red greater than blue, ($r > b$), or blue greater than red, ($b > r$), depending on the position of the red and blue fringes with respect to the black brush. If the brush is blue on its concave side and red on the convex side, then the dispersion is $r > b$. This apparently reversed situation can be explained readily by visualizing the interference figure, first with white light and then with blue and red filters. The photomicrograph of the RDX interference figure in the Frontispiece shows that RDX has strong dispersion of the optic axes, $r > b$. This can be confirmed by visualizing the photomicrograph with red and blue filters. This gives the same effect that would have been produced by illuminating the crystal, and taking the photomicrograph with red and blue light.

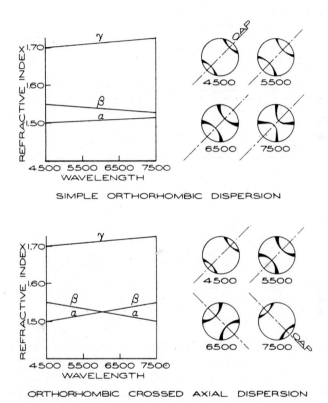

Fig. 33. Hypothetical examples of orthorhombic dispersion: upper, simple orthorhombic dispersion; lower, crossed axial plane dispersion.

Dispersion of the optic axes may be very pronounced in certain crystals. It is possible, for example, for the optic axial angle to change by 20–30°, or even more; instead of 2–3°, as in the usual cases. The photomicrograph of the optic axis interference figure of tetra-nitroaniline, TENA (Frontispiece; lower left), shows very strong dispersion, $b > r$. This photomicrograph was taken by Dr. E. E.

Jelley[14] of Eastman Kodak Company using a Didymium glass filter which has an absorption band in the yellow and green.   If white light had been used, only wide irregular bands of color but no definite brushes would have been observed.

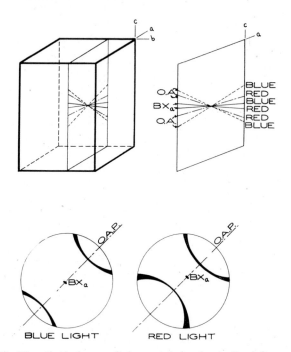

Fig. 34. Hypothetical monoclinic crystal showing inclined dispersion.

The more pronounced types of dispersion will be discussed in some detail because they are important and because they are not fully described elsewhere in a simple manner.

Orthorhombic dispersion is used to designate dispersion of the optic axes in the orthorhombic system.   Pronounced dispersion of the type to be discussed must be studied using monochromatic light, either through use of a monochromator, monochromatic light source or, best, with the microspectrograph (Section II,F).   It is then possible to determine the optic axial angle for any wavelength of light.

[14] A set of Dr. Jelley's excellent Kodachrome transparencies of interference figures is available through Ward's Natural Science Establishment, Inc., P. O. Box 24, Beechwood Station, Rochester 9, N. Y.

Two hypothetical examples of strong orthorhombic dispersion are shown in Figure 33, with the variations in the refractive indices that result in the interference figures of the type shown. The upper portion of the figure shows simple orthorhombic dispersion, while the lower portion shows orthorhombic crossed axial plane dispersion. The latter name is used, since below a certain wavelength the optic

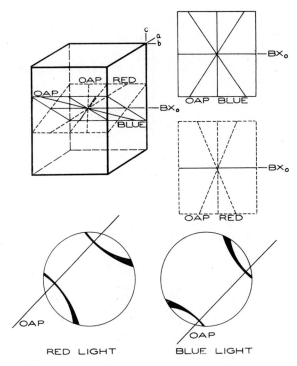

Fig. 35. Hypothetical monoclinic crystal showing horizontal dispersion.

axial plane is normal to its position above that wavelength (about 6000 A in the figure).

A variation of orthorhombic dispersion results when the beta refractive index crosses a line half-way between the alpha and gamma refractive indices. This causes the sign of double refraction to change numerical sign, and the acute and obtuse bisectrices to change positions with each other. This type of dispersion is called "orthorhombic dispersion with change of sign." If combined with crossed axial plane dispersion, the full name is "orthorhombic crossed axial plane dispersion with change of sign."

In the orthorhombic system the dispersion is the same whether the acute bisectrix is parallel to the *a*, *b*, or *c* crystallographic axes; however, in the monoclinic system it is possible to observe three different types of dispersion, depending on the orientation of the acute bisectrix with respect to the crystallographic axes.

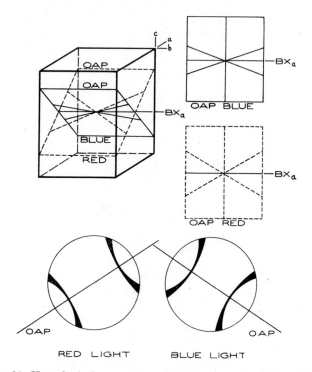

Fig. 36. Hypothetical monoclinic crystal showing crossed dispersion.

Inclined Dispersion. A monoclinic crystal in which the optic axial plane is *010* will show inclined dispersion (see Figure 34). This type of dispersion resembles simple orthorhombic dispersion, except that in the latter the change in position of the two optic axes with wavelength is symmetrical. In inclined dispersion the positions of the two optic axes can move independently. This difference is due to the fact that the acute bisectrix is fixed in the orthorhombic system but can vary in the monoclinic system (unless the acute bisectrix is parallel to b).

Horizontal Dispersion. If the optic axial plane is perpendicular to *010*, with the obtuse bisectrix parallel to the b axis, the crystal may show horizontal dispersion of the optic axes (see Figure 35).

Crossed Dispersion. If the optic axial plane is perpendicular to *010*, with the acute bisectrix parallel to the b axis, the crystal may show crossed dispersion of the optic axes (see Figure 36). Crossed dispersion must not be confused with crossed axial plane dispersion.

These three types of dispersion in the monoclinic system (inclined, horizontal, and crossed), may be regarded as simple monoclinic

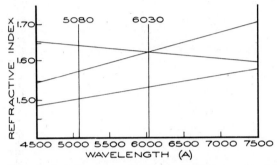

Fig. 37. Hypothetical dispersion of refractive indices in a biaxial crystal.

dispersion. It is possible for a monoclinic crystal to show a more pronounced dispersion involving two or more of the simple types of monoclinic dispersion. The first of these is designated by the general term, "monoclinic crossed axial plane dispersion," since it is of the same general type as orthorhombic crossed axial plane dispersion. In addition, some strongly dispersed compounds show crossed axial plane dispersion with change of sign, and a few like *HND* show a double change in sign.

In a hypothetical, and all-inclusive case, the refractive indices might vary as shown in Figure 37. No matter how these refractive indices are oriented with respect to the crystallographic axes, the following statements will hold:

1. The crystal has a positive sign of double refraction below 5080 A and above 6770 A.

2. The sign of double refraction is negative from 5080 A to 6770 A.

3. The optic axial plane changes to a position normal to the original position at 6030 A; the crystal is "uniaxial" at that wavelength.

4. The optic axial angle is 90° at 5080 A and at 6770 A.

5. The crystal shows crossed axial plane dispersion with a double change of sign.

The above crystal could be orthorhombic, triclinic, or monoclinic. If monoclinic, however, this crystal can also be said to possess all three simple types of monoclinic dispersion over short ranges of wavelength. The type exhibited at the different wavelengths depends on the orientation of the refractive indices with respect to the crystallographic axes. Since there are only three possibilities they are shown in Table XI.

TABLE XI

Dispersion in a Hypothetical Monoclinical Crystal[a]

Orientation at 4500 A		Type of simple monoclinic dispersion			
OAP[b]	BX_a	4500–5080 A	5080–6030 A	6030–6770 A	Above 6770 A
‖ 010	⊥ b	Inclined	Inclined	Horizontal	Crossed
⊥ 010	⊥ b	Horizontal	Crossed	Crossed	Horizontal
⊥ 010	‖ b	Crossed	Horizontal	Inclined	Inclined

[a] These data are based on the curves shown in Figure 37.
[b] Optic axial plane.

Triclinic crystals show triclinic dispersion in that the interference figure shows no elements of symmetry since the positions of the two optic axes, the acute and obtuse bisectrix, can change position with wavelength changes in a completely independent manner. To summarize, a centered BX_a interference figure for any orthorhombic crystal will show two planes of symmetry, one parallel to and one perpendicular to the optic axial plane. The corresponding figure for a triclinic crystal has no planes of symmetry, and for a monoclinic crystal the figure may have one plane of symmetry or none depending on the type of dispersion. The centered BX_a figure of a crystal showing crossed dispersion will show no planes of symmetry, with horizontal dispersion the plane perpendicular to the optic axial plane is a plane of symmetry, and with inclined dispersion the optic axial plane is a plane of symmetry in the BX_a figure.

Figure 38 shows the optic axial angles measured for a group of nitro and nitramine compounds as a function of wavelength. These measurements were made using a small constant deviation spectroscope as a monochromator. The optic axial angles were measured,

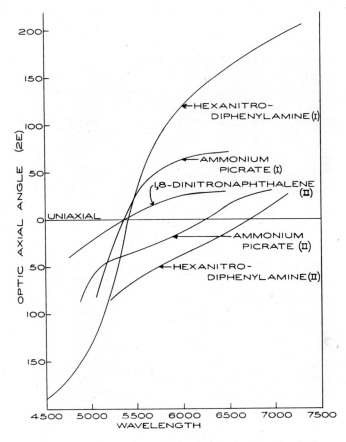

Fig. 38. Dispersion of the optic axial angle for several polynitro aromatic compounds and nitramines.

when necessary with an oil-immersion objective, but always on acute bisectric orientations. The following relationships were used to relate the various optic axial angles ($2E$, air; $2V$, crystal; $2H$, $n = 1.515$ immersion oil):

$$\sin E = \beta \sin V,$$
$$\text{and } \sin H = 0.66 \sin E$$

Measurements were made using the Mallard relationship which, stated in words, says that the linear distance between the optic axes in the interference figure is proportional to sin E, where E is one-half the optic axial angle in air. Other useful methods for the measurement of the optic axial angle are summarized by Jelley.[11]

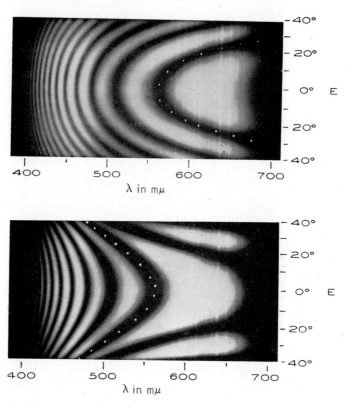

Fig. 39. Spectrogram showing dispersion of the optic axes for brookite showing orthorhombic crossed axial plane dispersion: upper, red end of spectrum; lower, crystal rotated 90° to show optic axis in blue end of spectrum (courtesy of Dr. E. E. Jelley).

The Jelley microspectrograph is also very useful for the determination of dispersion of the optic axial angle. By projecting the interference figure on the slit of the instrument, so that the slit passes between the two axes, a photographic record is obtained of the optic axial angles over the wavelength range from about 400 to 650 mμ, or into the near infrared if film sensitive in that region is used (Figure 39).

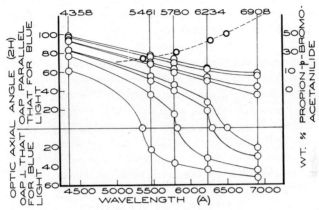

Fig. 40. Optic angle as a function of wavelength in the system propion- and acet-*p*-bromoanilides (courtesy of Dr. W. M. D. Bryant).

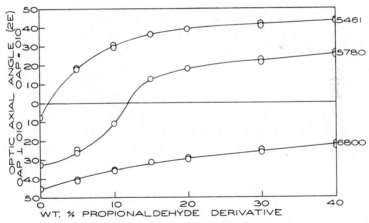

Fig. 41. Optic axial angle as a function of wavelength in the system acetalde- hyde- and propionaldehyde-2,4-dinitrophenylhydrazone (courtesy of Dr. W. M. D. Bryant).

W. M. D. Bryant[15,16] has also studied the anomalous dispersion of organic compounds and used the data for analytical purposes.   The

[15] W. M. D. Bryant, *J. Am. Chem. Soc.* **60**, 1394 (1938).
[16] W. M. D. Bryant, *ibid.* **55**, 3201 (1933).

dispersion of the optic axial angle, $2H$, has been found to vary greatly with wavelength for various solid solution compositions in the system acet-p-bromoanilide, propion-p-bromoanilide[15] (Figure 40). He has done the same for the 2,4-dinitrophenylhydrazones of acetaldehyde and propionaldehyde[16] (Figure 41).

Figure 42 shows a crystalline film of 1,8-dinitronaphthalene crystallized from the melt on a microscope slide. The deep blue polarization color visible in this photomicrograph and in the thymol mixed fusion shot of 1,8-dinitronaphthalene (Figure 44) is typical of optic axis views of crystals, and especially characteristic of acute bisectrix views of compounds showing crossed axial plane dispersion with small optic axial angles (HMX and 1,8-dinitronaphthalene). Figure 42 shows the interference figure of 1,8-dinitronaphthalene taken on the deep blue crystals in the adjacent photomicrograph.

5. Observations on Reheating

Reheating of a crystalline film already obtained by crystallization from the melt will often permit better observation of polymorphic transformations, and will also permit the formation of larger, better formed crystals which, in turn, are better suited for observation of optical and morphological properties.

A. MELTBACK

A meltback involves partial remelting of the preparation so that a portion of the solid remains as seed crystals. On cooling, crystals grow very slowly until the temperature falls 5–10°C below the melting point. Crystals grow slowly enough in most cases so that extinction and profile angles may be measured. The rate of cooling can be decreased further by placing the preparation on a heated brass block, on the hot stage, or on the hot bar. A temperature of 1–2°C below the melting point will give the largest possible crystals and the slowest growth rate.

B. MIXED FUSION

A mixed fusion is another excellent way of stabilizing the crystal front so that profile angles, extinction angles, etc., may be measured. This procedure is the basis for an identity test far more satisfactory

than the usual mixed melting point carried out in a capillary, and
also is the basis for the determination of composition diagrams (Section III,G).   The mixed fusion can also be used to make comparative
purity checks on different samples of the same compound, for the
determination of eutectic melting points, and to determine whether a
given mixture contains a given pure compound.

The first step in a mixed fusion (Figure 43) is to fuse the high-
melting component under the cover glass and allow it to resolidify
(a,b).   The low-melting component is then placed at the edge of the
cover glass (c) and heated so that it melts and runs under the cover
glass into contact with the first component (d).   Next, the preparation is reheated so that all the low-melting and most of the high-

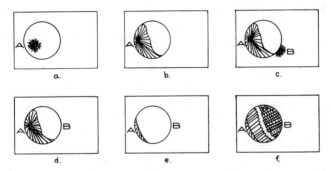

Fig. 43. Operations involved in a mixed fusion.

melting components are melted (e).   On cooling, crystals of both
components will, in general, grow up to the zone of mixing and stop.
The ideal low-melting component (for the purpose of studying well-
formed crystals of the high-melting component) should remain liquid
indefinitely and should be a solvent for the high-melting component.
Thymol, Canada balsam, aroclor, nitrobenzene, benzyl alcohol, tri-
cresyl phosphate, paraffin oil, and Cargille refractive index media have
all been used for this purpose.

This method of stabilizing the crystal front has another advantage,
in that crystals making up the crystal front digest in the eutectic
melt and become larger and better formed than crystals in the growing crystal front.   Good examples of this are picric acid and 1,8-
dinitronaphthalene.   From simple fusion, both compounds give a
regular crystal front but no measurable angles.   A mixed fusion,

however, gives a characteristic angular crystal front with measurable profile angles (Figure 44, and 47).

The mixed fusion is also the basis for an identity test superior to the mixed melting point, both in speed and dependability. The known and unknown are made the two components in a mixed fusion, and the crystal front of the higher melting component is observed as it grows toward the zone of mixing. If the two components are identical, the crystal front will continue to grow through the zone of mixing with no discontinuity in either rate of growth or form of the crystals. If the two are identical although one is more pure than the other, there may be a change in rate of growth and, perhaps, crystal size as the crystal front progresses through the zone of mixing. If the two components are different there will always be a discontinuity in the rate of crystal-growth, and almost always the type of crystals will change radically in the zone of mixing.

If the two components are different, of course, the composition diagram between them may be eutectic, addition compound, solid solution, or they may be completely insoluble. The type of composition diagram is, however, very easily recognized and the question of identity or nonidentity is easily, quickly, and unequivocally answered. The mixed fusion gives more definite and, therefore, more dependable results than the mixed melting point. When the two components form solid solutions (perhaps with identical melting points), when the two components are polymorphic forms of the same compound, or finally, when both are the same compound but one is very impure, there is no comparison between the two methods. The mixed fusion gives precise and accurate answers, whereas the mixed melting point would either give the wrong answer or be difficult, if not impossible, to interpret. It is far better to use the microscope so that the reasons for a particular behavior can be observed directly than to try to infer from observation of indefinite capillary melting point data whether two samples are different or identical.

The Koflers have used the mixed fusion, which they call a contact preparation, to determine the melting point of eutectics between their test substances and a group of standard compounds, such as azobenzene, benzil, and acetanilide. These melting points are tabulated in Chapter V, Table III, as additional identifying characteristics. Such melting points are analogous to the melting points of derivatives usually determined in organic qualitative analysis.

Another use of the mixed fusion is to determine whether a given

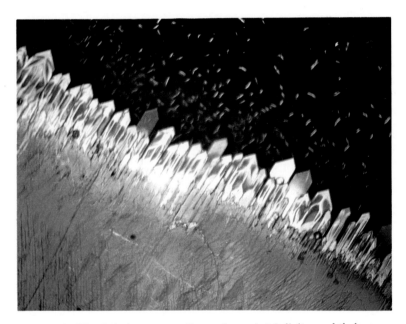

Fig. 44. Mixed fusion preparations: (upper) 1,8-dinitronaphthalene and (lower) picric acid.

mixture contains a small amount of a given pure compound. Each new component of a mixture causes a further lowering of the melting point of that mixture. If, then, a mixed fusion is run between the mixture and the compound in question, the eutectic melt in the zone of mixing will either have a lower melting point than the lowest melting eutectic in the mixture or there will be no lowering of the eutectic melting point. In the latter event the mixture already contained that particular pure compound. This determination is made as the mixed fusion preparation is heated in the hot stage.

6. Recrystallization from High-Boiling Solvents on a Microscope Slide

It is possible to go a step further than the meltback or mixed fusion for the preparation of well-formed crystals. Many compounds can be recrystallized from thymol or some other high-boiling liquid (benzyl alcohol, nitrobenzene, aroclor, etc.), on a microscope slide, to give well-formed characteristic crystals. This is quite useful since it eliminates the necessity of a macro recrystallization, or of recrystallizing from low-boiling solvents, such as alcohol or acetone, on a microscope slide. Such low-boiling solvents evaporate rapidly and spread readily over the slide making it very difficult to obtain well-formed crystals. Use of a solvent, such as benzyl alcohol, having a high boiling point and surface tension, eliminates these undesirable features and furnishes a method of recrystallization that is as simple as the common aqueous drop recrystallization of inorganic compounds. The procedure is based principally on the cooling of a hot saturated drop, rather than evaporation of the solvent. It can be carried out in an uncovered drop, or under a cover glass by heating the mixture until nearly all the solute is dissolved and then cooling to allow crystallization.

This technique is useful for the study of crystal morphology and optics, for the formation and study of unstable polymorphic forms, and finally for the isolation of well-formed crystals useful for x-ray studies or goniometry. Unstable polymorphic forms may often be obtained if the drop is cooled slowly and physically shocked after heating to a temperature high enough to dissolve all nuclei of the stable form. RDX, ammonium picrate, and hexanitrodiphenylamine crystallize under these conditions in very unstable high-temperature forms not obtainable in any other way.

The isolation of well-formed crystals is generally carried out in the same manner as above but with an uncovered drop. Crystals chosen for isolation and further study are teased out of the drop with a fine needle and dried by sliding across the clean slide away from the drop. Such a procedure permits the isolation of nearly perfectly formed crystals, which can then be mounted on a glass fiber for x-ray diffraction or goniometry.

7. Identification Schemes

To complete this section on the characterization and identification of fusible compounds, it remains only to discuss how the separate physical properties described above are integrated into analytical schemes for identification purposes.

A. IDENTIFICATION BY DESCRIPTIVE PROPERTIES

The simplest application is the use of the purely descriptive properties for the identification of one of a small group of known possibilities. An excellent example of this is the work of Gilpin on sterols.[17]

A summary of these easily determined and remembered properties is illustrated with the following descriptions of p-dichlorobenzene and p-dibromobenzene.

p-**Dichlorobenzene.** *Observations During Heating.* p-Dichlorobenzene melts at 53°C with sublimation (Figure 45) but no decomposition. Two habits are visible in the sublimate: plates and rods. The plates are rounded but show parallel extinction and 90° profile angles. The interference figures on these plates lie between the obtuse bisectrix and the optic axis. The rods are plates on edge and show oblique extinction. The extinction is usually about 15–20° but varies over a wide range.

Observations on Cooling. The melt supercools somewhat but always crystallizes spontaneously. The rate of crystal growth increases as the temperature falls to room temperature. The crystals show very high birefringence and grow as broad rods with an angular crystal front. The profile angles vary from 60° to 90° and the extinction angles from 15° to 27°.

The interference figures on these crystals are not very useful, although one or two crystals in the fusion preparation may show an

---

[17] V. Gilpin, *Anal. Chem.* **23,** 365 (1951).

off-center optic axis figure. An oil-immersion objective is necessary generally to determine the conoscopic properties that show p-dichlorobenzene to have an optic axial angle of about 88° with a positive sign of double refraction and very little or no dispersion.

The polarization colors increase with thickness in the normal way, in so far as the eye can tell. Most of the crystals show high order white polarization colors. A number of gas bubbles oriented along crystal imperfections can be seen, as well as shrinkage cracks between most of the grains. Occasionally, a crystal may show closely

Fig. 45. Sublimed crystals of p-dichlorobenzene II as they condense on the underside of the cover slip.

Fig. 46. Twin-bands in p-dichlorobenzene II mechanically induced by local pressure on the cover slip.

spaced twin-bands (Figure 46). These are slip-planes which form after crystallization as a result of strain during cooling. They can be introduced artificially by local pressure on the cover-slip using a needle and are easily visible between crossed polars as closely spaced parallel lines having different polarization colors.

Frequently during the crystallization of p-dichlorobenzene, a polymorphic transformation (I to II) is observed. This transformation proceeds rapidly at temperatures just below the melting point but slows down on cooling. The transition temperature is just above room temperature, hence the transition (II to I) is very slow in the range 20–30°C. If the temperature of the preparation containing some of form II is held just below the melting point, form I is transformed completely to form II. Good optic axis interference figures can be obtained on form II. The optic axial angle is about 80–85° with little or no dispersion; the sign of double refraction is positive.

Meltback. The crystals obtained on a meltback are little different from those obtained on spontaneous crystallization of the under-cooled melt.

Mixed Fusion with Thymol. Crystals of *p*-dichlorobenzene growing into thymol are well-formed rods or plates (Figure 47) that slowly dissolve after only one to two minutes. These crystals show profile angles varying between 60° and 90°. The extinction angle varies from 15° to 27° with an extinction angle of 15° for crystals having a profile angle of 63°. A profile angle of 90° corresponds to an extinction angle of 27°. The refractive index parallel to the length of these rods and plates is less than that of the thymol melt.

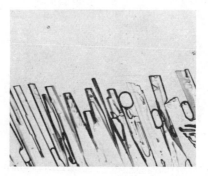

Fig. 47. Angular crystal front of *p*-dichlorobenzene II growing into thymol as a result of a mixed fusion.

p-Dibromobenzene. *Observations During Heating.* *p*-Dibromobenzene melts at 88°C with sublimation. The sublimate shows the same habits as *p*-dichlorobenzene, with the slight difference that the rods have a lower extinction angle (only 5–10° for the dibromobenzene) and do not round off so easily as the dichloro derivative.

Observations During Cooling. The melt supercools readily but always solidifies spontaneously to give feathery dendrites in the first region to crystallize; and large rods in the last portions of the melt to solidify.

Meltback. The rate of crystal growth increases as the preparation cools to room temperature. The crystal front is angular with a prominent profile angle of 90° and parallel extinction. Other rods growing through the preparation show lower birefringence and oblique extinction. The interference figure on these rods is usually an off-center, optic axis view which gives an optic axial angle, $2V$, of about 80° with little or no dispersion. The sign of double refraction is negative. The plate habit shows a figure which lies between the obtuse bisectrix and the optic axis.

These crystals do not show the mechanical twinning character-istic of p-dichlorobenzene, nor is there any evidence for polymor-phism of p-dibromobenzene.

Mixed Fusion with Thymol. Crystals of p-dibromobenzene grow-ing into thymol melt show two habits; one, plates; the other, rods. The plates show 90° profile angles and an interference figure between the obtuse bisectrix and the optic axis. The rods show variable angu-lar ends with an optic axis in the field ($2V$ about 80°; no dispersion; negative). All refractive indices of the crystals are higher than the index of the thymol melt.

B. KOFLER IDENTIFICATION TABLES

The Koflers[18] have done by far the best job to date of determining useful analytical data and tabulating it in a usable form. Their tables list nearly 1200 common organic compounds by increasing melt-ing point and include for each listing the eutectic melting points with two standard compounds, the refractive index of the melt, and nota-tions of important descriptive properties noted during the determina-tion. These data are included in the tables in Chapter V but have been retabulated to increase their usefulness by making four separate tables, each listing the compounds by a different analytical property, such as melting point, eutectic melting point, and refractive index of the melt.

C. LASKOWSKI'S USE OF CLASSIFICATION REAGENTS

Laskowski[3,4] has used the mixed fusion to characterize members of a class of organic compounds (aromatics) by the formation of a mo-lecular addition compound when 2,4,7-trinitrofluorenone (TNF) is used as second component. Compounds forming an addition com-pound when TNF is used as reagent in a mixed fusion are thereby proved to be aromatics (Figure 48). By heating such a mixed fusion preparation in the hot stage, four melting points in addition to that of TNF can be determined in one heating cycle; the aromatic unknown

---

[18] L. Kofler and A. Kofler, *Thermo-Mikro Methoden,* Universitätsverlag Wag-ner, Innsbruck, 1954.

itself, the addition compound and two eutectics: TNF-addition compound and addition compound-unknown (Figure 49) (Table XII).

The existence of several pairs of compounds in Table XII (1-bromonaphthalene and 1-iodonaphthalene; azobenzene and diphenyl; and p-aminoazobenzene and stilbene) whose melting point relationships are very close raises the question as to whether the four temperatures involved are actually independent.   Figure 50 shows the melting point of the addition compound to be completely random with respect to the melting point of the corresponding original compound.

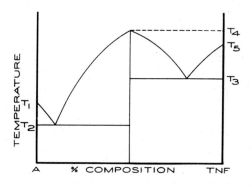

Fig. 48. Simple two-component phase diagram showing compound formation.

The same figure also shows that although the eutectic temperatures involved do not possess the same degree of randomness, it is sufficient to distinguish all but a few of the compounds involved.

If additional reagents can be found which, like TNF, give addition compounds with the members of a class of organic compounds, then a similar procedure will identify the members of that class of compounds by the four melting points corresponding to those in Table XII. Organic microqualitative analysis could then be carried out microscopically using the addition compound forming reagents as classification reagents, and the four melting points determined on one heating of the mixed fusion preparation as equivalent to the melting points of derivatives.   Picric acid may be used for organic bases, 2,4-dinitrophenylhydrazine for acids, aldehydes, and ketones, perhaps some Diels-Alder reagent may be found for systems of conjugated double bonds, many of the alkaloids form styphnates; organic acids form bromoanilides, primary alcohols form 3,5-dinitrobenzoic acid esters, phenols form *p*-nitrobenzoic acid esters, etc.

40°C   127°C

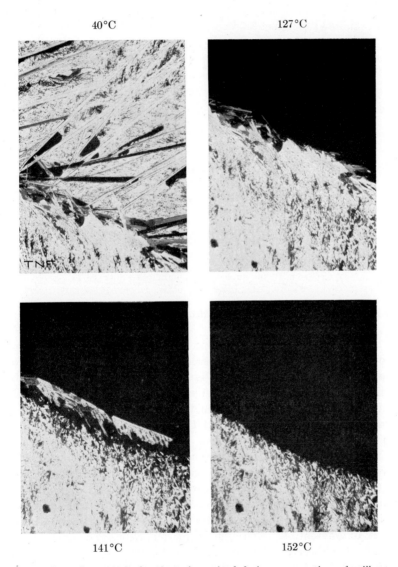

141°C   152°C

Fig. 49. Several stages in heating of a mixed fusion preparation of stilbene-2,4,7-trinitrofluorenone showing melting of successively higher melting phases.

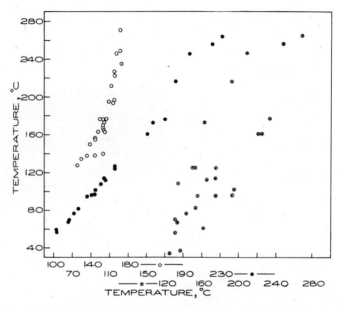

Fig. 50. Melting point relationships plotted from Table XII; open circles = T_3, full circles = T_2, and circled dots are T_4.

D. SCOPE AND LIMITATIONS OF FUSION METHODS IN IDENTIFICATION

The above techniques will, if the tables can be expanded, remove most of the objections to microscopic methods of identification of organic compounds. The methods can be used with a minimum of training, the equipment is not costly, the determination can be made quickly, and identification tables would then be available. It is possible at present to identify any compound in the tables, given as an unknown, within thirty minutes.

Both Kofler and Laskowski place great reliance on the eutectic melting point, which is far easier to determine than the melting point of the usual organic qual derivatives. Although the eutectic melting point is not always as independent a variable as might be hoped (Figure 50), several of them together are certainly sufficient, in most cases, to differentiate between different compounds of similar melting points (Table XIII). The melting point range for a given eutectic must lie below that of both components and, furthermore, within a range determined by the molar freezing point depression constants of

TABLE XII

Identification of Aromatic Compounds Using 2,4,7-Trinitrofluorenone

Original compound	Melting points[a]				Color of addition compound
	T_1	T_2	T_3	T_4	
6-Methylquinoline	. . .[b]	. . .[b]	. . .[d]	106.2[d]	Yellow—green yellow
1-Chloronaphthalene	. . .[b]	. . .[b]	147.1	162.3	Yellow—colorless[c]
1-Bromonaphthalene	. . .[b]	. . .[b]	152.5	171.5	Yellow—light yellow[c]
1-Iodonaphthalene	. . .[b]	. . .[b]	152.0	169.4	Yellow—green yellow[c]
2-Methylnaphthalene	35.5	. . .[b]	124.6	127.3	Yellow—orange[c]
Azoxybenzene	36.0	. . .[b]	135.4[d]	138.4	Yellow—green— colorless[c]
o-Hydroxydiphenyl	56.5	53.5	. . .[d]	II 131.7[d] I 133.4[d]	Red-orange—yellow green[c]
1-Nitronaphthalene	59.2	54.3	153.1	162.4	Pale yellow
Azobenzene	68	65.9	. . .[d]	132.8[d]	Orange—yellow[c]
Diphenyl	69.5	67.8	. . .[d]	131.9[d]	Bright yellow
8-Quinolinol	75.5	71.8	138.0	143.7	Orange-yellow
Naphthalene	81.0	78.0	143.5	153.7	Yellow—pale[c]
3-Aminoquinoline	94.0	86.5	143.7	155.6	Red
Acenaphthene	95.0	90.7	153.8	175.8	Red orange
1-Naphthol	96.0	93.5	162.0	192.5	Red
Phenanthrene	101.0	95.1	163.5	196.0	Yellow-orange[c]
N-Phenyl-2-naphthyl-amine	107.5	100.9	129.5	134.5	Black—translucent brown[c]
Acridine	110.5	106.3	152.1	167.1	Yellow-orange—pale[c]
2-Naphthylamine	112.0	105.0	150.1	175.8	Dark red
2-Naphthol	122.5	116.3	155.5	176.0	Red-orange—clear[c]
p-Aminoazobenzene	124.8	115.5	139.3	151.7	Red-yellow-orange[c]
Stilbene	124.0	116.4	139.2	149.5	Red-orange[c]
1,2-Benzanthracene	159.5	150.5	165.0	I 226.6 II 221.5	Red-red-orange[c]
1,3,5-Triphenylben-zene	171.5	157.5	152.5	163.2	Yellow
20-Methylcholan-threne	177.0	170.5	172.1	235.0	Dark brown
Anthracene	216.0	182.2	159.2	193.9	Red-red-orange[c]
Carbazole	244.8	198.8	161.3	210.9	Red-red-orange[c]
Chrysene	254.0	223.0	171.3	248.9	Orange—clear[c]
1,2,5,6-Dibenzanthra-cene	262.0	232.9	170.5	270.1	Red-orange—clear[c]
Naphthacene	335.0	. . .[b]	167.8	245.0[d]	Dark brown

[a] T_1 = original compound; T_2, eutectic: addition compound original compound; T_3, eutectic: TNF-addition compound; T_4, addition compound.
[b] Liquid at room temperature.
[c] Addition compound exhibits pleochroism.
[d] Peritectic reaction.

the two components.   In any identification scheme based on eutectic melting points it is wise to choose reference compounds not only melting in the same range as the test compounds, but to choose several reference compounds for the same range differing as widely as possible in their molar freezing point depression constants.   The latter will help to prevent predictable eutectic melting points.

TABLE XIII

Eutectic Melting Points for Closely Melting Compounds

Melting point, °C	Substance	Eutectic melting point, °C, with	
		Acetanilide	Phenacetin
135	Urea	102	122
135	Cinnamic acid	84	98
135	Cinnamaldehyde	79	96
135	Phenacetin	90	135
135	2,6-Dimethylpyrone	68	91
135–136	Malonic acid	62	84
136	1,4-Isobutylphenetidine	85	104
136	Phenyl propiolic acid	53	71
136	d-Galactonic acid-γ-lactone	109	128
136	Allyl-isobutyl barbituric acid	89	105
136	Sitosterol	105	115
136	Resorcylaldehyde	70	84

The eutectic melting point can be determined using a variety of kinds of sample preparation.   A mixed fusion preparation, an intimately ground mixture of the two components, a single crystal of one component crushed into contact with a sublimed crystalline film of the second component, or even two small single crystals in close proximity though not necessarily even touching.   All of these, even the latter, will show a lowering of melting point due to formation of the eutectic. The precise eutectic melting point is best determined by an equilibrium melting point determination on a mixture close to eutectic composition.   The next best, and wholly adequate, procedure is the determination of first melting of a 50:50 ground mixture of the two components.

Polymorphism is a definite threat to the determination of reproducible eutectic melting points since that temperature is dependent on the polymorphic forms involved.   The standard compound should always be one which shows no tendency to exist in an unstable crystal form under the test conditions used. If the test substance has several relatively stable crystal forms, there exists the possibility that different eutectic melting points may be obtained depending on the test conditions. Fortunately, this does not often occur and usually all reasonably similar test conditions will give the proper melting point as listed in Table III (Chapter V).

An example of an exception is sulfathiazole that can exist in several crystal forms of which the most stable are I (m.p. 201°C) and II (m.p. 174°C). All commercial preparations and most laboratory recrystallized samples of this compound are form II. On heating the melting point observed depends on the length of time before 174°C is reached. If slow enough, form II will transform completely to form I and the higher melting point will be observed. In the same way, the eutectic melting points will vary depending on the heating rates since the respective eutectic melting points are:

| Sulfathiazole | m.p., °C | Eutectic m.p. with | |
		Salophen	Dicyandiamide
I	201	172	167
II	174	159	152

The relatively small amount of confusion resulting from this behavior is, however, more than offset by the advantage of eutectic melting points in the identification of compounds that decompose at their melting points. Such compounds usually show sharp eutectic melting since those temperatures are normally below their decomposition range. A good example is acetyl salicylic acid (aspirin) that melts with considerable decomposition over the range 130–136°C in the hot stage, but which shows sharp eutectic melting points at 81°C with acetanilide and at 97°C with phenacetin.

The possible formation of addition compounds, solid solutions, and other such complications makes it a good general rule to carry out a mixed fusion between the test substance and the reference compound. In this way, the formation of new phases will be apparent and can be taken into account.

If, in a given system, an addition compound is formed two possible eutectic melting points may be observed depending on the composition of the mixture and other experimental conditions. As a rule, such mixtures, in powdered form, will show the lower melting eutectic,

As an example, the melting points of the binary and ternary mixtures as well as the pure dinitrobenzenes are:

| Compound | m.p., °C | Eutectic m.p. °C | |
		Binary	Ternary
m-Dinitrobenzene	91	m,o 64	
o-Dinitrobenzene	118	m,p 77	m,o,p 60
p-Dinitrobenzene	174	o,p 100	

If the original mixture contains the ortho and para isomers the eutectic should melt at 100°C. If the meta isomer is added a new eutectic melting at 60°C would be formed. It is not, of course, necessary to know all the melting points for this procedure to function, any lowering of the eutectic means a new component not present previously has been added to the mixture.

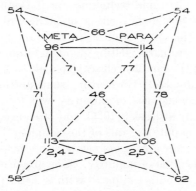

Fig. 51. Schematic representation of the eutectic melting points in all possible binary, ternary, and quaternary systems involving *meta*- and *para*-nitrophenol, and 2,4- and 2,5-dinitrophenol.

As the number of components in the mixture increases the increment by which the eutectic melting point decreases also decreases. Figure 51 shows the binary, ternary, and quaternary eutectic melting points for the possible systems involving m-nitrophenol, p-nitrophenol, 2,4-dinitrophenol, and 2,5-dinitrophenol. If a melting point of 58°C is obtained in the analysis of one of these mixtures, only the 2,4- and 2,5-dinitrophenol and the m-nitrophenol can be present; if *p*-nitrophenol is added, the eutectic melting point would drop to 46°C. Two ternary eutectics lie at 54°C, hence such a mixture must contain the *o*- and *m*-nitrophenols and either the 2,4- or 2,5-dinitro-phenols. In order to distinguish between these two possibilities either the 2,4- or 2,5-dinitrophenol is added to the mixture. A new eutectic melting point of 46°C means the added component was not previously present. If, on the other hand, the eutectic melting point remains at 54°C, the added component was already present.

C. DETECTION OF IMPURITIES AND ESTIMATION OF PURITY

It is often necessary to be able to estimate the purity of a given sample since usually it is a waste of time to determine physical prop-erties, such as ultimate analyses, melting points, refractive indices of the melt, etc., unless the sample is pure.

There are two quite rapid techniques for the estimation of purity: one, based on the hot stage melting point determination; and the second on observation of crystallization from the melt. The first of these involves an ordinary melting point determination with finely divided crystals of the sample well scattered about the field between a cover glass and half-slide. On heating, some portions of the sample containing high percentages of impurity will melt at the eutectic temperature, usually at least 5–10°C and often even more below the melting point of the pure crystals of the sample. The presence then of melted droplets over a range of temperature below the final melt-ing point is an indication of impurity. The absence of lower melting material indicates a pure sample. With a little practice the per-centage of impurity can be estimated crudely. The sensitivity of this method depends on the degree of dispersion of the impurity but usually can easily detect 1 per cent impurity.

Often it is more satisfactory to add a reference compound to the test substance and study the eutectic melting point than to study the melting point of the test substance directly. This is especially true for situations where the original sample contains an isomorphous im-purity, or where the original sample melts with decomposition. In the first case, the isomorphous impurity will usually not lower the melting point, but a reference compound will, in general, form a bi-nary or a ternary eutectic depending on the purity of the test substance. In the second case, the melting range of the compound that decom-

poses on melting will be lowered by the addition of a reference substance so that meaningful melting point data can be obtained.

The determination can be made somewhat more accurate by making
the melting point determination with a slightly larger sample so that
the temperature of the last melting of the sample as a whole can be
determined.   If, then, the lowering of melting can be determined, the
approximate purity can be calculated by the crude approximation of
1°C melting point depression corresponding, on the average, to about
2 weight per cent impurity.

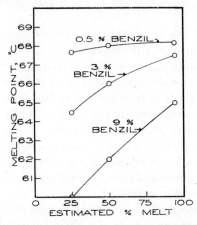

Fig. 52. Effect of degree of purity on melting range
determined by equilibrium melting points.

A more accurate method for the estimation of purity is based on the
equilibrium melting point determination.   As pointed out in the discussion of this method (Section III,B,1,d), the value obtained depends on the relative amounts of liquid and solid at the equilibrium
point.   If most of the sample is solid, the observed equilibrium melting point will be lower than when most of the sample is already
melted.   The difference between these two equilibrium melting points
is a fairly precise measure of the amount of impurity.   The only
problem is the estimation of the points (in terms of relative amounts
of crystals and melt) at which the two equilibrium melting points
should be taken.   This decision is easiest when the preparation has
been melted and recrystallized completely.   On reheating, the equilibrium melting points are determined at about 25 per cent melt, 75
per cent solid; and 90 per cent melt, 10 per cent solid.   An approxi-

mation to these results can be obtained more rapidly by making the melting point determination with a slow rate of heating (2°C/min.) and noting the temperature at the points where 25 per cent and 90 per cent of the sample is judged to have melted. Figure 52 shows these data for azobenzene at three stages of purification.

The melt itself should always be observed in order to look for high-melting insoluble impurities. As little as 0.25 per cent of insoluble impurity is detected easily, especially if the impurity is anisotropic. Changes in crystal habit on freezing may also indicate impurity; in certain cases this can be made semi-quantitative (Section III,E,4).

Observation of the crystallization process may also be used to estimate purity since impurities are left on freezing as eutectic melt dispersed throughout the crystalline preparation. The presence of this liquid eutectic usually is apparent as air bubbles suspended therein flow back and forth as freezing continues. The movement of air bubbles in the residual eutectic melt can be made more obvious by pressure on the cover glass with a needle. The observation of impurity in this way should be carried out on a melt-back (Section III, B,5,a) and within a few degrees of the primary freezing point. With some practice the amount of eutectic melt and thereby the amount of impurity can be roughly estimated.

Since all of these methods are approximate only, they cannot be used to tell whether one sample of a given compound is more or less pure than a second sample of that compound. The determination of relative purity usually can be done, however, very quickly by a mixed fusion between the two samples. The preparation is placed on the hot bar so that the zone of mixing lies parallel to the length of the bar and about half of the preparation is melted. The line of demarcation between melt and solid will be observed to be a straight line in each half of the preparation, but the two lines will not form a single line unless the two samples have the same melting point, i.e., the same purity. Differences in melting point amounting to as little as 0.2°C can be easily detected in this way.

D. METHODS OF PURIFICATION

All of the classical methods of purification (distillation, solvent extraction, crystallization, chromatography, etc.) can and have been adapted to micro samples.   Much of this has been well covered[19] so that only the techniques especially adapted to microscopic work and the use of fusion methods will be included here.

1. Crystallization on a Microscope Slide

The crystallization of any sample on a microscope slide depends on the availability of a solvent-slide combination such that the drop of solution will not spread in a totally unconfined manner.   This is solved by a choice of solvent (high surface tension like water, acetic

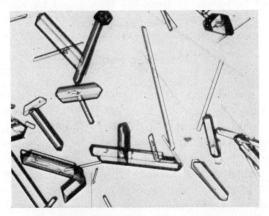

Fig. 53. Well-formed crystals of p,p'-DDT grown in a drop of thymol on a microscope slide.

acid, or other acids and bases; higher alcohols, aldehydes, ketones, esters, etc.), by ringing a small area of the slide with vaseline or other nonsoluble repellant media, or finally using slides of different materials (Teflon, polyethylene, celluloid, or other plastics) or coated with different materials not easily wetted by the desired solvents.

When a proper combination is found, the compound, usually in amounts of about 1 mg., is dissolved in the drop of solvent by warming.   Enough solute should be added, however, to saturate or nearly saturate the solution.   On slow cooling, crystals first appear near the edges of the drop.   These should be pushed back into the center using a fine glass tip.   When the drop is completely saturated, well-formed crystals can be observed growing throughout the drop (Figure 53). These may be studied *in situ* for optical properties; a cover glass may be placed over the drop to slow evaporation and permit time for crystal study, photomicrography, etc.; single crystals may be teased out of the drop with a glass tip and dried by sliding along the clean glass slide surface outside the drop; or, at the proper time, the drop may be "filtered" by touching with a small square of hardened filter paper. The crystals are pushed by the filter paper into a central spot and as much of the solution as possible is drawn out with the filter paper. The recrystallization may be repeated if necessary. The solution may be recovered from the filter paper by washing with a few drops of solvent.

2. Absorption Purification

An ingenious technique for purification has been developed by L. Kofler[20] based on the fact that, on heating, any mixture will melt partly to a liquid containing all the impurities and one solid component in excess. This solid component can be isolated if the eutectic melts are soaked into a porous medium, such as filter paper. In practice a small square of hardened filter paper (e.g., Schleicher and Schüll No. 575) about 1 cm. on edge is placed on a half-slide. The sample, usually not more than about 100 mg., is placed in the center of the filter paper, and a half-slide is placed over the sample at right angles to the lower half-slide. This "sandwich" is then placed on a hot bar and slowly moved toward higher temperatures until the sample just begins to melt, as indicated by a wet spot on the filter paper surrounding the solid sample. Movement of the slide is stopped at this point and, after applying pressure on the upper half-slide to squeeze the eutectic melt into the filter paper, the upper half-slide with the adhering solid sample is removed. The square of filter paper then is replaced and the sandwich is moved a few degrees higher on the hot bar. After repeating this procedure a few times the remaining solid crystals are pure enough for melting point determinations, refractive index of the melt, etc.

The number of steps, the amount of the sample absorbed at each step, and the final yield of pure compound are all interrelated as shown in Figure 54. The data plotted are based on the assumption

---

[20] L. Kofler and R. Wannenmacher, *Ber. Deut. Chem. Ges.* **73,** 1388 (1940).

that 100 mg. of a mixture of two components, A and B, forming a eutectic mixture at 60 per cent A, are present in equal quantities at the start.   Usually the compound to be isolated would be purer so that even fewer steps would be required.   In practice, something like half a dozen steps melting 25–30 per cent of the remaining sample at each step is recommended.   In general, there is no difficulty isolating sufficient pure crystalline solid to use for melting point determinations, refractive index of the melt, etc.

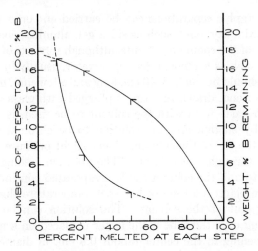

Fig. 54. Absorption purification; relationship between per cent of sample melted, weight of pure B left, and number of steps required.

Filter paper may be used for mixtures heated as high as 300°C if not held too long at that temperature.   Clay plates have been used at temperatures in this range and higher and behave very well.

The component isolated by the absorption technique is the last compound to melt during heating of the mixture.   Often it is desirable to isolate one of the minor components; one which, by the unmodified procedure, would be absorbed by the filter paper.   It is necessary in this case to change the composition of the original mixture so that a different component of the mixture becomes the one that would melt last on heating.   This is done by solvent extraction, sublimation, chromatography, etc.   Usually solubility differences are tried first since the major component may be assumed to be identified. Solvents in which the single identified constituent is highly soluble or only very slightly soluble are tried by observing the dry powder between the slide and cover glass as the solvent runs between into contact with a small portion of the powdered sample. If differences in solubility are noted, the entire sample may then be treated and either the undissolved portion or the extracted residue may be purified further by the absorption procedure.

3. Chromatography

Chromatographic separations can be carried out on a micro scale using standard adsorbents, such as silica gel, alumina, charcoal, etc., and with any of the common solvents, although solvents of intermediate polarity, such as acetone, ethanol, or water, usually function best. The column should be small, 5–10 cm. long and a few mm. inside diameter, the lower end, drawn to a tip, is plugged with glass wool. The adsorbent, in paste form with the solvent to be used, is drawn into the column by suction and the solution to be chromatographed is poured onto the top of the column. Very slight pressure then forces the solution through the column. The solution issuing drop-wise from the bottom of the column can be evaporated continuously as it strikes a slide placed on the hot bar at a temperature slightly below the boiling point of the solvent. The solution can be prevented from spreading over the slide if the latter is placed on a metal block having an opening in the center (about 0.8 cm. in diameter) above which the drop is centered. Under these conditions the solution evaporates quickly and the residue is concentrated at the coolest point on the slide (over the center of the opening in the block).

Occasional replacement of the slide will allow collection of several fractions, each differing in composition and some of which may give pure compounds directly, or when purified further by absorption of the melt (Section III,D,2).

4. Adsorption-Sublimation

One of the most useful devices for purification of mixtures has been suggested by W. Kofler.[21] This device is based on the use of gas-phase chromatography or, putting it another way, air or an inert gas saturated with the components of the mixture to be separated is passed through a preheated chromatographic adsorption column (under

[21] W. Kofler, *Monatsh. Chem.* **80**, 694 (1949).

vacuum if necessary).   About 80 per cent of all organic compounds are volatile enough to be purified at atmospheric pressure in this way.

The dimensions of the apparatus may be varied to suit the sample quantities involved, however, a convenient arrangement is shown in

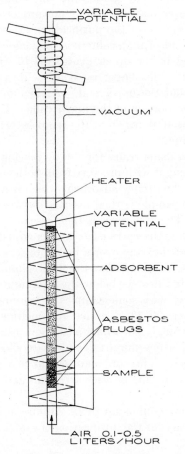

Fig. 55. Schematic drawing of an adsorption-sublimation unit.

Figure 55.   The adsorption column itself is 15 cm. long and 5 mm. inside diameter.   A glass tube about 6 cm. long and 10–12 mm. inside diameter is sealed to the upper end of the 5-mm. tube.   The adsorbent is held between two asbestos or glass wool plugs.   The upper plug is located at the junction between the narrow and wide tubing.

The sample, amounting to 5–10 per cent of the weight of the adsorbent, is placed just below the adsorbent and held in place with a third plug. A controlled slow stream of gas (0.1–0.5 l./hour) is passed upward through the column. The column is heated by an electrically wrapped 15-cm. glass tube surrounding the adsorption column. This heater may be moved upward or downward as necessary during the course of the purification. The sublimate issuing from the top of the adsorption column is condensed on a stainless steel cold finger inserted in the upper glass tube to within about 1 inch of the upper plug. This finger is cooled with a coil carrying cold water wrapped about the upper end. A vacuum connection also is placed in the upper portion of the upper tube. Finally, a thermometer is placed so that it registers the temperature of the adsorption column at equilibrium.

The apparatus is made ready for use by placing the upper plug in place and compacting it with pressure from both ends. The inverted column is next filled with dry adsorbent which is held in place with a second plug. The sample is then inserted between this second plug and a third one. The apparatus is then assembled; water is turned on in the cold finger, the carrier gas rate is adjusted, and the outer glass column is heated slowly over a period of several minutes with a voltage regulator setting such that the final column equilibrium temperature will be a few degrees below the melting point of the sample. It may be necessary with some samples to use higher temperatures, although more than 20–30°C above the melting point should be avoided. A less strongly adsorbing adsorbent usually is indicated in these cases. After a few minutes condensate should appear on the end of the cold finger. This sublimate should be removed periodically from the column by turning off the carrier gas and removing the cold finger.

Larger adsorption columns up to 15–20 mm. inside diameter have been used successfully for the purification of samples of several grams at one time.

The adsorbents ordinarily used in solution chromatography are too effective for gas phase adsorption, hence coarser adsorbent grains usually are used. Silica gel in about 0.5-mm. size grains can be used for samples subliming at temperatures up to about 150°C. Floridin XS in about 0.5 mm. grains may be used up to about 200°C if the fines are removed. Charcoal is very strongly adsorbing and should be used only for weakly adsorbed compounds or at higher temperatures. If temperatures above about 250°C. are used, however, a nonoxidizing gas must be used.

The fact that the adsorbent may catalyze decomposition of some adsorbed compounds, is a disadvantage of this technique Some compounds, normally stable at 40–50°C above their melting point, may decompose on an adsorption column at temperatures even below their melting point. It is often possible, however, to avoid decomposition by choosing a different adsorbent. For example, 1,2-benzanthracene, α-cinnamylbenzylcyanide, α- and β-naphthol, and α-naphthylamine decompose on silica gel but remain unchanged on Floridin XS. Some compounds, such as methylolbenzamide, 1,8-dioxyanthraquinone, α-naphthylaminothiourea, and veratryl cyanide, decompose on silica gel, Floridin, or charcoal. Pure benzamide is isolated from methylolbenzamide.

To summarize briefly, the usual operating conditions are: (1) temperatures a few degrees below the melting point, (2) a vacuum of 20–30 mm. mercury, and (3) a carrier gas velocity of about 0.1–0.5 l./hour. A complete adsorption sublimation usually requires 2–3 hours.

Even technical grade samples may be obtained completely pure by one adsorption in this apparatus. The double effect of sublimation and adsorption often give separations difficult, if not impossible, by other techniques. Mixtures of isomers, isomorphous substances, etc., may be separated as easily as widely differing substances.

E. ANALYSIS OF MIXTURES

There are only two widely applicable general fusion methods for quantitative analysis of binary mixtures: melting point depression and refractive index of the melt, of which the latter is usually by far the more accurate. In addition, there are a number of methods that are quantitative but of less general applicability: areal analysis when the two components are mutually insoluble, counting analysis on the crystals mounted in a differentiating refractive index medium, measurement of optical properties for isomorphous mixtures, change in crystal habit on crystallization from the melt, and rate of crystal growth. These methods are described below, more or less in increasing order of applicability.

1. Areal Analysis

Any sample which can be viewed in section and in which the components can be differentiated by area can be quantitatively analyzed for those components by areal analysis.   Used principally in metallography, where polished sections of alloys show relative areas of differ-

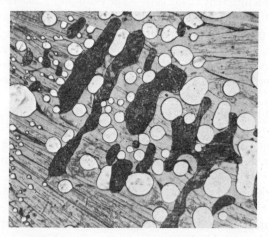

Fig. 56. Thin crystalline film of Amatol (TNT-
ammonium nitrate) suitable for areal analysis.

ent phases proportional to their volume ratios, this method is also of use, in special cases, for fusion preparations.   It is limited, however, to samples containing components wholly insoluble in each other, e.g., high explosives systems such as Amatol (TNT and ammonium nitrate, Figure 56), or RDX and wax.

The analysis itself may be carried out in any of a variety of ways which will give the relative areas of the components.   A drawing camera often is used to draw several representative fields onto cross-hatched paper, after which the number of squares representing each component may be counted.   Another simple way is to take photomicrographs of several fields; the components are then cut apart with scissors or a razor blade, collected, and weighed separately.   The percentage composition by weight can be calculated from the volume percentages using the known densities.

2. Counting Analysis

Any sample consisting of easily differentiated components in particulate form may be quantitatively analyzed by counting the number of each component in a number of representative fields.   The per cent by number is converted to weight per cent by correcting for the difference in average volume and density.

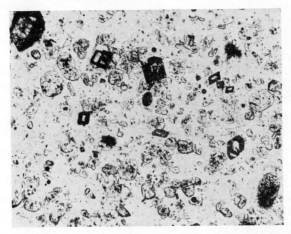

Fig. 57. Crystals of RDX (low contrast) and HMX (high contrast) dispersed in a medium of refractive index 1.590.

Differentiation between the components may be by differences in birefringence using crossed polars, in refractive index, shape, size, or color (natural or by staining).   Examples of this method of analysis include the determination of adulteration of diamond powder by quartz, corundum or silicon carbide, or the percentage of HMX in preparations of the high-explosive RDX.   Both of these determinations are based on use of refractive index and/or birefringence to differentiate between the components.   RDX-HMX mixtures, for example, should be mounted in a liquid having a refractive index of about 1.590 (Figure 57) since all three refractive indices of RDX are close to 1.590, and although HMX has one index near this value the other two are much higher.   With ordinary white light RDX shows very low contrast in this medium while HMX shows strong contrast (enhanced in certain positions with one polar).   A count of HMX should be made, usually about 5–10 per cent of the total sample, and a total count should also be made using crossed polars since RDX is difficult to count with ordinary light because of its low contrast. The particle sizes and shapes of these two components are usually so nearly the same that only the densities are needed to calculate the per cent by weight from the per cent by number. Since the weight per cent is to be determined, particle sizes below 5 microns, or other appropriate size, of both components may be ignored.

3. Measurement of Physical Properties in a System Showing Isomorphous Solid Solutions

When two compounds form a continuous series of isomorphous solid solutions the crystal properties (optical, morphological, and x-ray) vary continuously from the properties of one to the properties of the other, depending only on the composition. When the mixture is crystallized from the melt it is often convenient to measure the optic axial angle; this property when related to composition is useful for analysis.

Bryant[15,16] has used this method for the quantitative analysis of the p-bromoanilides of acetic and propionic acids (Figure 40), as well as the 2,4-dinitrophenylhydrazones of acetaldehyde and propionaldehyde (Figure 41).

4. Crystal Habit Change

The crystal habit of a compound grown from the melt is reproducibly affected by impurities. In binary systems this can often be used as a basis for analysis. Mitchell[22] has shown that the crystal habit in fusion preparations of adipic acid containing up to about 2 per cent of succinic acid can be used as a means of analysis (Figure 58). It is essential, of course, to control the temperature during crystallization so that habit variations due to temperature are eliminated.

5. Crystallization Velocity

The crystallization velocity depends on the composition, the temperature, and the geometry of the measuring system. If the latter

[22] J. Mitchell, *Anal. Chem.* **21**, 448 (1949).

100%   99.75%

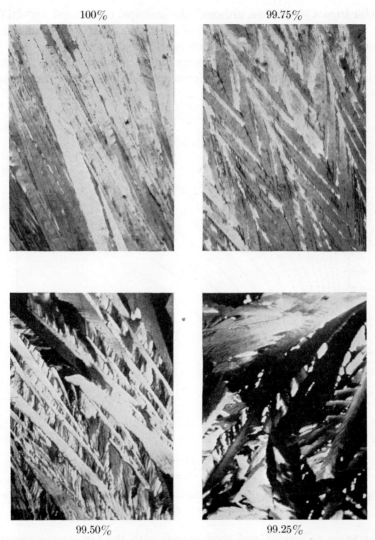

99.50%   99.25%

Fig. 58. Photomicrographs of adipic acid-succinic acid mixtures showing the effect of small percentages of the latter on the crystal habit of adipic acid.

two are kept constant the composition in terms of the component crystallizing can be determined. This has been accomplished for p,p'-DDT[23] in technical DDT with success. In this case the mixture

[23] W. C. McCrone, A. Smedal, and V. Gilpin, *Anal. Chem.* **18**, 578 (1946).

is far from a simple one, although the principal component p,p'-DDT is usually present to the extent of 70–80 per cent.   The remainder consists of a large number of other isomers and by-products.

The rate of growth differs depending on the form of the sample; whether capillary, glass tube, microscope slide, etc., hence the system

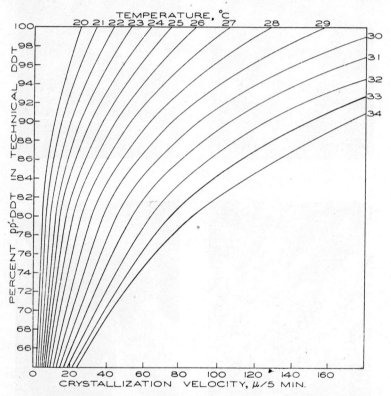

Fig. 59. Calibration curve for determination of per cent p,p'-DDT in technical DDT by measurement of crystallization velocity.

has to be calibrated and used always with the same experimental conditions.   For this work a slide and cover glass preparation was used.   The temperature was kept constant using the simple glass liquid circulation stage shown in Figure 3 in Section II,B,1.   Although the type of impurity, as well as the quantity, affects the rate of crystal growth, pure o,p'-DDT was found to simulate the effect of the wide variety of components in technical DDT, hence calibration curves were determined measuring the crystallization velocity as a function of temperature and relative proportions of o,p' and p,p'-DDT. The mixtures were weighed on a balance, mixed thoroughly in a melted drop by means of a glass needle, covered with a cover glass, and completely melted at about 80°C before placing on the temperature controlled stage. The results obtained are shown in Figure 59. Comparative analytical results based on the crystallization velocity and a recrystallization method are shown in Table XIV.

TABLE XIV

Analysis of Technical DDT by Rate of Crystal Growth

	Per cent DDT by	
Sample	Crystallization velocity	Ethanol recrystallization
I	75.3	76.0
II	73.5	73.7
III	71.9	71.9

6. Freezing Point Depression

In a binary system the depression of freezing point can be used as a precise measure of composition. Bryant[24] has used this method in a

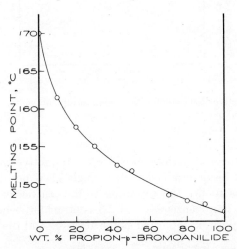

Fig. 60. Melting point as a function of composition in a system showing solid solution; acet- and propion-p-bromoanilides (courtesy of Dr. W. M. D. Bryant).

[24] W. M. D. Bryant, *J. Am. Chem. Soc.* **60**, 1394 (1938).

system showing solid solutions: *p*-bromoanilides of acetic and propionic acid (Figure 60). Many analysts have used the same procedure
for systems showing eutectic formation. Unfortunately, each system
must be calibrated precisely since the molar depression of freezing
points varies, at the worst, about tenfold. A depression of 0.5°C
for every weight per cent is usually used for very rough approxima-
tions of composition.

7. Refractive Index of the Melt

The use of refractive index of the melt as a tool for the identification
of pure compounds has been discussed in Section III,B,2,a. The
same function determined in the same manner may be used in the
analysis of binary mixtures.[25–27]

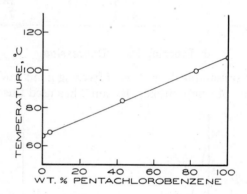

Fig. 61. Refractive index-composition relationship for melts of 1,2,3,4-tetra-
chlorobenzene and pentachlorobenzene with glass powder 1.5795 (courtesy of
Claude J. Arceneaux).

The simplest cases are those in which the refractive indices of both
substances can be determined with a single glass powder standard.
Arceneaux[28] has applied this technique to the analysis of binary mixtures of pentachlorobenzene and 1,2,3,4-tetrachlorobenzene (Figure
61). The composition is plotted as the abscissa, and the temperature

[25] E. Lindpaintner, *Arch. Pharm.* **277**, 398 (1939).

[26] F. Reimers, *Dansk Tidsskr. Farm.* **14**, 219 (1940); *Z. Anal. Chem.* **122**, 404 (1941).

[27] G. Dultz, Süddtsch, *Deut. Apoth. Ztg.* **81**, 277 (1941).

[28] C. Arceneaux, *Anal. Chem.* **23**, 906 (1951).

at which the refractive index of the melt and the glass standard are identical is plotted as the ordinate.   Obviously, the steeper the slope of this line the more accurate the determination of composition.

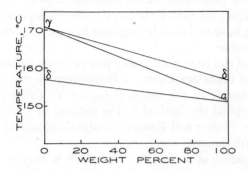

Fig. 62. Refractive indices of the melt in the systems alpha, gamma, and delta hexachlorocyclohexanes using glass powder 1.5101.

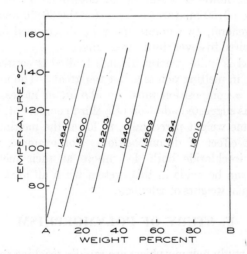

Fig. 63. Refractive indices of the melt in the system trional-Novatophane using a variety of glass powders.

For alpha and gamma hexachlorocyclohexane (Figure 62), for example, the slope is very low and the situation is even worse for other pairs of isomers of this compound.   On the other hand, for trional (methyl sulfonal) and novatophane (Figure 63) the change in refractive index is so great that seven glasses, in all, are required to cover the entire composition range.

For results accurate to 1 per cent or better it is necessary that the sample be very thoroughly mixed either as a drop of liquid on the slide (with a fine glass rod), by lifting the cover glass free several times and replacing it, or as a solid by grinding in a small mortar with a few drops of pure ether.

This method can be applied to any pair of compounds for which the indices of the melts are known. These may be determined when needed or taken from the tables (Chapter V, Table IV). Brandstätter has applied the method to the analysis of 2,4-dinitrophenyl-hydrazones[29]; Fischer and Kocher[30] analyze mixtures of vanillin and ethyl vanillin in the same way.

The preparation of the required diagram is very simple when a single glass powder suffices for the entire composition range. It is necessary only to draw a straight line between the temperatures for the two pure components. To be more certain that the relationship is linear, it is, however, desirable to determine at least one other value (for the 50:50 mixture) or two (for the 30:70 and 70:30 mixtures). In general, two points must be determined for each glass standard required to cover the desired range.

The method is quite general, though limited to systems in which the difference in melting points is not too great. The melts must be miscible and decomposition must be absent, or at least restricted. Lennartz[31] has suggested addition of a third component, always present in the same weight percentage, to lower the melting points and eliminate the effect of decomposition. For example, alypine and narcotine hydrochloride both decompose at their melting points, yet analyses can be made in this system when all mixtures are prepared with equal weights of salophen.

F. STUDY OF POLYMORPHISM

Those who study polymorphism are rapidly reaching the conclusion that all compounds, organic and inorganic, can crystallize in different crystal forms or polymorphs. In fact, the more diligently any system is studied the larger the number of polymorphs discovered. The

---

[29] M. Brandstätter, *Z. physik. Chem.* **191**, 227 (1942).

[30] R. Fischer, and G. Kocher, *Mikrochemie ver. Mikrochim. Acta.* **33**, 13₁ (1946).

[31] H. J. Lennartz, *Z. Anal. Chem.* **127**, 5 (1944).

fact that water has been observed in at least eight crystal forms is a measure of the amount of study devoted to this common compound.

Organic systems are certainly no exception. The number of organic compounds reported to exist in two or more crystal forms is so large that Deffet[32] has published a book listing in concise abbreviated style the information known on each such system. Many organic compounds are known to exist in four or more different polymorphic forms, e.g., 1,2,4-bromodinitrobenzene, 1,2,4-chlorodinitrobenzene, picrylchloride, veronal, 1,3,5-trinitrobenzene, cyclotetramethylenetetranitramine, and bis-(β-nitroxyethyl)nitramine. If studied more thoroughly most organic compounds would yield additional crystal forms.

The importance of polymorphism lies in the fact that all the properties (color, hardness, refractive indices, conductivity, melting point, etc.) of a given compound vary depending on the polymorphic form being studied. The situation is different from the inorganic polymorphic forms of carbon (graphite and diamond) only in degree. The following tabulation shows the variation in some of the physical properties of cyclotetramethylenetetranitramine known in the explosives industry as HMX.

TABLE XV

Physical Properties of the Various Polymorphs of HMX

Property	Form			
	I	II	III	IV
Crystal system	Monoclinic	Orthorhombic	Monoclinic	Hexagonal
Density	1.894	1.823	1.79	1.764
Refractive indices				
Alpha	1.589	1.563	1.537	1.607
Beta	1.594	1.564	1.585	1.566
Gamma	1.73	1.73	1.666	
Lattice parameters				
a	6.54	15.17	16.80	7.69
b	11.05	24.03	7.95	....
c	7.37	5.92	10.97	32.67

The color of a dye, the power of an explosive, the tensile strength of an alloy, and the thermal stability of a drug all depend on the poly-

[32] L. Deffet, *Répertoire des Composés Organiques Polymorphes*, Desoer, Liége, 1942.

morphic form. A detailed study of the various crystal forms: their preparation, stability, physical properties, etc., for a given compound is seldom wasted effort if quality standards for that compound are important. Often the performance of a given compound can be improved through change to a different polymorphic form.

1. Phase Diagrams

Before suggesting ways of answering some of the practical questions regarding polymorphism it is worth while to review the types of phase diagrams shown by systems involving polymorphs. This will be done starting with the simple case of a system of two forms only.

There will be only one liquid-vapor (boiling point) curve in the pressure-temperature diagram since both polymorphs give the identical liquid phase on melting. Each polymorph, however, has its own solid-vapor (sublimation or vapor pressure) curve. The two curves usually, but not necessarily, cross. The complete diagram, of course, contains both the liquid-vapor and the solid-vapor curves and these can be superimposed to give either of two possibilities; the liquid-vapor curve may, in general, intersect the two solid-vapor curves above or below their intersection. It is not unknown for the three curves to interest at the same point; when this occurs the melting points of the two polymorphic forms and the transition temperature coincide (e.g., β-naphthol and very nearly for γ-hexachlorocyclo-hexane, two of whose forms melt only 0.1°C apart).

The solid-liquid (melting point) curves can be drawn starting from either of the two possible intersections of the boiling point curve with the sublimation curves. The completed diagrams are then as shown in Figures 64. It is not necessarily true that the melting point and transition curves intersect at high pressures but the possibility exists. It is interesting to note in this case that the enantiotropic system becomes a monotropic system at high pressures and vice versa. Considering this situation and the general fact that most systems do not show an easily determined transition temperature, it becomes obvious that these two terms, enantiotropic and monotropic, are dangerous words indeed. In the first place, the first of these, enantiotropic, can be used only when the transition temperature has been found to be below the melting point. The converse, no transition temperature below the melting point, cannot usually be interpreted to mean the system is monotropic because the transition temperature may be below room temperature (or below the lowest temperature studied), or it may have been unobserved because of slow transition rates.

There is apparently no safe generalization that can be used to decide whether a given system is enantiotropic or monotropic. Most systems, however, follow the rule that the lower the temperature stability range for a given polymorph the higher, in general, the crystal density and the average refractive index. Given a system of two polymorphs, the physical properties determine the relative stabilities at

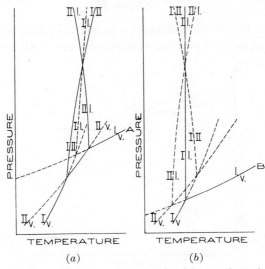

Fig. 64. Pressure-temperature diagrams for (a) enantiotropic system, and (b) monotropic system (at low pressures).

the melting point (the stable form in that temperature range has the lower vapor pressure and the higher melting point). If B, the lower density component of a given mixture, is the more stable at the melting point the system is enantiotropic; and if A, the higher density component, is more stable the system is monotropic. Furthermore, if A is the stable form at any temperature below the melting point, the transition temperature is above that particular temperature; on the other hand, if B is stable at that temperature, the transition temperature is lower. However, there are a few known exceptions to this general rule: hexagonal AgI to cubic AgI at 146°C, grey to white tin at 18°C, resorcinol I to resorcinol II at 74°C, and in each of these cases the high-temperature form has the higher density.

The possibility of this occurring is about the same as the chance that a solid will melt to a liquid of higher density (e.g., water).

The melting point of the unstable form cannot always be determined. Verstraete[33] has used the Le Chatelier equation to calculate this melting point. The transition temperature, T_t, in a monotropic system can never be measured directly, however, Schenk[34] has calculated it using the equation:

$$T_t = \frac{F_1 K_2 - F_2 K_1}{K_1 - K_2}$$

where F_1 and F_2 are the two melting points, and K_1 and K_2 are the molar freezing point depression constants for the two forms.

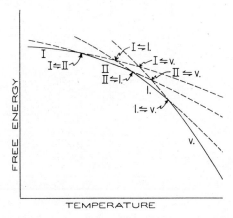

Fig. 65. Typical free energy-temperature diagram for an enantiotropic system.

On the matter of convention the various polymorphic forms should be designated by Roman numerals: I, II, III, IV, etc., as far as necessary. Form I should be the form most stable at room temperature. No rigid convention can be laid down for use of the higher numerals since further work is always attended by the possibility of discovering an intermediate form "2.5" difficult to designate with Roman numerals and impossible to insert without disrupting the previous assignments of numerals. A system as logical as it is simple is to number the forms in the order of their discovery which should, in general, follow their order of stability. Basing the assignment on

[33] K. Verstraete, *Bull. soc. chim. Belg.* **43**, 513 (1934).
[34] R. Schenk, *Z. physik. Chem.* **33**, 445 (1900).

melting points is not satisfactory since these data are not always available and, in many systems, cannot be determined. Kofler's suggestion that the Roman numeral be succeeded by the melting point in parentheses is a logical move subject to the preceding limitation.

The free energy-temperature diagrams at constant pressure are another, and perhaps clearer, way of showing phase diagrams, since

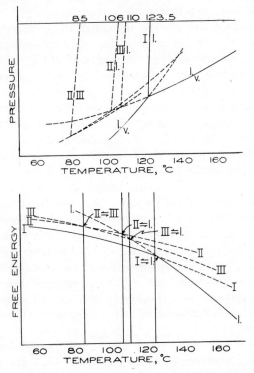

Fig. 66. Schematic phase diagrams for 1,3,5-trinitrobenzene: pressure-temperature diagram, and free energy-temperature diagram.

the phase having the lowest free energy at a given temperature is always the stable phase at that temperature. These diagrams are based on the thermodynamic relationship, $(dF/dT)_P = -S$. The free energy, F, plotted against the temperature, T, at constant pressure, P, gives a curve for each phase, the slope of which at any temperature will be the entropy, S. Figure 65 shows such a phase diagram for a hypothetical enantiotropic system.

The diagrams for systems having three or more polymorphic forms can be plotted in the same way. Figure 66 shows schematic P-T and F-T diagrams for TNB.

2. Does a Given Compound Show Polymorphism?

This section summarizes the known general fusion methods for crystallizing unstable polymorphic forms.

(a) Melt completely a small amount of the compound between a slide and cover glass and observe the solidification between crossed polars. If after spontaneous freezing a solid-solid transformation occurs spontaneously or can be induced by seeding or scratching, the compound exists in at least two polymorphic forms.

The problem, in this case, is to prevent crystallization of the stable form by inducing supercooling. Three steps can be taken to help induce supercooling. (1) The sample size should be very small, in fact, a number of separate droplets under the cover glass ranging in size from a few tenths of a mm. across to 1–2 mm. across is best, (2) The crystals should be melted *completely* by holding the melt for 30 sec. or so about 10–20°C above the melting point. (3) The melted preparation should be carefully set aside for several minutes without physical shock before examination. Only under these conditions can the very unstable form of 2,4,6-trinitrotoluene be obtained. To a lesser extent formation of the unstable form of acetanilide requires this same care. Even in spite of these precautions the unstable polymorphs of these two compounds are seldom observed; only the pseudomorph remains as evidence of the formation of the unstable form.

It is often of value to carry out a meltback (partial remelting), and seed the melt with some of the compound from the stock bottle (presumably the stable form). As freezing proceeds the junction of the two crystal fronts is observed for evidence of polymorphism. In general, if the two crystal fronts are made up of different crystalline modifications, one of them will grow into and through the other form on contact.

This method is satisfactory for a number of compounds; for example, pentaerythritoltetranitrate (PETN), carbon tetrabromide, mercuric iodide, ammonium nitrate, 1,3,5-trinitrobenzene (TNB), cholesteryl acetate, and others, always crystallize to give the high-temperature form if they are completely fused. Of this group,

PETN, CBr₄, and ammonium nitrate show spontaneous transformations on cooling, but trinitrobenzene must usually be scratched or seeded to induce a transformation.

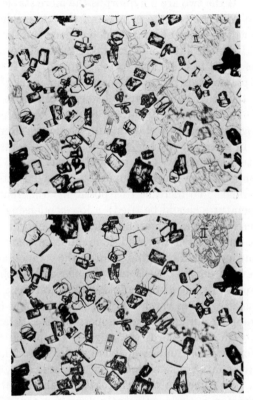

Fig. 67. Solution phase transformation between 1,8-dinitronaphthalene I and II in a drop of thymol on a microscope slide; twenty minutes elapsed between photomicrographs.

(b) Heat a sample of the compound in a hot stage and observe whether a solid-solid transformation occurs during heating. A transformation will always occur with some compounds which show enantiotropic transformations, e.g., ammonium nitrate, carbon tetrabromide, and ammonium picrate. Many other systems, even though enantiotropic, do not readily transform under these conditions. The chances are greater the larger the preparation, hence 10–20 mg. should be used.

(*c*) Sublime a small quantity of the compound and attempt to induce a solution-phase transformation between the sublimate and the original sample by mixing the two in a drop of saturated solution of one of them. If the two are polymorphs the more stable will be more insoluble and will grow at the expense of the more soluble unstable form. This will continue at a rate which depends on the difference in solubility and the absolute solubility until the unstable form is completely transformed to the stable form (Figure 67). If the two samples are not polymorphs but are different compounds, then one may dissolve but the other will not grow (except perhaps as the solution evaporates). If the two are identical forms of the same compound then no change will occur on standing in solution. (Remember that the solution in use is, at the beginning a saturated solution of either one of the two samples.) This method works only for systems in which the compound condenses on sublimation as a polymorph different from the original. To increase this possibility different condensing surface temperatures should be tried; a low-condensing surface temperature often favors the formation of an unstable form.

(*d*) Reflux an excess of the solid compound in a small amount of solvent boiling as near the melting point of the compound as possible. Reflux for several hours, then isolate the suspended solid by decantation followed by drying at the refluxing temperature. Any method of quickly isolating these crystals or, at least, keeping the temperature from dropping during the entire operation is satisfactory. Test the product with a sample of the original compound for solution-phase transformation as outlined above under (*c*). This procedure works for any enantiotropic system, e.g., styphnic acid, in which the material can be refluxed in the temperature range of the high-temperature form for a time sufficiently long for the solution-phase transformation to occur.

(*e*) Recrystallize the compound from a small amount of solution by cooling very rapidly (pour onto ice, or drop drop-wise on a chilled microscope slide, etc.), and observe a portion of the precipitate suspended in a drop of the mother liquor. The drop may then be seeded with the original compound to check for solution-phase transformation. If the precipitate is a different polymorph a solution-phase transformation should take place. This method of obtaining polymorphs has been used successfully for hydroquinone and for HMX.

A very useful modification of this test involves the use of high-boiling solvents, such as thymol, benzyl alcohol, and nitrobenzene.

If these compounds are used it is possible to carry out the recrystallization in a drop on a microscope slide. Under these conditions cooling will be very rapid and it is possible to obtain high-temperature polymorphic forms that have not been prepared by any other method. For example, RDX (cyclotrimethylenetrinitramine) and hexanitrodiphenylamine were found to exist in at least two polymorphic forms by recrystallizing from thymol after all other methods of detecting the presence of polymorphs had failed.

3. Are Two Given Samples Polymorphic Forms of the Same Compound?

(a) If two samples have different crystal properties, i.e., axial ratios, refractive indices, densities, and x-ray powder patterns, and can be converted into each other through the solution phase (by recrystallization), or through the solid phase, they are polymorphic forms of the same compound.

(b) If the two compounds are different in all crystal properties, as in (a), yet melt to give a liquid having the same refractive index of the melt and the same temperature coefficient of refractive index, the two samples are likely to be polymorphs of the same compound.

(c) If a mixed fusion between the two samples shows identity yet the crystal properties were different, as in (a), then the two samples are polymorphs of the same compound.

(d) If one of the samples is fused and allowed to supercool slightly below the melting point, the melt can be seeded at different points with each of the solid samples. If the resulting solidification is observed using a low-power microscope having crossed polars, observation at the junction of the two solids will indicate the presence or absence of polymorphism. If, at the junction, one of the two forms continues to grow through the other solid, the two forms are polymorphs. If the two solids grow together with no subsequent change, even on rewarming and long standing, then the two samples are identical and not polymorphs (assuming that one of the seed crystals did not transform during the seeding operation). Seeding, alone, is not, however, proof that the crystal form of the seed material and the growing crystals are the same phase, or even necessarily the same compound. Seeding with any material involves some physical shock which is often sufficient by itself to cause nucleation.

(e) If the two samples are mixed dry on a microscope slide beneath a cover glass, they can be wetted by allowing a liquid to run in under the edge of the cover glass.   If they are wetted with a saturated solution of either component in a suitable solvent, the occurrence of a solution-phase transformation will show the two to be polymorphic forms of the same compound (Figure 67).

(f) If several crystals of each sample are heated close together in a hot stage, a solid-solid transformation of one component followed by melting of both at the same temperature would strongly indicate (but not prove) that the two were polymorphs.   If, on heating, one form melted first then resolidified due to seeding by the other form followed by uniform melting on further heating, the two forms would definitely be polymorphs.

(g) There might also be a vapor-phase transformation during heating of the two samples in intimate mixture.   This would also be definite evidence of polymorphism.

G. DETERMINATION OF TEMPERATURE-COMPOSITION DIAGRAMS

1. Introduction

A temperature-composition diagram is a convenient means of expressing the melting point as a function of composition of all solid phases present in two- or three-component systems.   The determination of such a diagram is usually regarded, however, as a research problem requiring laborious cooling-curve determinations and considerable amounts of time and material.   This is true when conventional methods are used.   In contrast, the essential characteristics of even a ternary composition diagram can be determined microscopically in a few hours;   generally 2–4 hours for a simple binary eutectic diagram and about two days for a ternary diagram.   Each polymorphic form doubles the time required, and the presence of solid solutions, addition compounds, etc., can usually be handled without complication in times measured by hours rather than days.   In addition, the use of the microscope permits the determination of composition diagrams on minute amounts of material, on decomposable substances, and on systems involving unstable polymorphic forms.

Such diagrams are especially useful in any system where the physical properties are dependent upon the physical phases present in the final mixture.   They are also important in fields where crystallization procedures, drying treatments, heating and cooling operations, and washing or melting techniques may result in the formation of new crystalline modifications, hydrates, addition compounds, or solid solutions.　A determination and study of the appropriate composition diagram will often explain variations in physical characteristics, such as melting point, color, and hardness, or performance characteristics, such as rate of solution and thermal stability.

Another use of the composition diagram is the determination of the melting point of any mixture of those components, as well as the percentage of the mixture still fluid at any temperature below the

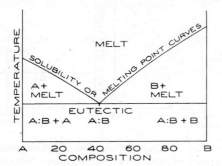

Fig. 68. Binary composition diagram in a system
showing simple eutectic formation.

final melting point.　The heat of fusion of a component can also be calculated from the composition diagram using the Clapeyron equation.

Some knowledge of the behavior of the various types of temperature-composition diagrams is essential to an understanding of the fusion methods used for their elucidation.　The simplest diagram, and perhaps a trivial one, expresses the relationship between two (or more) components insoluble in each other, not only in the solid but also in the melted (liquid) state.　Neither melt dissolves any of the other component, hence no lowering of either melting point can occur. Such systems are encountered in research and not only in systems where one component is organic and one inorganic.　Azobenzene with either oxalic acid or phloroglucinol constitute two such systems. In general, high-melting highly polar compounds are mutually insoluble in low-melting compounds of low polarity.　Some important systems, organic-inorganic systems, such as the high-explosive mixture Amatol (ammonium nitrate and TNT), fall in this class also. Pharmaceutical preparations, being mixtures of salt-like compounds and sugars as well as the usual organic types of compounds, often show this behavior.

The simple eutectic diagram is usually the starting point for any discussion of temperature-composition diagrams. Figure 68 shows such a diagram for a simple two component system in which the two components are completely miscible in the liquid state and form neither

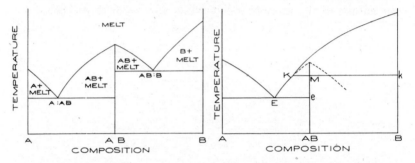

Fig. 69. Composition diagram for an addition compound system with congruently melting addition compound.

Fig. 70. Composition diagram for an addition compound system with incongruently melting addition compound.

solid solutions nor addition compounds. The lowest melting mixture is the eutectic which crystallizes as a fine-grained physical mixture of the two components. The two melting point curves express the lowering of melting point of each pure component by addition of the other component or, in another sense, these curves represent the solubility limits of each component in the melt of the other component. Any mixture of these components will, on heating, begin to melt at the eutectic melting point, and will be melted completely at the higher temperature indicated by the appropriate point on the upper melting point curve. At all temperatures above the eutectic melting point only one solid phase can exist along with the melt. On one side of the eutectic the solid phase will be A, on the other side B.

A system in which a molecular addition compound is formed is, in the simplest case, simply two eutectic diagrams (Figure 69), and the behavior of such systems is understood readily on this basis. This is true, however, only for an addition compound system, as shown in

Figure 69, in which the addition compound melts congruently (i.e., to give only melt). The addition compound may, however, melt incongruently (i.e., to give melt plus one of the pure components as solid crystals); this is also called a peritectic reaction (Figure 70). In such a system mixtures to the left of point K behave like a simple eutectic system, but to the right of point K all mixtures exhibit the peritectic reaction. On heating, mixtures between K and M the eutectic, and there is only one, melts at $E - e$ leaving crystals of the addition compound. When the temperature reaches the line $K - k$ the addition compound melts incongruently to yield melt plus pure component B. A mixture between M and k will consist of AB + B

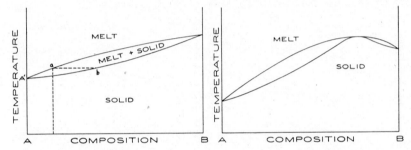

Fig. 71. Composition diagram for a system showing Roozeboom Type I solid solution.   Fig. 72. Composition diagram for a system showing Roozeboom Type II solid solution (maximum).

until melting at $K - k$, at which point AB will melt incongruently to give additional B plus melt of composition K.

On cooling, the reverse behavior is observed *if sufficient time is allowed for equilibrium.* Very often on cooling in any system conditions are such that the equilibrium phases do not nucleate and the system proceeds to do the best it can without them. For example, in a eutectic system, the eutectic may not nucleate because of rapid supercooling and, in this case, the two types of molecules slowly and laboriously diffuse through the eutectic melt to the proper crystal front and soon, unless the viscosity is too great, the system is completely crystallized without a fine-grained eutectic mixture. In a similar way, heating of a mixture between K and M in Figure 70 may lead to congruent melting of the addition compound at its unstable melting point simply because crystalline component B fails to nucleate at the peritectic temperature. It is not impossible for an addition compound to be missing entirely due to lack of nuclei and, in this case, the system will appear to show a simple eutectic, e.g., picric acid-diphenylamine, veronal-pyramidon, benzil-1,3,5-trinitrobenzene, and picric acid-azobenzene. Slow temperature changes and large amounts of material (5–10 mg.) are the best safeguards against nonequilibrium conditions.

There are five general types of solid solutions (Roozeboom Types). Three of these (Figures 71, 72, and 73) are simple in the sense that they represent continuous solid solution systems (i.e., showing linear, maximum, and minimum melting point curves). Two of them (Figures 74 and 75) are more complex in that they represent systems

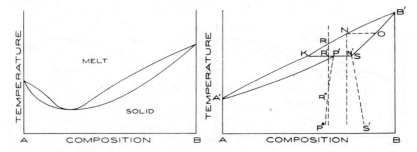

Fig. 73. Composition diagram for a system showing Roozeboom Type III solid solution (minimum).

Fig. 74. Composition diagram for a system showing Roozeboom Type IV solid solution.

showing only partial solid solubility. Type I (Figure 71) is the simplest case; linear solid solubility between the melting points of the two components. The upper line is the liquidus line, the lower the solidus line. Between these two lines both melt and crystals are stable together. On solidification of a mixture, such as a, the first crystals to form have the composition b; since the melt, thereby, becomes richer in a, the next crystals to form are richer in a. The net result is, that on continued cooling the melt composition changes along aA', the crystals along bA'. If cooling is very slow there is an exchange between the A rich melt and the B rich crystals so that the final product is a crystalline solid of composition a. On rapid cooling the crystals formed are richer at the centers in the higher melting component.

A solid solution system which shows a minimum melting point (Figure 73) behaves in a similar manner, except that on cooling the composition changes toward the minimum melting composition rather than the lower melting component.   The system with a maximum melting solid solution (Figure 72) likewise behaves similarly, except that on cooling all compositions change away from the maximum melting mixture toward either of the two pure components (unless the original mixture has the same composition as the maximum in which case solidification occurs with no composition changes in solid or melt).

The first of the two noncontinuous solid solution systems is shown in Figure 74.   This system, Roozeboom Type IV, is little different from the continuous solid solution system shown in Figure 71, except that solid solutions having compositions between $P'P''$ and SS' are incapable of forming.   There will be, at the temperatures represented by line KS, a peritectic reaction similar to that which occurs in some addition compound systems (Figure 70).   Here, however, mixtures to the left of K and right of S behave like systems shown in Figure 71 (continuous linear solid solution).   Between P' and S (mixture N, for example) the melt, on cooling, first separates a crystalline solid solution of composition O.   On further cooling the composition of the melt changes along NK and the solid along OS until the temperature along KS is reached.   At this temperature the solid phases represented by the extension of OS are forbidden, hence a change occurs and some of the B-rich solid solution crystals (S) transform to solid solution crystals richer in A (P') and as cooling continues the melt composition changes along KA', the solid composition along $P'A'$.   In so far as equilibrium allows, however, the B-rich crystals (S) change to contain less A since the solid solubility of A in B and B in A decreases as the temperature falls.   During this change the A-rich solid solution is also changing so that, again equilibrium permitting, the final solid mixture will contain a mixture of the two solid solutions found on SS' and $P'P''$.

If the original mixture has the composition R then, on cooling to KS, all the B-rich phase (S) already formed will transform to the relatively A-rich phase (P'), and on further cooling the curves KA' and $P'A'$ will be followed.   With full equilibrium the A-rich solid solutions would change at R'' to a mixture containing some B-rich phase from SS'.

The fifth type of solid-solution system (Figure 75) is a simple eutectic system in which some crystals of A may contain a few per cent of B and vice versa.   The eutectic mixture is made up of the two saturated solid solutions, m and l, rather than the two pure components,

A and B.   Mixtures having compositions between m and l behave like a simple eutectic system in which, however, m and l replace the pure components.   Mixtures between pure A and m and B and l behave, under equilibrium conditions, like simple linear solid solution systems.   With rapid cooling the final composition of the solid will be a mixture approaching that of a eutectic mixture of m and l plus either one of these partial solid solutions in excess depending on the original composition (A to m, excess m; B to l, excess l).

2. Determination of Temperature-Composition Diagrams Using the Hot Stage

The determination of a temperature-composition diagram is undertaken in a preliminary way by preparing a mixed fusion.   Careful observation of the zone of mixing during the crystallization process

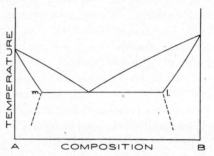

Fig. 75. Composition diagram for a system showing Roozeboom Type V solid solution.

indicates the existence of a eutectic (Figure 76), addition compound (Figure 77), solid solutions (Figure 78), and unstable polymorphs (Figure 78).   The slide is then placed in a carefully calibrated hot stage so that the zone of mixing can be observed as the temperature is raised.   This permits, usually during a single heating, the measurement of the melting points for all solid phases present.

As shown in Figure 49, the appearance of the zone of mixing during melting also betrays the type of system involved.   Sharp melting of the entire zone of mixing leaving the two pure components on either side indicates a eutectic (Figure 79).   With an addition compound, there is the successive melting of the two eutectics formed by the addition compound with each of the pure components at the edges and the addition compound between the two molten eutectics (Figure 49). If a peritectic reaction is involved, only one eutectic is noted. In this case the addition compound melts congruently only from the

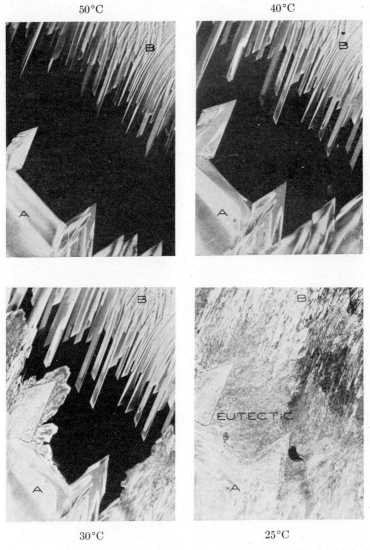

Fig. 76. Formation of a eutectic during spontaneous cooling of a mixed fusion between azobenzene and bromocamphor (crossed polars).

normal eutectic side with transformation to the adjacent crystalline component apparent on the other side (incongruent melting point). In the special case lying intermediate between the congruently

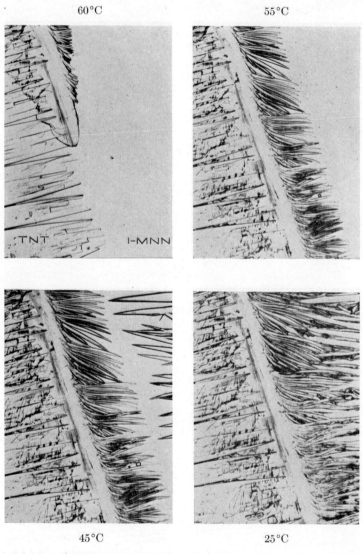

Fig. 77. Crystallization during spontaneous cooling in the system 1-mononitro-naphthalene-TNT. This system shows an addition compound.

80°C   70°C

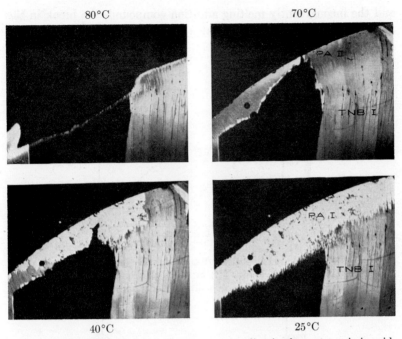

40°C   25°C

Fig. 78. Crystallization during spontaneous cooling in the system picric acid-
TNB I.   Picric acid II and TNB I form continuous solid solutions (Figure 91),
but picric acid II transforms to picric acid I on further cooling.

Fig. 79. Appearance of mixed fusion preparation on partial remelting of
a eutectic system (picric acid-DDT).

and the incongruently melting addition compound, the break in the melting point curve falls just at the maximum. The system, β-

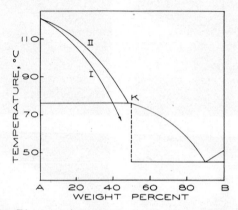

Fig. 80. Binary composition diagram for the system β-naphthol (A) and α-naphthylamine (B) in which the composition of the addition compound falls near point K (Kofler and Brandstätter).

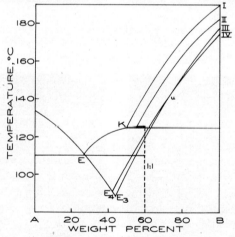

Fig. 81. Binary composition diagram for the system Dimethylpyrone (A) and veronal (B).

naphthol and α-naphthylamine (Figure 80), is almost of this type as is dimethylpyrone with either veronal III or IV (Figure 81). If the addition compound is unstable it may melt incongruently by virtue of the fact that it decomposes below the eutectic melting point of the two components, e.g., α-naphthol and β-naphthylamine forms an equimolar addition compound which decomposes (melts) at 50°C with separation of crystals of β-naphthylamine, since the eutect c between α-naphthol and β-naphthylamine melts at 57°C.

Complete solid solubility is indicated by continuous melting through the zone of mixing. Melting may start in the zone of mixing, or may occur last at that point if the solid solution curves form a minimum or a maximum melting point. Any system may melt to give two liquid melts only partially miscible, e.g., acetamide with benzil (Figure 82). Each melt is saturated with the other component and the compositions become more nearly alike on further heating until identical

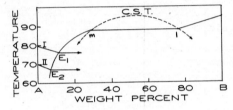

Fig. 82. Binary composition diagram for the system benzil (B) and acetamide (A) showing two liquid layers in the melt phase.

compositions are reached and the meniscus disappears at the critical solution temperature (C.S.T.). Resorcinol and triphenylmethane show this behavior in a mixed fusion.

The use of fusion methods makes it possible to determine phase equilibria involving unstable polymorphic forms, however, at the same time these methods increase the likelihood of mistaking an unstable phase for a stable one. The literature, for example, reports that the system, anthracene with 2,6-dinitrotoluene, possesses a eutectic melting at 54°C. That it does, but with an unstable polymorph; the stable form of 2,6-dinitrotoluene melts at 66°C, and the eutectic between this phase and anthracene melts at 62°C.

The type of diagram can even vary with the polymorphic forms involved; trinitrobenzene I (m.p. 123.5°C) and picric acid II (m.p. 75°C) show continuous solid solutions, yet trinitrobenzene I with picric acid I (m.p. 122°C) shows a simple eutectic (Figure 83; see also Figure 78). This behavior and others more complex are very common. Usually, however, in any given system, the same phases always will appear and behave in a consistent manner. The melting points of solid phases, such as eutectics and addition compounds, are noted during reheating of the mixed fusion preparation in the hot stage. The preparation of the mixed fusion takes about one minute and a complete heating cycle usually not more than fifteen minutes. By this time, the general type of diagram and melting points of the pure components, eutectics, addition compounds, and maximum or minimum melting solid solutions are known.

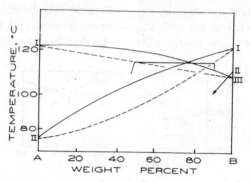

Fig. 83. Composition diagram for the system 1,3,5-trinitro-benzene I, II, and III (B), and picric acid I and II(A).

Compositions of eutectic mixtures, addition compounds, etc., are determined by successive approximation. A portion of a well-mixed carefully weighed mixture is heated in the hot stage until the eutectic melts. The mixture (1–3 mg.) is covered with a one-quarter section of a cover glass, since equilibrium will be more easily attained in a smaller area. Careful observation of the mixture just above the eutectic melting point indicates the component in excess, and the amount of the excess component is an indication of how far from the eutectic composition that mixture lies. This excess component usually can be recognized easily by the characteristic pattern of the crystals remaining after the eutectic melts (Figure 84a and c). If, however, there is any doubt as to the identity of the component in excess, the temperature is lowered slowly and the characteristic appearance of the growing crystals can be used as further identification (Figure 84b and d). If necessary, measurement of angles and other optical data may be utilized in this identification. Another way to tell on which side of the eutectic composition a given mixture lies is

by a mixed fusion between that mixture and either pure component.
On heating the mixed fusion preparation, a thin band of eutectic melt

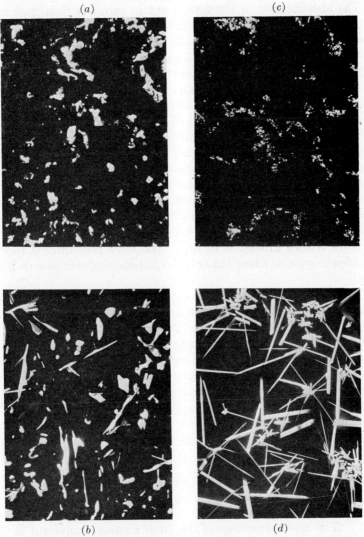

Fig. 84. Melting of mixtures close to and on either side of the eutectic composition showing on one side excess adipic acid just above the eutectic melting
point (a), on slight cooling (c); and on the other side of the eutectic excess anthranilic acid just above the eutectic melting point (b), and on slight cooling (d).

will appear between the two components if they lie on opposite sides of the eutectic; if both lie on the same side no melting will occur between them before the mixture melts uniformly throughout.

The identification of the component in excess is then used as a guide in correcting the composition of the next mixture. Usually four to six mixtures are sufficient to determine the composition of a eutectic to within a few tenths of a per cent. The weighing, mixing, and observation of one composition takes about 15 minutes.

Physical mixing of the components in a sufficiently intimate mixture is a difficult process. If neither of the two components decomposes nor sublimes, the most effective method to insure intimate mixing is to melt the two components on the hot bar in a mortar, mix them while molten, and grind the recrystallized mixture thoroughly. If one or both components sublime to any degree, it is unwise to melt the components since sublimation would change the composition of the mixture. In this case, mixing is done in a small mortar after wetting the mixture with a few drops of a volatile liquid (i.e., clean ether) which does not react with either component, and the mixture is then ground until dry. The same procedure is recommended in systems where one or both components decompose on heating.

The prediction of approximate eutectic compositions can, of course, save considerable time. This can be estimated by noting the melting points of the eutectic mixture and the two pure components since, in general, a high-melting component will be represented by a lower percentage in the eutectic. The method is based on the observation that the cooling curves in most eutectic type diagrams are of approximately the same slope. By substituting the respective temperatures in the following relationship an approximate prediction of the eutectic composition can be made.

$$X_1 = \frac{100(T_2 - T_e)}{T_1 + T_2 - 2T_e}$$

where T_1 = melting point of the lower melting component
T_2 = melting point of the higher melting component
T_e = eutectic temperature
X = mole percentage of the lower melting component in the eutectic mixture.

In one test, nine of the sixteen predictions made using this formula were within 3.5 per cent of the experimentally determined composition, and all the rest were within 9 per cent (Table XVI).   This good agreement may be accounted for by the fact that structurally all these compounds are quite similar.   In another series of compounds made up of two different classes of organic molecules, aromatic nitro and aliphatic nitramine compounds, the agreement is not so good.   In this series it is necessary, for good results, to use a more elegant way of predicting the melting point curves and eutectic composition The following relationship is, therefore, used in these cases.

$$\ln \frac{P}{100} = \frac{L_f}{RT_0} \cdot \frac{(T_0 - T_f)M}{T_f}$$

where P = mole per cent compound in mixture
L_f = heat of fusion of pure compound
R = gas constant
T_0 = melting point of pure compound
T_f = melting point of mixture
M = molecular weight of pure compound.

This relationship can be used, of course, only when the heat of fusion is known, or when it can be estimated from known data for a compound of similar structure (the entropy of fusion, L_f/T_0, is nearly constant for closely related compounds).

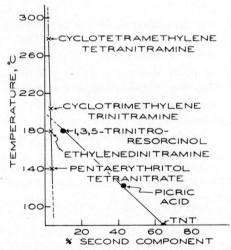

Fig. 85. Eutectic composition in a number of binary systems having one common second component, methylenedinitramine, as a function of melting point of the first components.

TABLE XVI

Comparison Between Eutectic Compositions Measured and Calculated

System[a]	Eutectic composition, mole per cent		Difference
	Calculated	Measured	
$\alpha:\beta$	99.5	99.5	0
$\alpha:\gamma$	22	24.3	2.3
$\alpha:\delta$	40	36.5	3.5
$\beta:\gamma$	99.8	99.8	0
$\beta:\delta$	97	99.3	2
$\gamma:\delta$	66	58	8
γ:TCB[b]	71	68	3
γ:HMB[c]	76	67.4	8.6
γ:TMB[d]	26	32.7	6.7
γ:HCB[e]	96	95.0	1
TCB:HMB	61	56.7	3.3
TCB:TMB	17	25.1	8.1
TCB:HCB	12	19.5	7.5
HMB:TMB	11	17.2	6.2
HMB:HCB	88	90.4	2.4
TMB:HCB	4.5	9.5	5.0

[a] α, β, γ, and δ are geometrical isomers of hexachlorocyclohexane.
[b] 1,2,4,5-Tetrachlorobenzene.
[c] Hexamethylbenzene.
[d] 1,2,4,5-Tetramethylbenzene.
[e] Hexachlorobenzene.

The importance of structural similarity in governing constancy of the entropy of fusion is well illustrated in Figure 85. Here the mole per cent of component B in the eutectic mixture is plotted as a function of the melting point of component B. All the aromatic structures fall on a single line, whereas all of the aliphatic and alicyclic structures fall on a separate line.

If the heat of fusion for the common component in all these systems, methylenedinitramine, is calculated using the above relationship, the following values are obtained (Table XVII).

Those values obtained in the systems with HMX (4.7), RDX (7.1), and EDNA (8.5) should approximate the true value for the heat of fusion of methylenedinitramine, since those compounds should form more nearly ideal systems with methylenedinitramine. The heat of fusion for methylenedinitramine should be, on this basis, 6–7 cal./gram. Unfortunately, there is at this time no experimental value for comparison.

Prediction of the eutectic composition enables the analyst to

SEC.

extra
to th
AII t
the e
the e
of co
AII,
ponei
accui
melti

choose a starting composition closer to the actual eutectic mixture and thus considerably shortens the time needed for the determination. Another method for rapid determination of eutectic composition is described in Section III,G,4; in some cases it may be quicker than the procedure outlined here.

Although it is generally unnecessary to determine points on the cooling curves for most systems, this can be done if necessary by noting the final melting point of mixtures of known compositions. Care must be taken if this procedure is used, however, since thorough mixing during heating on a microscope slide is difficult. Ordinarily, lines connecting the eutectic melting point and the melting point of each of the two components are arbitrarily drawn bowed upward slightly.

TABLE XVII

Calculated Values of Heat of Fusion for Methylenedinitramine from Several Binary Melting Point Curves

System		L_f, cal./gram
Methylenedinitramine	: PETN	2.4
"	: HMX	4.7
"	: RDX	7.1
"	: EDNA	8.5
"	: Styphnic acid	14.3
"	: Picric acid	23.2
"	: Tetryl	36.8
"	: TNT	80.6

Figu
as tr
unst:
Tl
is ca
syste
durii
the
high
than
crys
com
zone
pone
proc
In a

A system involving a congruently melting addition compound is determined in the same manner with the realization that it is, in reality, two eutectic diagrams; each of the two pure components forming a eutectic with the addition compound. The melting points of the eutectics of the addition compound with each of the two components are different; hence, the eutectic melting point observed indicates which side of the addition compound that mixture lies. Since the addition compound must have a stoichiometric ratio of the two components, determination of the composition of this phase is relatively easy. If a mixture has the composition of the addition compound, there will be no melting until the melting point of the compound is reached, at which temperature the entire mixture will melt. In certain cases, a mixture having the composition of the

TABLE XVIII

Melting Point and Composition Data for 16 Binary Systems

System	Melting points, °C	Eutectic properties melting point, °C	Composition mole per cent
$\alpha:\delta$	α, 160.4 δI, 138.0[a] δII, 143.0 δI $\rightleftarrows$ δII, 132.5	113.0 $\alpha:\delta$I 110.5 $\alpha:\alpha$II	61.5 ± 0.5 δI[a] 63.5 ± 0.5 δII
$\beta:\delta$	β, 325 δII, 143.0	136.5	0.7 ± 0.3 β
$\alpha:\beta$	α, 160.4 β, 325	158.5	0.5 β^b
TMB:TCB	TMB, 80.0 TCB, 141.5	63.5	25.1 ± 1 TCB
HMB:TCB	HMB, 167.5 TCB, 141.5	98.5	56.7 ± 0.5 TCB
TMB:HMB	TMB, 80.0 HMB, 167.5	67.0	17.2 ± 0.8 HMB
$\beta:\gamma$	β, 325 γI, 114.2	113.8	0.2 β^b
$\alpha:\gamma$	α, 160.4 γI, 114.2	96	24.3 ± 0.7 α
$\delta:\gamma$	δI, 138.0[a] δII, 143.0 γI, 114.2 γII, 111.0[a] γIII, 114.3 δI $\rightarrow$ δII, 132.5 ± 0.5 γII $\rightarrow$ γIII, 88.0 ± 0.5 γI $\rightarrow$ γIII, 113.8	88.0 γI:δI 84.0 δII:γI 80.0 δII:γII	61.2 ± 0.5 γII 58 γI[a]
TMB:γ	TMB, 80.0 γI, 114.2 γII, 111.0[a]	59.5 TMB:γI 55.5 TMB:γII	32.7 ± 0.6 γI 38 γII[a]
TCB:γ	TCB, 142 γI, 114.2	95.0	68.2 ± 0.5 γ
HMB:γ	HMB, 167.5 I, 114.2 II, 111.0[a]	88.5, HMB:γI 82 HMB:γII	67.4 ± 1.0 γI 72 γII[a]
HCB:γ	HCB, 231 γI, 114.2	108	95.0 ± 0.5 γ
HCB:TMB	HCB, 231 TMB, 80	72.5	9.5 ± 1.0 HCB
TCB:HCB	TCB, 142 HCB, 231	127.5	19.5 ± 1.0 HCB
HMB:HCB	HMB, 167.5 HCB, 231	158	90.4 ± 1.0 HMB

TABLE XVIII (*Continued*)

System	Melting points, °C	Eutectic properties melting point, °C	Composition, mole per cent
$\alpha:\gamma:\delta$	α, 160.4	73.5	19.5 ± 1.0 α
	γI, 114.2		46.5 ± 1.0 γ
	δII, 143.0		34.0 ± 2.0 δ
TMB:HMB:TCB	TMB 80.0	53.5	61 ± 2.0 TMB
	HMB 167.5		17 ± 2.0 HMB
	TCB 141.5		22 ± 2.0 TCB

[a] Value estimated, extrapolated from m.p. of II parallel to m.p. curve of I.
[b] Calculated value based on equal slopes for melting curves.

made on form II and the compositions involving form I were extrapolated from this value.

For this same reason, the actual determination of the binary system delta:gamma was carried out on mixtures of gamma II and delta II. In all other systems involving gamma, the transformation of gamma II → gamma I was quite rapid, almost instantaneous. The presence of the delta isomer, however, seems to inhibit this transformation at the lower temperatures, thus making it more convenient to obtain data on mixtures of delta II and gamma II and extrapolate the other compositions. Eutectic temperatures noted are, in all cases, measured directly. This is one example of a system whose composition diagram could not be determined in its entirety except by microscopic fusion methods.

The binary eutectic compositions listed in Table XVIII have been determined to within at least one per cent; the ternary compositions to within at least two per cent. In systems involving no sublimation, the determination can be made to within one- or two-tenths of a per cent. All these systems have, however, involved sublimation, usually to a marked degree. Subliming materials necessitate special precautions, not only in mixing the components but also in obtaining melting points. The portion of the mixture to be used in determining the excess component is fused between a microscope slide and whole cover glass and immediately placed upside down on a cold metal surface to reduce sublimation from the edges of the cover glass. Ideally, only a small portion of a cover glass should be used to speed attainment of equilibrium between solid and melt, however, in these determinations whole cover glasses were used since the sublimation during fusion undoubtedly changed the composition of the mixture in contact with the edges. After the fusion operation, the edges of the cover glass were sealed with methyl phenyl silicone to insure no further sublimation during the determination of the excess component. For the latter determination, the center of the preparation was observed since the composition at the edges might have been changed slightly. Each preparation was used for only one heating cycle.

Table XIX includes the data for several binary and ternary systems involving aromatic nitro and aliphatic nitramine compounds.

Kofler has determined the data necessary for three binary systems. These data are:

For the system: azobenzene-acenaphthene-benzil:

Binary eutectics:

> Azobenzene-acenaphthene, 47°C and 34 per cent acenaphthene.
> Azobenzene-benzil, 52°C and 38 per cent benzil.
> Benzil-acenaphthene, 63°C and 43 per cent acenaphthene.

Ternary eutectic:

> 38°C, 46 per cent azobenzene, 26 per cent acenaphthene, and 28 per cent benzil.

For 2,4-dinitrophenol-acetanilide-benzil:

Binary eutectics:

> 2,4-Dinitrophenol-acetanilide, 79°C and 47 per cent acetanilide.
> Benzil-acetanilide, 78°C and 32 per cent acetanilide.
> 2,4-Dinitrophenol-benzil, 69°C and 63 per cent benzil.

Ternary eutectic:

> 58°C, 42 per cent Benzil, 36 per cent 2,4-dinitrophenol, and 22 per cent acetanilide.

For 1,3,5-trinitrobenzene (T), fluorene (F), benzil (B):

> This system contains two molecular compounds; one, a congruently melting equimolar compound between fluorene and trinitrobenzene (M_1), and an incongruently melting compound between trinitrobenzene and benzil ($M_2 = 2:1$).

Binary eutectics:

> T-F, 100°C and 22 per cent T, M = 106°C, $e_2 = 88$°C and 22 per cent T.
> T-B, $e_1 = 74$°C and 34 per cent T, $k = 90$°C and 62 per cent T.
> B-F, 69°C and 38 per cent F.

Ternary eutectics:

> E_1 (B, F, M) 60°C, 22 per cent T, 33 per cent F, and 45 per cent B.
> E_2 (B, M_1, M_2) 64°C, 40 per cent T, 12 per cent F, and 48 per cent B.
> E_3, (T, M_1, M_2) 78°C, 61 per cent T, 13 per cent F, and 26 per cent B.

TABLE XIX

Eutectic Composition and Melting Point Data for Systems of Several Nitramine and Nitro Compounds

Two-component systems — methylenedinitramine (A)	Eutectic composition, mole per cent	Temperature, °C
Picric acid (B)		
AI:BI	43.0 ± 1.5 B	84.8 ± 0.2
AII:BI	61.0 B	82.0
PETN (B)		
AI:BI	4.3 ± 0.5 B	104.0
Tetryl (B)		
AI:BI	19.6 ± 0.6 B	93.0
Styphnic acid (B)		
AI:BI	10.0 ± 0.3 B	93.0
AI:BII	17.0 ± 2.0 B	83.0
AII:BI	8.0 ± 2.0 B	88.0
AII:BII	15.0 ± 2.0 B	79.0
TNT (B)		
AI:BI	65.2 ± 0.6 B	74 ± 0.5
AII:BI	63 B	72
EDNA (B)		
AI:BI	3.0 ± 1.5 B	95 ± 1
AII:BI	2 ± 1.0 B	92.5
RDX (B)		
AI:BI	4.0 ± 2.0 B	93.5 ± 1.5
HMX (B)		
AI:BI	98 ± 1.0 B	98
PETN (A):picric acid (B)		
AI:BI	22.4 ± 0.3 A	105.5
TNT (A):picric acid (B)		
AI:BI	71.3 ± 0.5 A	61.0
TNT (B)	14.0 ± 1.0 AI	59.0
Picric acid (C)	54.0 ± 2.0 BI	
	32.0 ± 2.0 CI	
PETN (B)	52.0 ± 1.0 AI	82.5
Picric acid (C)	4.0 ± 1.0 BI	
	44.0 ± 1.0 CI	

The composition diagram can be used to furnish rough estimates of the ratios of solid to melt at any temperature. This is often desirable when the flow properties of mixtures at different temperatures is of interest. For binary diagrams any mixture will, of course, be 100 per cent solid below the eutectic melting point; very slightly above that temperature the percentage of melt formed depends on the

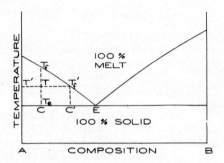

Fig. 87. Eutectic diagram as used to calculate percentage of liquid melt at any temperature and composition.

SYSTEM α : γ : δ

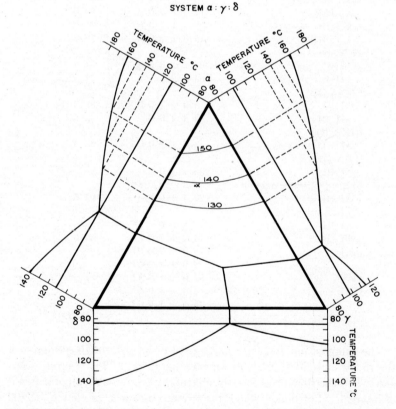

Fig. 88. Binary and ternary composition diagrams in the system α-, γ- and δ-hexachlorocyclohexane.

composition. The eutectic composition would be 100 per cent melt, but the approximate per cent melt in any other mixture just above the eutectic temperature may be calculated from the expression 100(100-C/100-E), where C is the composition of the mixture and E

SYSTEM D: HMB · TCB

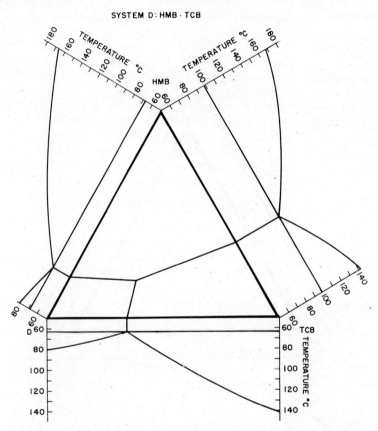

Fig. 89. Binary and ternary composition diagrams in the system hexamethyl-benzene (HMB)—1,2,4,5-tetramethylbenzene (D)—1,2,4,5-tetrachlorobenzene (TCB).

is the eutectic composition. C and E must be in terms of per cent A for mixtures to the left of E, and in terms of per cent B for mixtures to the right of point E. Above the eutectic melting point the percentage of melt increases starting from the base calculated above and reaching 100 per cent at the melting point curve. The total percentage of melt is then 100 per cent at the melting point curve. The total percentage of melt at any temperature, T, and composition, C, is then 100(100-C/100-C'), where C' is the composition of the melt at the temperature, T (Figure 87).

In a ternary system, isothermal lines are drawn on the diagram to represent all compositions whose final melting points are the same.

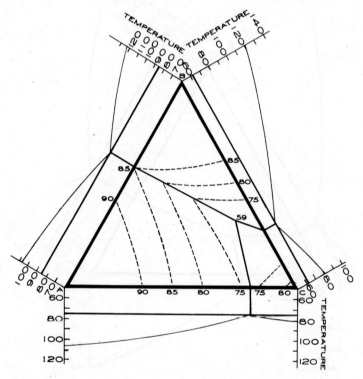

Fig. 90. Ternary composition diagram in the system methylene-dinitramine (A)—picric acid (B)—TNT (C).

These lines are drawn by reading the temperatures from the corresponding binary systems, projecting these temperatures to the ternary diagram, and then connecting similar temperatures between two binary diagrams (Figure 88). These connecting lines are curved slightly to simulate the curved surface of the three-dimensional ternary diagram. The per cent solid at any temperature can be calculated for any ternary diagram in a manner analogous to that used for the binary system.

Additional ternary diagrams in these systems are shown in Figures 89–91.

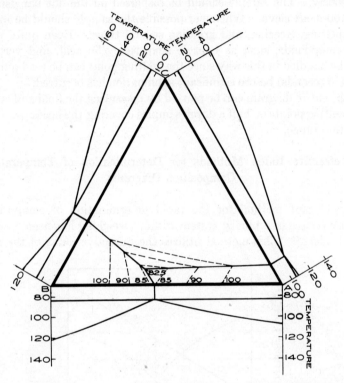

Fig. 91. Ternary composition diagram in the system methylene-dinitramine (A)—picric acid (B)—pentaerythritol tetranitrate (C).

3. Determination of Temperature-Composition Diagrams Using the Hot Bar

Composition diagrams can be very quickly and simply determined using the hot bar.[35] A mixture placed on the hot bar as a long strip of scattered crystals will, in general, show three distinct zones: completely melted droplets, completely unmelted crystals, and partly

[35] L. Kofler and H. Winkler, *Arch. Pharm.* **283**, 176 (1950); *Monatsch. Chem.* **81**, 746 (1950).

melted droplets. The two demarcation lines corresponding to the
eutectic melting point and the final melting point can be measured
easily to ±1°C using a small hand magnifier. Melting points accurate to ±0.5°C can be determined if standards are used simultaneously. The sample should be dispersed on the hot bar using a
60–100-mesh sieve. Whenever possible the sample should be mixed
by melting, freezing, and grinding several times. Even quite volatile compounds, such as benzoic acid, salicyclic acid, and veronal,
can be handled in this way since the melting point can be read quickly
(in 4–5 seconds) before significant sublimation has occurred.

The entire diagram can be plotted by measuring the final and eutectic melting points on half a dozen samples covering the necessary composition range.

4. Refractive Index Methods for Determination of Temperature-Composition Diagrams

An elegant method for the rapid determination of composition
of any phases in a binary system without weighing has been used by
the Koflers.[36] This method utilizes the refractive index of the melt

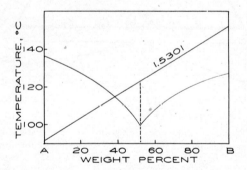

Fig. 92. Determination of binary eutectic composition by use of standard
glass powder, 1.5301, in a mixed fusion preparation of phenacetin (A) and benzamide (B).

(Section III,B,2,a) and is carried out in the following way: A small
quantity of the proper glass powder is placed on a half-slide and a
mixed fusion involving the two test substances is prepared incorporating the glass powder throughout. On heating, the eutectic melts first

---

[36] L. Kofler, Z. Anal. Chem. **133**, 27 (1951).

and a single glass particle in the center of the eutectic is observed until it disappears. This temperature corresponds to the composition of the eutectic, which can be determined from the composition-refractive index relationship for that system. For example, in the system, phenacetin-benzamide, the eutectic lies at 99°C and 51 per

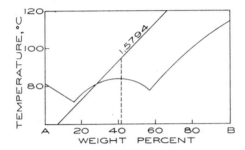

Fig. 93. Determination of addition compound composition by use of standard glass powder, 1.5794, in a mixed fusion preparation of TNT (A) and fluorene (B).

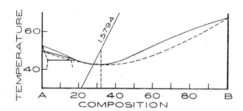

Fig. 94. Determination of minimum melting composition by use of standard glass powder, 1.5794, in a mixed fusion preparation of dibenzyl (A) and azobenzene (B).

cent benzamide as determined using the hot stage. A glass particle of index 1.5301 observed at the exact spot in the zone of mixing corresponding to the first material to melt disappears at 122°C. This corresponds to 51 per cent benzamide, the eutectic composition (Figure 92).

The composition of an addition compound can be determined in a similar fashion (Figure 93). The composition of maximum and minimum melting solid solutions are determined in this way more accurately than any other (Figure 94). Dibenzyl-azobenzene solid solutions, for example, have a very flat minimum difficult to locate by the usual methods.   The glass powder method, however, shows this minimum to be at 32 per cent azobenzene.

It may be necessary, or at least desirable, in some systems to use the highest possible index glass in order to avoid high temperatures and consequent mixing by diffusion and convection.   In any case, the values found can be checked quickly by weighing out a mixture of the proper composition and observing completeness of melting, component in excess, etc.

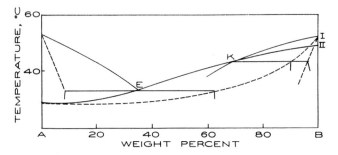

Fig. 95. Stabilized intermediate phase in the system benz-
alaniline (A)—dibenzyl (B).

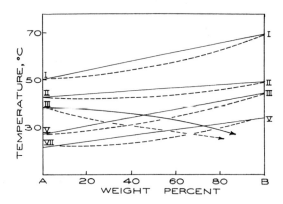

Fig. 96. Parallel isopolymorphism in the system 1,2,4-chloro-
dinitrobenzene (A)—1,2,4-bromodinitrobenzene (B).

Another particularly useful application of this method is for the determination of the composition of two liquid layers in a system such as acetamide-acenaphthene.   The compositions of these two liquids are easier to determine by the glass powder method than

by any other means.   Acetamide is supercooled easily and shows an
index of 1.4339 at 58°C, whereas acenaphthene shows an index of
1.5898 at 121.5°C.   In a mixed fusion, the acetamide-rich melt near
one side of the meniscus shows an index of 1.4339 at 102°C, and near
the other side of the meniscus an index of 1.5898 at 113°C.   From

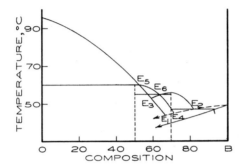

Fig. 97. Addition compounds in the system α-naphthol
(A)—α-naphthylamine (B) showing one that melts congruently and one that melts incongruently (peritectic).

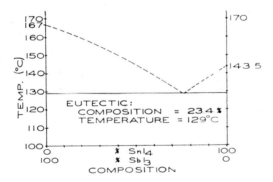

Fig. 98. Simple eutectic in the system SnI_4—SbI_3.

these data and the known temperature-composition functions for this
system, it can be calculated that acetamide dissolves 13 per cent
acenaphthene while acenaphthene dissolves only 2 per cent of acetamide.

The surprising result of studying organic binary and ternary diagrams is the realization that these systems are as complex as many
metal systems and that the behavior of most metals and alloys can

be illustrated at low temperatures with transparent substances using organic systems. One of the complications is, of course, polymor-

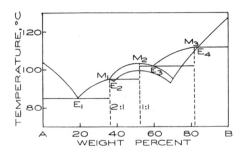

Fig. 99. Addition compounds in the system pyrocatechol (A)—nicotinamide (B).

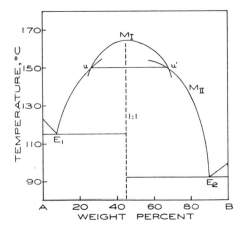

Fig. 100. Addition compound in the system trinitrobenzene (A)—phenanthrene (B).

phism. Some of the typical composition diagrams in which poly-morphism plays a part are shown in Figures 95 and 96. One figure (95) shows an unusual phenomenon; one of the unstable lattices for one of the pure compounds becomes the stable lattice over a definite composition range.

The term isodimorphism has been used to describe systems such that two different series of complete solid solubility exist in the same system (Figure 96). The system, 1,2,4-chlorodinitrobenzene–

1,2,4-bromodinitrobenzene (Figure 96), shows this idea carried to an extreme with at least four such series.

A system showing a peritectic reaction is shown in Figure 97. A few systems have simple eutectics (Figure 98), whereas a large number show addition compounds; other examples are shown in Figures 99 and 100.

5. Quasi-eutectic Syncrystallization

Finally, a most unusual behavior apparently first observed by Tammann and studied by many others in various metal systems, has

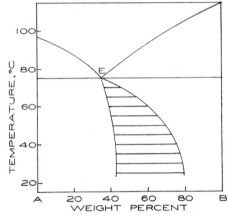

Fig. 101. Quasi-eutectic syncrystallization in the system benzil (A)—acetanilide (B).

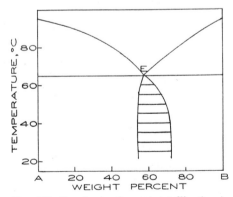

Fig. 102. Quasi-eutectic syncrystallization in the system acenaphthene (A)—benzil (B).

been observed also in organic systems. This behavior called quasi-eutectic syncrystallization is denoted only on freezing of super-cooled mixed melts by the strange behavior of the eutectic. Instead

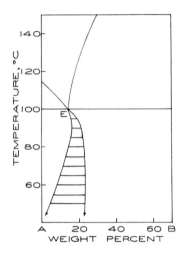

Fig. 103. Quasi-eutectic syncrystallization in the system 2,4-dinitrophenol (A)—anthracene (B).

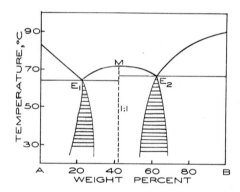

Fig. 104. Quasi-eutectic syncrystallization in the system TNT (A)—anesthesin (B).

of a single eutectic composition, at lower temperatures mixtures over a range of composition can freeze as a single phase in all respects like a eutectic. The range of quasti-eutectic composition, furthermore, does not necessarily even include the true eutectic composition. A few systems showing this type of behavior are shown in Figures 101–104. The same phenomenon also exists in ternary systems as shown in Figure 105.

The real meaning of this behavior seems to be based simply on the relative crystallization velocities of the quasi-eutectic and the pure components. The rates of crystal growth of the two components are usually at a maximum when each is present in the pure state. The

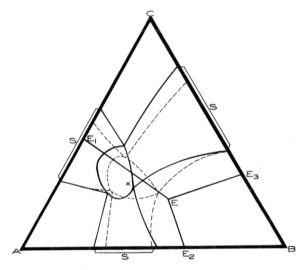

Fig. 105. Quasi-eutectic syncrystallization in the ternary system 2,4-dinitrophenol (A)—acetanilide (B)—benzil (C) supercooled to 50°C (dotted lines), supercooled to 20°C (full lines). X marks the ternary eutectic composition according to Tammann.

rates, then, decrease with increasing percentages of the other component and become equal at the eutectic composition (Figure 106). When the mixtures are supercooled, however, the rates of growth of the pure components and of the secondary crystallization of the supercooled quasi-eutectic change. Instead of a single composition where the eutectic grows as a secondary growth, there is a range of composition where the crystallization velocity of the secondary growth (quasi-eutectic) is greater than the crystallization velocity of the pure components. The boundaries of this quasi-eutectic syncrystallization region, then, is defined as the region within which the crystallization velocity of the quasi-eutectic exceeds that of the pure components.

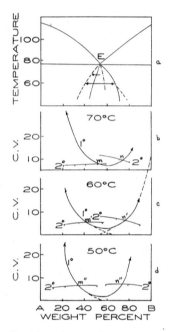

Fig. 106. Isothermal crystallization velocity curves in the system acetanilide (A)—2,4-dinitrophenol (B) supercooled to 70°, 60°, and 50°C.

CHAPTER IV

APPLICATIONS OF FUSION METHODS

Wherever possible the applications of fusion methods have already been used as illustrations of the various techniques. A few, however, which more properly represent research problems solved by means of fusion methods are described below.

A. KINETICS OF CRYSTAL GROWTH

The rate of growth of a crystal front depends on temperature and composition. In binary mixtures at a given temperature the rate of growth may be greater or less than the rate characteristic of the pure compound. Little is known concerning the reasons for wide variations in the effect of impurities on rate of crystal growth, however, the best evidence indicates that the rate is basically a function of the mobility of the melt. Impurities which increase fluidity (i.e., decrease viscosity) increase the crystal growth rate and vice versa. Some evidence for these conclusions is presented below.

Curves relating the rate of crystal growth and composition at various temperatures can be used for quantitative analysis. An example is shown in Figure 59 and Section III,E,5. A similar set of curves for p,p'-DDT and 1,3,5-triphenylbenzene (TPB) is shown in Figure 107.[1] The effect of different amounts of several impurities on the growth rate of p,p'-DDT is shown in Figure 108. It is readily apparent that whereas o,p'-DDT and TPB both decrease the rate of crystal growth of DDT, thymol increases the rate.

Other compounds, especially low-boiling highly fluid solvents, increase the rate of crystal growth of p,p'-DDT much more strongly than thymol. Some of these data are shown graphically in Figure 109 where the maximum rate of growth of p,p'-DDT is plotted against the fluidity of the added component. The maximum rate of growth is readily measured in a mixed fusion between p,p'-DDT and the desired

[1] V. Gilpin, et al., *J. Am. Chem. Soc.* **70**, 208 (1948).

second component by measuring the most rapidly growing crystal front in the zone of mixing.   It is not an easy matter to measure the fluidity of the actual supercooled composition which shows the high rate of crystal growth, hence the assumption is made that the fluidity of that mixture will be approximately proportional to the fluidity of the pure second component, since p,p'-DDT is a common component in all mixtures.   This assumption is valid, of course, only to the

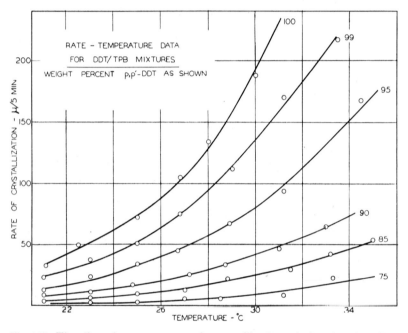

Fig. 107. The effect of temperature on the crystallization velocity of p,p'-DDT—triphenylbenzene mixtures.

extent that these mixtures form ideal solutions and that the most rapidly growing mixtures have the same percentage composition. However, the data seem to confirm with sufficient clarity that the rate of crystal growth is a function of the fluidity.

The kinetics of crystal growth can be further explored by plotting these data according to an Arrhenius type relation:

$$C.V. = Be^{-E_c/RT}$$

where $C.V.$ is the crystallization velocity, B is a constant, and E_c is the activation energy for the crystallization process.   Figures 110 and 111 show that at low temperature the data follow this relation very well. An activation energy of about 33 Kcal/mol can be calculated.   Thymol and other highly mobile liquids decrease this activation energy considerably indicating that the activation energy for crystalliza tion is a function of viscosity of the melt.

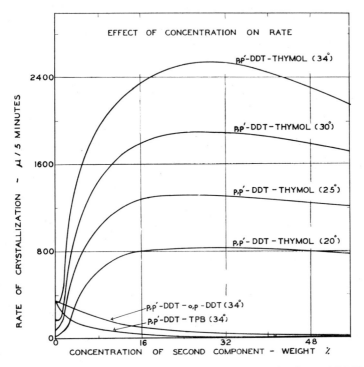

Fig. 108. The effect of impurities on crystallization velocity for p,p'-DDT.

The importance of B is not known.   It may contain an entropy term suggesting that structural symmetry of the second component, which must play a role, may enter in this term.   However, B also depends strongly on other factors, perhaps also on viscosity, as indicated by the large change in B during increase in thymol content of thymol mixtures as compared with TPB or o,p'-DDT mixtures. Much more work should be done in this interesting direction.

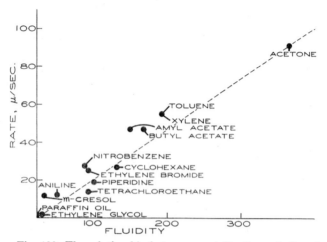

Fig. 109. The relationship between crystallization velocity of p,p'-DDT and the fluidity (reciprocal viscosity) of pure second components of corresponding mixtures.

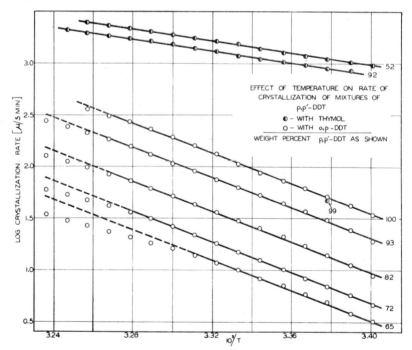

Fig. 110. Arrhenius-type relations for mixtures of p,p'-DDT with o,p-DDT and thymol.

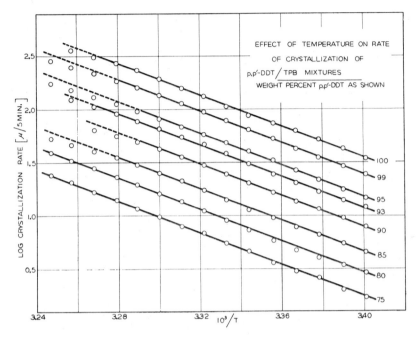

Fig. 111. Arrhenius-type relations for p,p'-DDT with triphenylbenzene.

B. THERMAL STABILITY OF DECOMPOSABLE
COMPOUNDS

Many organic compounds are unstable at their melting points, e.g., sugars (Figure 112), polynitroaromatics, nitramines, amino acids, and many alkaloids. Some of these decompose slowly at relatively low temperatures. Many of these compounds can, however, be stabilized, to some extent at least, since the decomposition is almost always autocatalytic. Any chemical additive, therefore, which neutralizes or otherwise accounts for the products of decomposition will lower the decomposition rate. This is especially important in the explosives and pharmaceuticals industries.

The following account covers the development of a fusion method for determining the thermal stability of a given sample and a study of methods of stabilizing one particular compound, methylenedinitramine. The initial experiments were based on the fact that the products of decomposition cause lowering of the melting point of the

sample, and as further decomposition occurs the melting point will
progressively decrease. The simplest means of determining the
thermal stability was finally found to be by measurement of the time
for complete melting (TCM) as the solid sample is held in the hot
stage at constant temperature.

A small sample, about 2 mg., is mounted between two large cover
slips and placed in a hot stage previously heated to the desired test
temperature. The temperature of the stage will fall about 1°C as the
sample is introduced, however, it will recover quickly and this deviation can be ignored. The test temperature should be chosen so
that the TCM values fall within a convenient range (5–30 minutes).

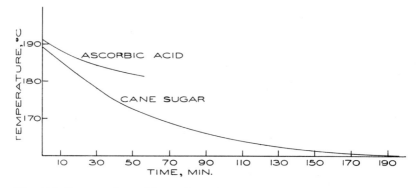

Fig. 112. Decrease in melting point of two thermally unstable compounds
(ascorbic acid and cane sugar) as a function of time.

This is controlled easily, of course, since the higher the temperature
the lower the TCM.

The appearance of the preparation during a determination is very
much like a very slow melting point determination with the added
evidence of decomposition, gas bubbles. The percentage of crystalline solid gradually decreases until only melt is left. TCM is measured in minutes from the introduction of the sample to the complete
disappearance of the last crystal residue.

The hot stage is most suitable for the determination of TCM at
constant temperature, although a hot bar may be used for routine
determination by sprinkling the sample through a 100-mesh screen
and noting TCM at the desired temperature. Although there is some
sacrifice of accuracy using the hot bar, this apparatus is a great help
in determining TCM values rapidly as a function of temperature,

since it is only necessary to sprinkle the sample through the screen
over the range near the melting point and measure the temperature
at which melting occurs as a function of time. The effect of temperature on TCM is shown in Figure 113 and is discussed in more detail below.

For samples of methylenedinitramine TCM at 90°C or 95°C were
found to be most conveniently determined. It was found, at once,
that TCM varied considerably from sample to sample of the sup-
posedly pure material. TCM (95°C), for example, varied from about

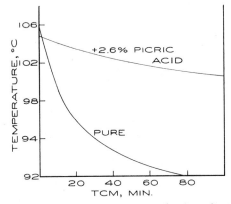

Fig. 113. The effect of temperature on the time of complete
melting (TCM) for methylenedinitramine.

10 minutes to about 40 minutes, depending only on the purity of the
original sample. Since nitramines are notoriously unstable, it was
decided to use picric acid as a stabilizer. The stabilization of one
sample by picric acid is shown in Table XX. The accuracy of these
data could, if desired, be corrected for the lowering caused by picric
acid itself since the mixture containing 2.30 per cent picric acid is
more stable than is indicated by the value found for TCM since 2.3
per cent of picric acid lowers the melting point of methylenedinitramine
by more than 1°C. This correction would, in this case, amount to
about a 10 per cent increase in TCM (95°C). Higher percentages of
picric acid or TCM measured at higher temperatures would, however,
require correspondingly higher corrections.

Styphnic acid, probably because it possesses two phenolic OH
groups, is about two times as effective as picric acid in stabilizing
methylenedinitramine (Table XXI).

TABLE XX

Stabilization of Methylenedinitramine by Picric Acid

Picric acid, weight per cent	TCM (95°C), minutes
0.00	30.6
0.40	177
0.86	308
1.70	395
2.30	431

TABLE XXI

Comparative Stabilizing Effects of Picric and Styphnic Acids on Methylenedinitramine

Per cent stabilizer		TCM (100°C), minutes
Picric acid	Styphnic acid	
0	0	12
0.5	0	17
1.0	0	25
1.5	0	40
0	0.5	30
0	1.0	52
0	1.5	76

The effect of temperature on TCM is shown for methylenedinitramine in Figure 113. The same sample of methylenedinitramine was used for both series of experiments; one, however, was first mixed with 2.6 per cent picric acid. Each of these curves can be extrapolated to zero time to give the melting point of the undecomposed samples; 106.0°C for the pure material and 104.8°C for the mixture with picric acid. This is another, and very precise, method for the determination of melting point for a compound that decomposes at its melting point.

The TCM procedure can be adapted easily to the determination of melting points of decomposable compounds on the hot bar and gives more direct results than the hot stage. The hot stage requires a longer time to establish equilibrium (up to 1 min. for a slide preparation; up to 0.5 min. with a preparation between 2 cover slips) and a series of separate determinations must be made. When the hot bar is used, the sample is sprinkled through a 100-mesh sieve over the melting region of the bar and the change in melting point with time is measured. Only 4–5 seconds is required to reach equilibrium and a series of 10 or more melting points may be determined in 5 minutes, each

representing a TCM value for a different temperature.   These data
may be extrapolated back to zero time to give an accurate melting
point.

Melting point data for a number of compounds taken in this way
are shown in Figure 114.

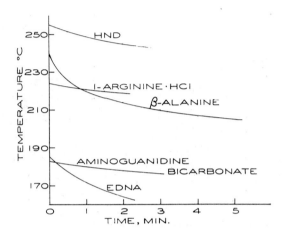

Fig. 114. Change in melting point with time for a
number of thermally unstable compounds.

C. STUDY OF POUR-POINT DEPRESSANTS IN LUBRICATING OIL

In order to achieve a lubricating oil that starts easily at winter
temperatures and still lubricates well at high motor temperatures,
refiners have always striven to keep a low temperature coefficient
of viscosity (expressed reciprocally as a viscosity index).   Oils
containing relatively large percentages of long straight-chain paraffin
hydrocarbons have naturally high V.I.'s and are, therefore, desirable
except that these same compounds tend to crystallize as waxes at
low temperatures.   These waxes can cause the oil to suddenly lose all
mobility at temperatures within the required winter-operating temperature range.

It seemed reasonable to suppose that the mechanisms by which an
oil suddenly "froze," i.e., ceased to pour (hence the word pour-point),
is connected in some way with crystallization of the wax.   Accord-
ingly, it was decided to study the cooling of representative oils using

fusion methods.[2]   This required a cold stage which could be used with phase contrast accessories.   No such stage was available at the time, hence a simple stage which could be heated or cooled and with which phase accessories could be used was designed and built[3] (see Section II,C,5).

(a) (b)

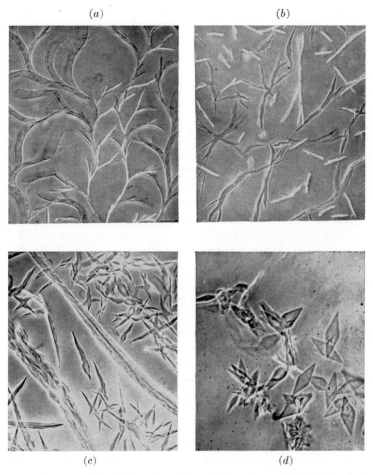

(c) (d)

Fig. 115. Wax crystals in lubricating oil showing the effect of gradually increasing the amount of pour-point depressant in (a) through (d).

[2] G. Gavlin, E. A. Swire, and S. P. Jones, *Ind. Eng. Chem.* **45**, 2327 (1953).

[3] This stage has been subsequently modified by A. H. Thomas Co. and is now available through their Philadelphia office.

Samples of tube oil cooled below their pour-points ($-20°C$) were found to look like the photomicrographs in Figure 115. The wax crystals are easily visible using phase contrast and form long, branched and probably a three-dimensional network analogous to the two-dimensional one shown in Figure 115a. By this means then, the oil, even though still fluid, is immobilized completely in pockets within a semirigid wax structure. The effect of various pour-point depressants is shown in the other photomicrographs; notice the change in crystal habit of the waxes making them more free-flowing.

Such a hypothesis suggested that this network could be broken up if the length of the wax crystals could be decreased. If growth of the wax crystals could occur on the sides of the needles and rods shown in Figure 115a instead of the ends, the crystals might then remain separate and remain suspended in the oil thus permitting flow.

The optical properties of these wax crystals confirmed that the long-chain molecules were lined up parallel to each other and that the direction of rapid growth was perpendicular to the length of the paraffin chains. The optical properties used to ascertain this were the refractive indices and birefringence. Since the crystals showed one high refractive index and two low indices, it was reasonable to assume that the molecules are lined up parallel to the direction of the high refractive index and this direction is normal to the length of the long crystals in Figure 115a, hence the crystals must grow more rapidly in the other two directions.

The problem was then to find or synthesize molecules that would be adsorbed on the rapidly growing faces of the wax crystal. This requires a molecule of low solubility in the first place and a molecular structure, part of which fits or is adsorbed on the proper crystal faces, i.e., the ones on which the long-chain paraffin molecules lie flat. This suggested a polymer with long paraffin side-chains and since these were easy to synthesize in the acrylate series, a number of derivatives were synthesized in which the length of the side chain and the molecular weight of the polymer were varied.

The various new additives were tested by their effect on the habit of the wax crystals growing from the lubricating oil on cooling in the cold stage. Many of the samples showed excellent pour-point depression, and in preparations of each of these samples the wax crystals were found to be separate and massive rather than elongated (Figures 115b,c, and d).

D. RECRYSTALLIZATION AND GRAIN GROWTH

It has long been known that metals show grain growth on annealing and that this growth involves a reorientation of metal atoms along a grain boundary in such a way that the average grain diameter increases and some grains disappear entirely.[4]

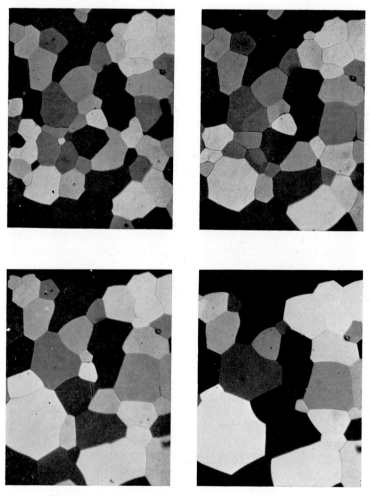

Fig. 116. Grain growth in octachloropropane at 136°C.

[4] H. C. H. Carpenter, and C. F. Elam, *J. Inst. Metals* **24**, 123 (1920).

In 1929 Tammann[5] published data showing that certain compounds (camphor, pinene hydrochloride, and ice) show a behavior very similar to that observed in metals.   In 1946 Buerger and Washken[6] showed that some minerals (e.g., anhydrite, fluorite, periclase, and

Fig. 117. Recrystallization in p,p'-DDT (upper) and TNT (lower).

[5] G. Tammann and K. L. Dreyer, *Z. Anorg. u. Allgem. Chem.* **182**, 289 (1929).

[6] M. J. Buerger and E. Washken, *Am. Mineralogist* **32**, 296 (1947).

corundum) when compressed and heated to temperatures well below the melting point would also show grain growth similar to metals. In 1949 the study of octachloropropane (Figure 116) was suggested[7] as an aid in the study of recrystallization in metals.

During the past several years a number of organic compounds quite dissimilar to octachloropropane in lattice properties have been shown to exhibit recrystallization. For example, Kofler[8] reported in 1941 that an organic compound, TNT, shows a somewhat similar behavior in that crystals once formed undergo a further recrystallization in the solid phase so that one crystal grows into and through its neighbor (Figure 117). DDT has also been reported,[9] and several other organic compounds (unreported) have been observed to show similar behavior (Figure 117). In each of these cases and in contrast with the metals, camphor, fluorite, octachloropropane, etc., it is apparent that these highly anisotropic organic compounds show recrystallization in which the direction is dependent on the orientation of the crystal lattice within the grains.

Metals, octachloropropane, camphor, pinene hydrochloride, ice, fluorite, anhydrite, etc., show grain growth of one crystal into another in such a way that the orientation of the lattice cannot be an important factor. On the other hand, recrystallization by TNT, DDT, vitamin K, DINA, etc., is definitely dependent on orientation of the crystals. Furthermore, the crystals will grow in a direction which can be predicted for a given compound from the known relative orientations.

Two different types of recrystallization are therefore recognized. The two types will be described throughout as the DDT type, in which orientation controls the direction of growth; and the octachloropropane type, in which orientation has little or no effect on the direction of growth.

The DDT type of recrystallization (Figure 117) is of particular interest since, as stated above, the direction of growth is dependent on lattice orientation. Any theory covering the mechanism of recrystallization must take into account, for crystals of this type, the effect of difference in orientation of the two lattices in contact. DDT, for example, grows in such a way that the (001) face will penetrate either the (100) or (010) planes of adjacent crystals. If, on the other

[7] W. C. McCrone and P. T. Cheng, *J. Appl. Phys.* **20**, 230 (1949).

[8] A. Kofler, *Z. physik. Chem.* **188**, 201 (1941).

[9] W. C. McCrone, *Anal. Chem.* **20**, 274 (1948).

hand, crystals of this type are aligned parallel to each other, no growth will occur. Maximum growth will occur, therefore, when crystals elongated parallel to c intersect at 90° angles.

TNT shows a very similar behavior although it does not recrystallize as rapidly as DDT, DINA, and vitamin K. It does, however, grow in much the same manner and in such a way that the direction

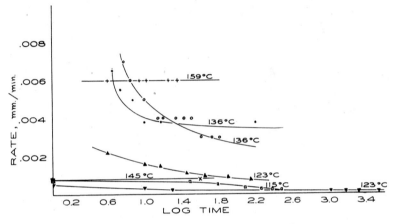

Fig. 118. Rate of grain growth for octachloropropane at different temperatures as a function of time.

of growth can always be predicted from the orientation of the crystals. In this case the (010) face will always grow into the (001) and (100) faces (Figure 117).

During the past 20 or 30 years there has been considerable discussion regarding the possible mechanism by which recrystallization occurs.

Most of this discussion has been on grain growth of the octachloropropane type and most of it has concerned metals. Harker and Parker[10] have advanced the argument that grain shape or, in a sense, surface tension governs the extent and direction of grain growth. This results in movement of the grain boundaries in such a way that straight boundaries meet at angles of 120°. By this criterion little or no grain growth should occur when these conditions are satisfied. The effect of lattice deformation on grain growth is not discussed by them. Most other investigators have assumed that strain energy,

[10] D. Harker and E. R. Parker, *Trans. Am. Soc. Metals* **34**, 156 (1945).

due to cold-working and resultant plastic deformation, is the driving force.

To test these hypotheses a group of samples of octachloropropane were melted, chilled quickly to room temperature on a metal block, then annealed in a hot stage at constant temperature.[11] Photomicrographs (Figure 116) were taken at regular intervals so that the average grain size could be measured as a function of annealing temperature and time.   Four identical samples prepared in this way were annealed each at a different temperature (136°, 123°, 115°, and 103°C). The results are shown in Figure 118. In addition, a single preparation was made up with no heat treatment at all; a small sample, about 5 mg., was compressed under a cover glass with a mechanical force of about 500 psi. This sample was then annealed at 136°C. Finally, two preparations were made up in a manner such that strain was minimized. The melted samples were placed in the hot stage directly at a temperature of 159°C, the other at a temperature of 145°C. The data for these three samples are also plotted in Figure 118.

These data show that the two samples annealed at the same temperature, 136°C, behave very similarly in spite of the fact that one was strained by a thermal procedure, the other mechanically. All the curves, except the two unstrained samples annealed at 145°C and 159°C, start at high rates of growth and gradually decrease apparently asymptotically to a value proportional to the temperature. The two unstrained samples, on the other hand, maintain an apparently constant rate of growth over the time period covered.

These results are interpreted to mean that the unstrained samples show grain growth almost entirely as a result of surface tension. The other strained samples, on the other hand, show growth in the early stages due to strain but as the strain is alleviated only the surface tension contribution remains. The latter should, of course, decrease with time as the remaining grains become 6-sided with 120° angles. The rate of growth of the 159°C sample is less by far than that expected of a strained sample annealed at that temperature; it is high, however, probably because at this temperature, so close to the melting point, surface tension forces are very strong.

Octachloropropane, annealed in this way has been shown to follow the same mathematical relationship followed by metals.[12]   It seems

---

[11] W. C. McCrone, *Discussions Faraday Soc. No.* **5**, 158 (1949).
[12] P. A. Beck, *J. Appl. Phys.* **19**, 507 (1948).

probable that a great deal can be learned about grain growth in metals using octachloropropane at least as a guide.

An attempt has also been made to determine the mechanism for the anisotropic type of grain growth which occurs with DDT, TNT, vitamin K, and DINA.   TNT seemed to be the most suitable subject for experimentation, hence an attempt was made to determine the effect of thermally induced strain on recrystallization in TNT. First, a small sample (5–10 mg.) of TNT was melted and cooled to about 50°C before crystallization.   This preparation was then placed in an already heated hot stage at 78°C and observed for a period of 40 min.   During this time the crystals grew into adjacent crystals a distance of 0.5 mm.   Figure 117 shows the type of growth observed.

A second preparation of TNT was then melted and placed in the hot stage at 80°C before crystallization occurred.   On seeding, crystals of TNT were made to grow slowly into contact at right angles. Observation of this and similar preparations over a period of 60 min. at 80°C showed no indication of crystal growth.   The conclusion from this information is that recrystallization in TNT and presumably in DDT and other compounds of this type is due entirely to lattice strain and relative crystal orientation.   Such compounds might be expected to possess a high anisotropy of elasticity with considerable variation in coefficients of expansion, hardness, etc., in the three principal directions in the crystal.[13]

[13] Color movies showing grain growth of octachloropropane and recrystallization of TNT, DDT, and DINA have been assembled into a film titled "Grain Growth and Recrystallization," which is available on loan from the author.

IDENTIFICATION TABLES

A. INTRODUCTION

Four analytical tables useful for the identification of organic compounds are included in Chapter V. Table I lists the compounds alphabetically with their melting points and with an identifying code number. The latter will be used in lieu of the chemical name in Tables III and IV. Table II lists the compounds by code number in the order of increasing melting point. Table III gives the eutectic melting points of each compound with several standard compounds. The compounds are listed by code numbers in the order of increasing eutectic melting point for each standard compound in succession. Table IV covers the refractive index of the melt and the temperature coefficients of that index. The data are listed in the order of increasing temperatures for each glass index standard along with the corresponding temperature coefficient; each set of data are identified by code number.

These tables are based principally on the work of the Koflers. The data have been retabulated, however, into a more useful analytical form. Given the melting point of an unknown compound, the melting points of its eutectics with two standard compounds, and given the refractive index of the melt, reference to Tables II, III, and IV will give the code numbers of the compounds having values close to the values found. Comparison of the code numbers from each table will show in nearly every case only one code number in common. The compounds corresponding to the code number can be identified by Table I. In case two or more code numbers appear in common a mixed fusion (Section III,B,5,b) between the unknown and one or more of the possibilities should establish the true identity.

The melting points (Table II) may be taken in any of the ways described in the text and for which corrections are known, based on melting points in an identical manner of known standards. The eutectic melting points (Table III) are observed usually on a mixed fusion preparation and with the second components chosen from the following depending on the melting point.

199

For melting points between	Standard second component
20–100°C	azobenzene, benzil
100–120	benzil, acetanilide
120–140	acetanilide, phenacetin
140–170	phenacetin, benzanilide
170–190	benzanilide, salophen
190–240	salophen, dicyandiamide
240–340	phenolphthalein

The refractive index of the melt is determined as described in Section III,B,2,a. When known, the temperature coefficient is also listed. As a matter of passing interest it might be noted that, as expected, this coefficient increases with refractive index of the melt. On the other hand, for a group of compounds having roughly the same refractive indices of the melt the temperature coefficient of refractive index decreases as the melting point increases. On closer study, one would expect to find that the higher melting compounds are, on the average, more polar which would raise their melting points in relation to their temperature coefficient of refractive index

TABLE I

Alphabetical Listing of Compounds with Melting Points
and Identifying Code Numbers

Compound	Melting point, °C	Code number
Abasin	108–110	388
Acenaphthalene	93	280
Acenaphthene	94	288
Acenaphthenequinone	261	1122
Acetaldehyde-2,4-dinitrophenylhydrazone	165	725
Acetamide	80	229
p-Acetaminobenzenesulfonamino-acetonitrile	190	871
3-[4-Acetaminobenzenesufamino]-benzonitrile	237	1079
N-[4-Acetaminobenzenesulfonyl]-p-phenylenediamine	235	1074
p-Acetaminobenzenesulfothiourea	190–194	901
p-Acetaminobenzoic acid	262	1125
p-Acetaminobenzonitrile	205	966
[4-Acetaminobenzyl]-benzoylamine	186	848
4-Acetaminodiphenyl	170	745
Acetanilide	115	415
p-Acetanisidide	130	515
Acetbadional	190–194	901
α-Acetnaphthalide	161	701
Acetoacetic anilide	84	243
Acetoacetic ester-p-nitrophenylhydrazone	118	440

TABLE I (*Continued*)

Compound	Melting point, °C	Code number
β-Acetonaphthalide	134	540
Acetone chloroform	97	305
Acetone-2,4-dinitrophenylhydrazone	128	497
Acetonethiosemicarbazone	174–178	801
Acetophenonoxime	59	112
o-Acetoxyacetophenone	90	263
Acet-m-toluidide	65	152
Acet-o-toluidide	110	379
Acet-p-toluidide	151	640
1-Acetylaminoanthraquinone	220	1038
p-Acetylaminobenzenesulfonylguanidine	263–266	1132
N-Acetyl-4-bromo-1-naphthylamine	191	887
N-Acetyl-N'-diethylbromoacetylurea	108–110	388
Acetyldiphenylamine	103	332
N-Acetyl-5-ethyl-5-phenylhydantoin	177–180	816
Acetyl-α-naphthylamine	161	701
Acetyl-β-naphthylamine	134	540
Acetylnirvanol	177–180	816
β-Acetylphenylhydrazine	129.5	512
Acetylsalicylic acid	130–136	551
O-Acetylsalicyltheobromine	190–196	912
2-[N⁴-Acetylsulfanilamino]-pyridine	228	1057
Acetylthiourea	120	449
Acoin	174–177	795
Aconitine	180–195	905
Aconitine nitrate	186–188	858
Acridine	110	378
Adermin hydrochloride	207–214	1002
Adipic acid	152	643
Adipic amide	227	1054
Adonite	102	328
Adonitol	102	328
Adrenalin	203–208	978
Adrianol	141–143	586
Aesculin	148–150	637
Alantolactone	67–70	175
Albucid	184	833
Aldomedonanhydride	178	807
Alizarin	289	1165
Allantoin	225–230	1063
Alloxantin	235–242	1084
N-Allyl-N-butyl-N'-acetylurea	158	683
5-Allyl-5-butylbarbituric acid	129	505

(*Continued*)

TABLE I (*Continued*)

Compound	Melting point, °C	Code number
5-Allyl-5-phenylbarbituric acid	159	690
2-Allylphenyl cinchonate	36	12
N-Allyl-N-isopropyl-N'-acetylurea	193	897
5-Allyl-5-isopropylbarbituric acid	142	578
5-Allyl-5-n-propylbarbituric acid	131	519
Allylthiourea	71	180
Aludrin	120–125	478
Alypin hydrochloride	170	743
Alypin nitrate	163.5	713
p-Aminoacetanilide	163	710
Aminoacetic acid	247–257	1119
p-Aminoacetophenone	106	357
4-Aminoanisole	57	106
α-Aminoanthraquinone	255	1115
p-Aminoazobenzene	125	479
Aminoazophenylene	99	317
o-Aminobenzaldehydephenylhydrazone	216–220	1025
2-[p-Aminobenzenesulfamino]-5-ethylthiadiazole	188	863
p-Aminobenzenesulfonamide	166	730
p-Aminobenzenesulfonamide-β,β-dimethylacrylamide	181	821
2-[p-Aminobenzenesulfonamino]-pyrimidine	254–257	1120
p-Aminobenzenesulfoneacetamide	184	833
p-Aminobenzenesulfonylguanidine monohydrate	190	872
m-Aminobenzoic acid	178	805
o-Aminobenzoic acid	145	592
p-Aminobenzoic acid	187	851
m-Aminobenzonitrile	54	84
p-Aminobenzonitrile	87	255
p-Aminobenzylcyanide	45	43
o-Aminodiphenyl	49	57
α-Amino-β-methylvaleric acid	280–290	1168
2-Amino-4-nitrotoluene	107	361
m-Aminophenol	122	463
o-Aminophenol	175	785
p-Aminophenol	185	845
p-Aminophenyl acetic acid	198–207	973
4-[4'-Aminophenylsulfonamido]-phenylsulfonamide	112–134	537
4-[4'-Aminophenylsulfonamido]-phenylsulfondimethylamide	195	910
4-[4'-Aminophenylsulfonamido]-phenylsulfonemethylamide	151	642
Aminopyrene	108	369
2-Aminopyridine	56	96
p-Aminosalicylic acid	130–135	547

TABLE I (*Continued*)

Compound	Melting point, °C	Code number
p-Aminosalicylic acid hydrochloride	205–220	1024
p-Aminotoluene	44	37
Ammonium salicylate	145–148	611
Amphetamine hydrochloride	250–265	1131
5-Amylbarbituric acid	226–228	1055
5-*sec*-Amyl-5-[β-bromallyl]-barbituric acid	155–164	715
p-tert-Amyl phenol	94	289
1-1-Amyltheobromine	110–115	414
tert-Amylurea	162	705
Amytal	156	670
Androsterone	184	832
Anesthesine	90.5	266
Aneurin hydrochloride	232–237	1078
Anhydromethylene citric acid	185–195	911
Aniline hydrochloride	197	919
Anisaldazine	170	746
Anisic acid	185	843
p-Anisidine	57	106
Anisil	131	524
Anision 4,4′-dimethoxybenzoin	110	381
Anthracene	215	1012
Anthracene picrate	141–143	588
Anthralin	181	819
Anthranilic acid	145	592
Anthraquinone	286	1159
Antifibrin	115	415
Antipyrene	111.5	393
Antipyrene salicylate	92	274
Antistin	248	1100
Apoatropine hydrochloride	238–240	1081
Apomorphine hydrochloride	220–270	1136
L-Arabinose	157–162	704
Arachidic acid	75.5	211
Arbutin	165	720
Arecoline hydrobromide	177	796
Arecoline hydrochloride	163	708
D-Arginine	220–230	1068
Aristoquin	187	855
Artemisine	200–204	961
L-Ascorbic acid	185–190	869
Aspidospermine	204–208	979
Aspirin	130–136	551
Atophane	213	1001

(*Continued*)

TABLE I (*Continued*)

Compound	Melting point, °C	Code number
2,4-Atoquinol	36	12
Atropine	116	418
Atropinebromomethylate	228–230	1067
Atropine hydrobromide	147–149	624
Atropine hydrochloride	170	744
Atropine sulfate	190–192	889
Azelaic acid	106.5	360
Azobenzene	68	166
p,p'-Azoxyanisole	118	442
2,2'-Azoxydiphenyl	141	575
Barbituric acid	252–254	1109
Benzalacetone	40	20
Benzalacetophenone	57	105
4-Benzalamino-antipyrene	176	791
Benzalaniline	52	72
Benzalazine	94	286
Benzamide	128	498
m-Benzamino benzonitrile	143	587
p-Benzamino benzonitrile	169	739
Benzanilide	163	712
1,2-Benzanthracene	165	724
Benzanthrone	172	760
Benzbromanilide	204	955
2,3-Benzdiphenyleneoxide	208	985
Benzedrine hydrochloride	250–265	1131
1-Benzeneazo-2-naphthol	132	529
1,2,3-Benzenetricarboxylic acid	196	915
Benzhydrazide	113	406
Benzidine	129	502
Benzil	95	293
α-Benzildioxime	242	1085
Benzilic acid	145–150	632
Benzimidazole	173	770
7,8-Benzoflavone	157	674
2,3-Benzofluorene	212	996
Benzoic acid	122.5	467
Benzoic-*p*-sulfonamide	284–286	1158
Benzoin	134	538
α-Benzoinoxime	151–153	650
Benzonaphthol	107	362
Benzophenone	48	53
Benzophenonehydrazone	99	316
Benzophenonoxide	176	788
Benzopyrazole	147	604

TABLE I (*Continued*)

Compound	Melting point, °C	Code number
5,6-Benzoquinoline	92	275
1,4-Benzoquinone	113	404
Benzosol	61	132
Benzothiophene	31	6
Benzotriazole	99	317
Benzoylacetone	57	107
N-Benzoylaminoacetic acid	190	875
Benzoylaminoacetonitrile	142	577
β-Benzoylaminoethanol hydrobromide	141	576
o-Benzoylbenzoic acid	127	496
2-Benzoyl-2-dimethylaminomethyl-1-dimethylamino-butane nitrate	163.5	713
Benzoyl-1-ecgonine	200–203	949
Benzoyl eugenol	68	169
Benzoyl-α-naphthylamine	161	702
Benzoyl peroxide	108	370
N-Benzoylpiperidine	50	66
o-Benzoylresorcinol	118	435
o-Benzoylsulfimide	228	1056
N-Benzoyltetrahydropapaverine	159	689
Benzylaniline	36	15
Benzyl benzoate	19	2
Benzyl cinnamate	38	18
Benzyl-3,5-dinitrobenzoate	105	347
Benzyl-p-hydroxy benzoate	112	399
Benzylidenephenylhydrazine	148–153	653
Benzylphenyl carbamate	144	590
5-Benzyl-5-propylbarbituric acid	210	991
N⁴-Benzylsulfanilamide	178	803
S-Benzyl thiuroniumacetate	135–139	562
S-Benzylthiuronium-3,5-diiodo-4-hydroxybenzene-sulfonate	192–194	903
S-Benzyl thiuroniumformate	144–147	600
S-Benzylthiuronium-4-sulfosalicylate	189–200	933
Benzylurea	149	627
Berberine hydrochloride	182–188	857
Berberine sulfate	275–280	1148
Betol	94	285
4,4'-Bis-acetaminodiphenylsulfone	293	1172
2,2-Bis-p-chlorophenyl-1,1,1-trichloroethane	109	377
α,β-Bis-diphenylenethane	246	1094
Bis-Ethylsulfone dimethylmethane	126.5	491
Bis-[p-methoxyphenyl]-azimethylene	170	746

(*Continued*)

TABLE I (*Continued*)

Compound	Melting point, °C	Code number
Boldin	151–158	680
Borneol	208	984
Bornyl chloride	128–131	522
Bourbonal	77	218
Bromoacetamide	90	264
3-Bromo-4-acetaminotoluene	119	445
p-Bromoacetanilide	169	740
α-Bromoacetic acid	49	58
p-Bromoacetophenone	52	76
ω-Bromoacetophenone	50	64
p-Bromoaniline	64	144
p-Bromobenzalacetophenone	105	349
m-Bromobenzoic acid	155.5	666
o-Bromobenzoic acid	149	623
p-Bromobenzoic acid	220 (dec.)	1040
p-Bromobenzoic anhydride	218	1021
3-Bromo-d-camphor	76	213
Bromodiethylacetylurea	120	450
4-Bromo-1,2-dinitrobenzene	73	195
4-Bromo-1,3-dinitrobenzene	72	184
p-Bromodiphenyl	89	261
β-Bromoethylnitrobenzene	70	178
N-[β-Bromoethyl]-phthalimide	83	236
Bromohydroquinone	110	384
p-Bromoiodobenzene	91	268
2-Bromonaphthalene	50	67
1-Bromo-2-naphthylamine	63	141
4-Bromo-1-naphthylamine	103	334
m-Bromonitrobenzene	55	94
o-Bromonitrobenzene	41	27
p-Bromonitrobenzene	127	495
p-Bromophenolbenzoate	104	342
dl-α-Bromostearic acid	59	113
dl-Bromosuccinic acid	161	699
p-Bromotoluene	27	4
N-[α-Bromoisovaleryl]-piperazine	183	823
α-Bromoisovalerylurea	152	646
Bromural	152	646
Brucine	170–178	800
Brucine hydrochloride	190–205	964
Brucine nitrate	220–244	1088
Bulbocapnine hydrochloride	230	1062
1,2,3,4-Butane tetranitrate	61	133
1,2,3,4-Butanetetrol	119.5	446

TABLE I (*Continued*)

Compound	Melting point, °C	Code number
Butolan	144	590
Butoxy-cinchoninic acid diethylethylenediamine		
hydrochloride	99	314
5-Butylbarbituric acid	200–208	976
5-*sec*-Butyl-5-[β-bromoallyl]-barbituric acid	132	525
Butylmalonic acid	105	348
5-Butyl-5-propylbarbituric acid	154	656
n-Butyraldehyde-2,4-dinitrophenylhydrazone	122	464
Butyrchloral hydrate	91	269
n-Butyric amide	116	423
Caffeic acid	190–215	1007
Caffeine	236	1076
Caffeine citrate	155–164	714
Camphane	140–155	665
Camphor	174–176	787
d-Camphor carbonic acid	128	499
d-Camphoric acid	190	877
Camphoric acid imide	190–210 (dec.)	988
d-Camphoroxime	120	451
Cane sugar	185–190	870
Cantharidine	218	1020
Carbamylcholine chloride	195–204	953
Carbanilide	247	1098
Carbazole	245	1092
2-Carbmethoxyl-1-naphthol	78	221
Carbon tetrabromide	95	295
Cardiazole	59	110
Cetyl alcohol	49.5	62
Cevadine	195–207	971
Chloralformamide	124	474
Chloral hydrate	55–57	100
Chloralurethane	106	353
Chloramide	124	474
Chloramine T	171–173	765
Chloranil	280 (dec.)	1153
Chloretone	97	305
Chloracetamide	119	443
p-Chloroaniline	71	181
p-Chlorobenzalacetophenone	99	315
p-Chlorobenzaldehyde	48	50
o-Chlorobenzoic acid	140	566
p-Chlorobenzoic acid	243	1086
6-Chloro-*m*-cresol	64	147

(*Continued*)

TABLE I (*Continued*)

Compound	Melting point, °C	Code number
α-Chlorocrotonic acid	100.5	325
4-Chloro-1,3-dinitrobenzene	51	70
p-Chloroiodobenzene	54	88
α-Chloralose	186	850
β-Chloronaphthalene	60	125
m-Chloronitrobenzene	45	42
o-Chloronitrobenzene	33	9
p-Chloronitrobenzene	83	240
2-Chloro-4-nitrotoluene	65	150
p-Chlorophenol	43	36
p-Chlorophenol benzoate	88	259
p-Chlorophenyl carbonate	151	641
2-Chlorophenyl salicylate	52	74
4-Chlorophenyl salicylate	73	194
4-Chlorothymol	61	131
Cholein acid	188	859
Cholesterol	148	616
Cholesteryl acetate	115	416
Cholic acid	196–200	930
Chrysazine	194	902
Chrysene	254	1110
Cignolin	181	819
Cinchonidine	204	954
Cinchonidine sulfate	195–208	974
Cinchonine	264	1128
Cinchonine hydrochloride	208–218	1018
Cinnamein	38	18
trans-Cinnamic acid	135	545
Cinnamic anhydride	135.5	549
Cinnamic amide	149	630
Cinnamide	149	630
Cinnamoyl-p-hydroxyphenylurea	270–275	1142
Cinnamoyl-p-oxyphenylurea	190–195	908
α-Cinnamylbenzylcyanide	120	453
Cinnamyl cinnamate	44	40
Citraconic acid	92	272
Citric acid	151–154	659
Citrophen	167–179	808
Clopane hydrochloride	114	413
Cocaine	98	307
Cocaine hydrochloride	189–191	885
Cocaine nitrate	55–59	119
Codeine	156	669
Codeine hydrate	55–60	128

TABLE I (*Continued*)

Compound	Melting point, °C	Code number
Codeine hydrochloride	260–270	1138
Codeine hydrochloride dihydrate	165–170	742
Codeine phosphate	220–235	1075
Colchicine	140–150	636
Compral	76	214
Coniine hydrobromide	212	998
Coniine hydrochloride	215–218	1019
Conteben	220–224	1044
Coprosterol	105	344
Cortin	161	700
Cortiron	161	700
Cotarnine hydrochloride	182–188	856
Cotoin	130	517
Coumarin	69	172
trans-2-Coumarinic acid	215–220	1031
trans-4-Coumarinic acid	206–215	1009
Creatine	258–268	1133
m-Cresolol	76	215
m-Cresol carbonate	48	54
o-Cresol carbonate	55	93
p-Cresol carbonate	113	403
β-Cresotinic acid	165	722
γ-Cresotinic acid	177	797
Cyanoacetamide	120	452
ω-Cyanobenzylbenzoate	59	118
p-Cyanoethylbenzoate	51	71
Cycloform	65	151
5-Cycloheptenyl-5-ethylbarbituric acid	174	774
5-Cyclohexenyl-5-ethylbarbituric acid	173	766
Cyclopentadecanone	65	155
5-Cyclopentenyl-5-allylbarbituric acid	140	570
1-Cyclopentyl-*N*-methyl-2-propylamine	114	413
DDT	109	377
Decamethylenedicarboxylic acid	129	508
1,10-Decamethylene glycol	73	190
Decanedioic acid	133	531
Dehydracetic acid	112	394
Dehydrocholic acid	234	1071
Desoxycholic acid-palmitic or stearic acid (8:1)	188	859
Desoxycorticosteroneacetate	161	700
α-Dextrin	290–300	1179
β-Dextrin	280–290	1169
Dextrose	145–148	621

(*Continued*)

TABLE I (*Continued*)

Compound	Melting point, °C	Code number
2,2'-Diacetoxy-4,4'-dimethyldiphenylsulfone	199	925
2,4'-Diacetoxy-3',5-dimethyldiphenylsulfone	121	455
4,4'-Diacetoxy-2,2'-dimethyldiphenylsulfone	116	424
2,2'-Diacetoxydiphenylsulfone	192	890
3,3'-Diacetoxydiphenylsulfone	102	329
4,4'-Diacetoxy-3-nitrodiphenylsulfone	167	733
4-Diacetylamino-2,3'-dimethylazobenzene	74	198
Diacetyldioxyphenylisatin	240–246	1095
Diacetylmorphine	170–172	757
Diacetylphenolphthalein	142–147	605
Diacetyltetrabromopyrocatechin	215	1011
Dial	174	777
5,5-Diallylbarbituric acid	174	777
2,4-Diaminoazobenzene-4'-sulfonamide	223–230	1065
4,4'-Diaminodiphenyl	129	502
3,3'-Diaminodiphenylsulfone	171	753
2,4-Diamino-6-phenyl-1,3,5-triazine	225	1050
2,6-Diaminopyridine	121	457
2,4-Diaminotoluene	99	312
Dianisyloxide	104	341
Dianisylphenetyl guanidine hydrochloride	174–177	795
Dianisylsulfide	45	45
Dibenzal hydrazine	94	286
Dibenzoylmethane	78	224
Dibenzyl	53	79
Dibenzylamine hydrochloride	about 265	1130
Dibenzylidene acetone	112	397
Dibenzyl succinate	47	49
Dibenzyl succinate hydrochloride	195–216	1014
Dibenzylsulfoxide	133	533
4,4'-Dibromoazoxybenzene	176	792
p-Dibromobenzene	87.5	256
α,β-Dibromohydrocinnamic acid	200–202	947
5,7-Dibromo-8-hydroxyquinoline	198	924
3-[β,γ-Dibromopropyl]-5-diethylbarbituric acid	131	518
ω,ω'-Dibromo-o-xylene	93	281
ω,ω''-Dibromo-p-xylene	147	602
Diisobutylamine hydrobromide	300–320	1184
Diisobutyramide	175	786
2,4-Dichloraniline	64	148
2,5-Dichloraniline	50	68
4,4'-Dichloroazobenzene	187	854
p-Dichlorobenzene	54	85
1,4-Dichloronaphthalene	66	158

TABLE I (*Continued*)

Compound	Melting point, °C	Code number
4,6-Dichlororesorcinol	95	297
Dicyandiamide	210–212	994
4,4′-Dicyandiphenylsulfone	250–253	1108
o-Diethoxybenzene	43	32
N,*N*-Diethyl-*N*′-acetylurea	208	982
Diethyl allyl acetamide	73	189
3-Diethylamino-2,2-dimethylpropyl-*p*-aminobenzoate hydrochloride	197–199	929
2-Diethylaminoethyl-1-phenylcyclopentanecarboxylate hydrochloride	148.5	622
5,5-Diethylbarbituric acid	188–190	874
p,*p*′-Diethylbenzophenone	47	47
Diethylbromoacetamide	66	157
3,3-Diethyl-2,4-dihydroxytetrahydropyridine	94	287
Diethylmalonamide	224	1045
Diethylstilboestrol	168	737
Diethylstilboestrol diacetate	120	448
Diethylstilboestrol dipropionate	108	368
N,*N*′-Diethylurea	112	398
Difluorenyl	246	1094
Digitonin	240–245	1091
9,10-Dihydroanthracene	109	374
cis,cis,trans,trans-Dihydrocholesterol	105	344
trans,trans,trans,trans-Dihydrocholesterol	142.5	583
Dihydrocodeinebitartrate	188–190	866
9,10-Dihydronaphthacene	208	983
α-Dihydrophyllocladen	75	208
1,8-Dihydroxy-x-anthranol	181	819
1,2-Dihydroxyanthraquinone	289	1165
1,4-Dihydroxyanthraquinone	201	942
1,5-Dihydroxyanthraquinone	280	1151
1,8-Dihydroxyanthraquinone	194	902
2,4-Dihydroxybenzaldehyde	136	556
2,5-Dihydroxybenzaldehyde	100	324
3,4-Dihydroxybenzaldehyde	154	658
1,2-Dihydroxybenzene	104	339
1,4-Dihydroxybenzene	172.5	764
2,4-Dihydroxybenzoic acid	204–208	981
3,4-Dihydroxybenzoic acid	203	950
3,4-Dihydroxycinnamic acid	190–215	1007
4,4′-Dihydroxy-α,β-diethylstilbene	168	737
2,6-Dihydroxy-3,5-dimethoxyaporphin	151–158	680
2,2′-Dihydroxy-4,4′-dimethyldiphenylsulfone	197	917

(*Continued*)

TABLE I (*Continued*)

Compound	Melting point, °C	Code number
2,2'-Dihydroxy-5,5'-dimethyldiphenylsulfone	206	968
2,4'-Dihydroxy-3',5-dimethyldiphenylsulfone	183	826
2,2'-Dihydroxydiphenyl	110	380
o,o'-Dihydroxydiphenylsulfone	194	900
o',m-Dihydroxydiphenylsulfone	129	506
o,p'-Dihydroxydiphenylsulfone	185	844
p,p'-Dihydroxydiphenylsulfone	247	1097
p,p'-Dihydroxyditane decamethylene ether	74	202
1,2-Dihydroxy-3-iodopropane	46–48	51
Dihydroxy-4-methoxy benzophenone	130	517
1,8-Dihydroxy-3-methyl anthraquinone	195	906
1,3-Dihydroxynaphthalene	124	475
1,6-Dihydroxynaphthalene	137	558
2,3-Dihydroxynaphthalene	163	711
2,6-Dihydroxynaphthalene	215–220	1026
2,7-Dihydroxynaphthalene	190	880
m,m'-Dihydroxyphenylsulfone	195	907
3,5-Dihydroxytoluene	110	382
p-Diiodobenzene	129	501
Diiodoform	190	878
8,9-Diiodoricinstearolic acid	68	168
3,5-Diiodotyrosine	204	960
Dikodid hydrochloride	175–185	840
Dilaudid hydrochloride	300–330	1188
Dilituric acid	185–190	879
3,4-Dimethoxybenzaldehyde	43	35
1,4-Dimethoxybenzene	57	104
4,4'-Dimethoxybenzil	131	524
3,4-Dimethoxy benzoic nitrile	115	417
4,4'-Dimethoxy benzoin	110	381
3,4-Dimethoxybenzylcyanide	65	154
2,2'-Dimethoxy-3,3'-dimethyldiphenylsulfone	147	607
2,2'-Dimethoxy-4,4'-dimethyldiphenylsulfone	194–196	916
2,2'-Dimethoxy-5,5'-dimethyldiphenylsulfone	228	1058
2,4'-Dimethoxy-3',5-dimethyldiphenylsulfone	181	882
4,4'-Dimethoxy-3,3'-dimethyldiphenylsulfone	141	574
2,2'-Dimethoxydiphenylsulfone	198	923
2,3'-Dimethoxydiphenylsulfone	125	484
3,3'-Dimethoxydiphenylsulfone	90	265
4,4'-Dimethoxydiphenylsulfone	127	493
4,4'-Dimethoxydiphenylsulfone-2,2'-dicarboxylic acid	250–255	1116
2,6-Dimethoxyphenol	56	98
p-Dimethylaminoazobenzene	117	425
p-Dimethylaminobenzaldehyde	73	191

TABLE I (*Continued*)

Compound	Melting point, °C	Code number
p-Dimethylaminobenzylidene rhodanine	262–272	1140
2-Dimethylaminoethyl-4-butylaminobenzoate hydro-chloride	147	603
m-Dimethylaminophenol	87	253
3,3′-Dimethylbenzidine	130	516
3,4-Dimethylbenzoyl-*p*-aminobenzenesulfonamide	215–220	1032
2,3-Dimethylbutanediol-2,3	36–41	24
Dimethylcarbanilide	123	471
β,β-Dimethyl-γ-diethylaminopropyl-*p*-aminobenzoate	54	86
5,5′-Dimethyldihydroresorcinol	146–150	639
N,N′-Dimethyl-*N,N′*-diphenylurea	123	471
Dimethylglyoxime	238	1080
2,3-Dimethylnaphthalene	105	346
2,6-Dimethylnaphthalene	111	390
2,7-Dimethylnaphthalene	97	303
N,N′-Dimethyloxamide	about 200	938
2,5-Dimethylphenol	75	210
3,4-Dimethylphenol	62.5	139
3,5-Dimethylphenol	64	145
2,6-Dimethylquinoline	60	126
Dimethyl terephthalate	141	573
N,N′-Dimethylurea	108	371
2,6-Dimethylyron	135	548
β,β′-Dinaphthyl	187	853
Di-α-naphthylamine	113	405
Di-β-naphthylamine	171	751
1,5-Dinaphthylenediamine	188–190	867
peri-Dinaphthylenethiophene	278	1146
2,4-Dinitroaniline	179	811
2,4-Dinitroanisole	88	257
3,5-Dinitroanisole	107	363
m-Dinitrobenzene	91	267
o-Dinitrobenzene	118	439
p-Dinitrobenzene	174	775
3,5-Dinitrobenzoic acid	206.5	970
4,6-Dinitro-1,5-dimethyl-3-*tert*-butyl-2-acetylbenzene	134	541
3,3′-Dinitrodiphenylsulfone	201	939
3,5-Dinitroguaiacol	121	458
3,5-Dinitro-1-hydroxy-2-methoxybenzene	121	458
1,8-Dinitronaphthalene	171	752
2,4-Dinitro-1-naphthol	138	559
2,4-Dinitrophenetol	85.5	249
2,4-Dinitrophenol	113	401

(*Continued*)

TABLE I (*Continued*)

Compound	Melting point, °C	Code number
2,5-Dinitrophenol	106	355
2,6-Dinitrophenol	63.5	143
2,4-Dinitrophenylhydrazine	196–198	922
3,5-Dinitrosalicylic acid	172	763
N,N'-Dinitrosopiperazine	160	695
2,2'-Dinitrostilbene	199	928
2,4-Dinitrotoluene	71	182
2,6-Dinitrotoluene	66	161
3,4-Dinitrotoluene	60	124
Dionin	149–156	667
2,2'-Diphenic acid	228	1059
o,o-Diphenol	110	380
Diphenyl	70	176
Diphenylacetylene	60	127
2-Diphenylacetyltriethylamine hydrochloride	117	427
Diphenylamine	53.5	83
1,3-Diphenylbenzene	83	239
1,4-Diphenylbutadiene	152	644
Diphenylcarbazide	159–162	703
Diphenylcarbazone	155–158	677
Diphenyl carbonate	80	230
Diphenylene ketone	83	237
Diphenylene oxide	85	247
Diphenylene sulfide	100	321
α-Diphenylglyoxime	249	1101
N,N'-Diphenylguanidine	148	620
5,5-Diphenylhydantoin	298	1176
Diphenylimide	245	1092
Diphenylmaleic imide	210	1035
Diphenylnitrosamine	68	167
Diphenylsulfone	127	492
Diphenylthiocarbazone	141–147	597
N,N'-Diphenylthiourea	153	652
N,N'-Diphenylurea	247	1098
Diphenylurethane	73	188
Diplosal	145–148	610
Dipropionamide	154	657
Dipropylamine hydrochloride	278–280	1154
5,5-Dipropylbarbituric acid	148	618
α,α-Dipyridyl	70	177
Diquinine carbonate	187	855
Dithizone	141–147	597
N,N'-Di-o-tolyguanidine	152–172	756
N,N'-Di-o-tolylthiourea	166	728

TABLE I (*Continued*)

Compound	Melting point, °C	Code number
N,*N'*-Di-*p*-tolylthiourea	184–190	868
Dodecanoic acid	44	38
Dormin	160	693
Dormovit	172	762
Doryl	195–204	953
Dulcin	173	768
Dulcit	189	865
Durol	80	226
Eicosanoic acid	75.5	211
Elaidic acid	44.5	41
Elbon	190–195	908
Eldoral	217	1017
Emetine dihydrochloride	205–215	1008
Emodin	262	1123
l-Ephedrine	40	22
Ephedrine hydrochloride	220	1036
rac-Ephedrine hydrochloride	190	873
Ephetonin	190	873
Epicarin	200–205	965
cis,trans,trans,trans-Epidihydrocholesterol	188	860
Ergotinine	225–227	1053
Erythritol	119.5	446
Erythritol tetranitrate	61	133
Eserine	106	352
trans-Estradiol	175	783
p-Ethoxyphenylurea	173	768
N-Ethylacetanilide	53	81
5-Ethyl-5-allylbarbituric acid	160	693
Ethyl *p*-aminobenzoate	90.5	266
m-Ethylaminophenol	57	101
p-Ethylbenzalacetophenone	62.5	138
Ethyl-4-benzaminobenzoic acid	150	635
p-Ethylbenzoic acid	114	412
N-Ethyl-*N*-butyl-*N'*-acetylurea	117	431
5,5-Ethylbutylbarbituric acid	126	486
Ethyl carbamate	49	55
5-Ethyl-5-cyclohexylbarbituric acid	202	945
DL-Ethyl-*α,β*-dibromohydrocinnamate	78	222
Ethyl 3,5-dinitrobenzoate	93	283
Ethylenediamine hydrochloride	300–330	1186
Ethylene periodide	190	878
Ethyl hippurate	59.5	121
Ethyl *p*-hydroxybenzoate	116	419

(*Continued*)

TABLE I (*Continued*)

Compound	Melting point, °C	Code number
Ethylidene diurethane	125	481
Ethylmalonic acid	112	395
5-Ethyl-5-[1-methylbutyl]-barbituric acid	114	410
Ethyl-1-methyl-4-phenylpiperidine-4-carboxylate	187	852
Ethylmorphine hydrochloride	149–156	667
Ethyl-α-naphthyl carbamate	81	232
Ethyl-β-naphthyl ether	35	11
Ethylnarceine hydrochloride	195–207	972
Ethyl m-nitrobenzoate	41	25
Ethyl p-nitrobenzoate	56	99
Ethyl p-nitrobenzoyl salicylate	103	335
Ethyl p-nitrocinnamate	139	565
Ethyl-2-phenyl-6-methyl cinchoninate	71–73	192
N-Ethyl-N-phenylurea	66	159
5-Ethyl-5-isopropylbarbituric acid	204	957
5-Ethyl-5-n-propylbarbituric acid	146	594
Ethylpropylketone-2,4-dinitrophenylhydrazone	148	616
N⁴-Ethylsulfanilamide	216	1015
Ethyl-dl-tartaric acid	92	277
Ethylurea	92	278
Ethyl vanillin	77	218
β-Eucaine	275–278	1147
Euchinin	92	273
Eucodal	235–260	1121
Eucupine	153–154	660
Eugenol benzoate	68	169
Eupaverine hydrate	150–157	672
Euphorin	50	63
Evipan	146	596
Exalgin	100	323
Exalton	65	155
Ferropyrine	199–204	958
Ferulic acid	171	754
Fluoranthene	109	376
Fluorene	114	408
Fluorenone	83	237
Formaldehyde-2,4-dinitrophenylhydrazone	167	735
Formaldomedon	192	892
Formanilide	49	59
Formyldiphenylamine	74	199
D-Fructose	100–104	337
Fumaric acid	about 290	1166
5-Furfuryl-5-isopropylbarbituric acid	172	762
β-Furyl-2-acrylic acid	140	567

TABLE I (*Continued*)

Compound	Melting point, °C	Code number
d-Galactonic-γ-lactone	136	554
Gallacetophenone	171	750
Gallic acid	258–265	1129
Gelsemine	154–165	719
Genatropine hydrochloride	160–177	794
d-Gluconic-δ-lactone	140–153	651
Gluconicphenylhydrazide	199–201	941
d-Glucose	145–148	621
Glucose-β-pentacetate	133	532
Glutamic acid	195–200	934
Glutaric acid	99	313
Glycerol-α-monoiodohydrin	46–48	51
Glyceryl tribenzoate	76.5	216
Glyceryl trimyristate	53–55	92
Glycine	247–257	1119
Glycocol	247–257	1119
Glycol dibenzoate	73	193
Glycol diphenyl ether	98	306
Guaiacol	28.5	5
Guaiacol benzoate	61	132
Guaiacol carbonate	88	260
Guajen	105	346
Guanicaine	174–177	795
Guanidine hydrochloride	178–185	839
Guanidine nitrate	214	1004
Guanidine sulfate	280–288	1161
Hebaral	124	473
Hedonal	80	228
Helenin	67–70	175
Heliotropine	36	16
Helmitol	169–172	758
Hematoxylin	144–147	599
Hemimellitic acid	196	915
Heptadecanoic acid	61.5	136
Heroin	170–172	757
Hexachlorobenzene	228	1061
α-Hexachlorocyclohexane	158	687
β-Hexachlorocyclohexane	260–300	1180
γ-Hexachlorocyclohexane	113.5	407
δ-Hexachlorocyclohexane	138	560
Hexachloroethane	180–190	881
1,2-Hexachloroindene-3-one	148	615
Hexadecanedicarboxylic acid	126	489

(*Continued*)

TABLE I *(Continued)*

Compound	Melting point, °C	Code number
Hexaethylbenzene	129	509
Hexal	184	831
Hexamethylbenzene	166	729
1,6-Hexamethyleneglycol	41	26
Hexamethylenetetramine	250	1103
2,4,6,2',4',6'-Hexanitrodiphenylamine	246–250 (dec.)	1104
Hexophan	270–280	1152
5-Hexyl-5-ethylbarbituric acid	124	473
Hippuric acid	190	875
Histadyl	164	717
Homatropine	100	322
Homatropine hydrobromide	215–217	1016
Homatropine hydrochloride	225–230	1064
Hordenine	118	437
Hordenine sulfate	200–212	995
Hydrastine	132	526
Hydrastine hydrochloride	148–150	638
Hydrastinine hydrochloride	200–235	1072
Hydrazine sulfate	240–244	1087
Hydrazobenzene	126	485
Hydrocinnamic acid	49	60
Hydroquinine	165–175	782
Hydroquinone	172.5	764
Hydroquinone dimethyl ether	57	104
Hydroquinone monomethyl ether	54	89
p-Hydroxyacetophenone	109	375
m-Hydroxybenzaldehyde	104	340
p-Hydroxybenzaldehyde	117	426
m-Hydroxybenzoic acid	202	946
o-Hydroxybenzoic acid	158	682
p-Hydroxybenzoic acid	214	1003
o-Hydroxybenzyl alcohol	85.5	251
Hydroxybrasilin	144–147	599
2-[4-Hydroxy-3-Carboxyphenyl]-quinoline-4-carboxylic acid	270–280	1152
trans-2-Hydroxycinnamic acid	215–220	1031
trans-4-Hydroxycinnamic acid	206–215	1009
o-Hydroxydiphenyl	59	116
p-Hydroxydiphenyl	165	726
4-Hydroxy-3-ethoxybenzaldehyde	77	218
Hydroxylamine hydrochloride	156–161	697
Hydroxymalonic acid	150–158	679
N-Hydroxymethylbenzamide	108	367
2-Hydroxy-5-methylbenzoic acid	152	648

TABLE I (*Continued*)

Compound	Melting point, °C	Code number
2-Hydroxy-3-methoxy-benzaldehyde	44	39
7-Hydroxy-4-methylcoumarin	188	862
1-Hydroxy-2-naphthoic acid	192–196	913
3-Hydroxy-2-naphthoic acid	222	1042
Hydroxynaphthyl-*o*-hydroxy-*m*-toluic acid	200–205	965
3-Hydroxy-4-nitrotoluene	53	80
o-Hydroxyphenylacetic acid	149	628
β-[*p*-Hydroxyphenyl]-α-aminopropionic acid	260–270	1137
[4-Hydroxyphenylethyl]-dimethylamine	118	437
1-[*m*-Hydroxyphenyl]-2-methylaminoethanol	141–143	586
1-[*p*-Hydroxyphenyl]-2-methylaminoethanol tartrate	183–189	864
2-Hydroxypyridine	108	372
4-Hydroxypyridine	150	634
4-Hydroxyquinoline	195–198	921
6-Hydroxyquinoline	193	894
8-Hydroxyquinoline	74	196
2-Hydroxy-1,3-toluic acid	165	722
4-Hydroxy-1,5-toluic acid	165–171	755
3-Hydroxy-1,4-toluic acid	177	797
4-Hydroxy-1,2-toluic acid	179	809
Hydroxyurea	135–143	585
Hyoscyamine	107	366
Hyoscyamine hydrobromide	147–149	624
Hyoscyamine hydrochloride	148–154	654
Hyoscyamine sulfate	180–195	904
Idobutal	129	505
Idryl	109	376
Indazole	147	604
Indole	52	73
β-Indolyl acetic acid	168–170	741
meso-Inositol	222–225	1047
Inulin	180–185	842
p-Iodoacetanilide	186	849
5-Iodo-2-aminopyridine	130	514
4-Iodoantipyrene	160	696
o-Iodobenzoic acid	162	706
7-Iodo-5-chloro-8-hydroxyquinoline	180–181	818
Iodoform	123	468
Iodogorgonic acid	204	960
5-Iodo-2-hydroxypyridine	190–195	909
m-Iodonitrobenzene	36	14
α-Iodoisovalerylurea	183	827
Iosen	75	208

(*Continued*)

TABLE I (*Continued*)

Compound	Melting point, °C	Code number
Ipral	204	957
Isatin	204	956
Isoamyl carbamate	64	146
Isoamyl dihydrocupreine	153–155	660
Isoamyl-3,5-dinitrobenzoate	60	129
5-Isoamyl-5-ethylbarbituric acid	156	670
5-Isoamyl-5-propylbarbituric acid	135–139	564
Isoborneol	215	1010
5-Isobutyl-5-allylbarbituric acid	139	561
Isobutylamine hydrochloride	178	804
Isobutyl-*p*-aminobenzoate	65	151
Isobutyl carbamate	66	160
Isobutyraldehyde-2,4-dinitrophenylhydrazone	184	834
Isobutyryl-*p*-phenetidide	136	552
l-Isoleucine	280–290	1168
ω-Isonitrosoacetophenone	126	487
4-Isopropyl antipyrene	103.5	336
5-Isopropylbarbituric acid	213	1000
N-Isopropylbenzanilide	131	521
5-Isopropyl-5-[β-bromoallyl]-barbituric acid	183.5	829
Isopropyl carbamate	93	282
Isopropyl-3,5-dinitrobenzoate	122	466
5-Isopropyl-5-*n*-propylbarbituric acid	175	784
Kryptopine	215–230	1066
Lactamide	78	220
Lactoflavin	280–290	1167
Lactophenetidine	118	441
Lactophenin	118	441
Lactose	206–216	1013
Larocain	197–199	929
Lauric acid	44	38
Levulose	100–104	337
Lithocholic acid	190	876
Lobeline	115–125	476
Lobeline hydrochloride	175–185	841
Lophine	277	1145
Luminol	175	779
Lysidine bitartrate	190–194	899
Maleic anhydride	53	82
Maleic anhydride adduct with 8,10-heptadecadiene-1-carboxylic acid	102	330
dl-Malic acid	131	520
Malonamide	166	732
Malonic acid	136	550
Malonylurea	252–254	1109

TABLE I (*Continued*)

Compound	Melting point, °C	Code number
dl-Mandelic acid	119	444
Mannite	166	731
d-Mannitol	166	731
Mannitol hexanitrate	110–113	400
d-Mannose	128–133	534
Marbadal	172–177	793
Marfanil	250–255	1112
Meconic acid	260–280	1149
Medomine	174	774
Mellitose	132–135	542
l-Menthol	42	29
l-Menthyl-3,5-dinitrobenzoate	155	644
2-Mercaptobenzothiazole	179	813
Mesaconic acid	202	948
Metaldehyde	150–160	692
p-Methoxylacetophenonazine	198–200	931
o-Methoxybenzaldehyde	37	17
p-Methoxybenzoic acid	185	843
m-Methoxy-*p*-hydroxycinnamic acid	171	754
2-Methoxy-4-methyl-5-brombenzenesulfonamide	169	738
2-Methoxyphenyl-3,5-dinitrobenzoate	140	569
1-[*p*-Methoxyphenyl]-1-phenylethylene	75	206
6-Methoxyquinoline-4-carboxylic acid	286–295	1175
N-Methylacetanilide	100	323
Methyl-3-amino-4-hydroxybenzoate	143	584
Methyl-4-amino-3-hydroxybenzoate	125	483
2-Methylanthracene	206	969
Methylarbutin	176	789
2-Methylbenzoic acid	106	354
Methyl benzoylmandelate	77	219
Methyl-*p*-bromobenzoate	81	233
Methyl-*n*-butylketone-2,4-dinitrophenylhydrazone	110	383
Methyl-isobutylketone-2,4-dinitrophenylhydrazone	96	299
Methyl carbamate	54	90
Methyl-*p*-chlorobenzoate	43	33
Methyl cinnamate	36	13
p-Methyldibenzoylmethane	85	250
Methyl-3,4-dimethoxyphenyl-cyanoacetate	75	209
Methyl-3,5-dinitrobenzoate	107	365
N-Methyl-*N*-ethyl-*N'*,*N'*-diphenylurea	118	433
Methylethylketone-2,4-dinitrophenylhydrazone	117	432
N-Methyl-5-ethyl-5-phenylbarbituric acid	179	810
N-Methylglycine	210–211	992

(*Continued*)

TABLE I (*Continued*)

Compound	Melting point, °C	Code number
N-Methylglycine anhydride	147	601
Methyl-*m*-hydroxybenzoate	72	186
2-Methyl-3-hydroxy-4,5-di[hydroxymethyl]-pyridine hydrochloride	207–214	1002
Methyl-1-hydroxynaphthoate-2	78	221
2-Methylindole	60	130
3-Methylindole	95	296
5-Methylindole	59	109
7-Methylindole	85	246
p-Methylmandelic acid	147	606
Methyl-*p*-methoxybenzoate	48	52
N-Methyl-5-methyl-5-cyclohexenylbarbituric acid	146	596
Methyl-3,4-methylenoxyphenyl cyanoacetate	69	174
N-Methyl-α-methyl-β-phenylethylamine hydrochloride	174	778
2-Methylnaphthalene	34	10
2-Methyl-1,4-naphthoquinone	106	359
Methyl nicotinate	40	21
Methyl-*p*-nitrobenzoate	96	298
2-Methyl-4-nitrophenol	95	292
N-Methylolbenzamide	108	367
p-Methylphenyl acetic acid	94	290
5-Methyl-5-phenyl barbituric acid	226	1051
N-Methylphenylthioacetamide	64	149
dl-[2-Methylpiperidino]-propanol hydrochloride	173	769
2-Methyl-5-isopropylbenzoquinone-1,4	47	48
Methyl-*n*-propyl carbinol urethane	80	228
Methyl propyl ketone-2,4-dinitrophenylhydrazone	144	591
1-Methyl-7-isopropyl phenanthrene	98	308
5-Methyl resorcinol	110	382
Methylsulfonal	76	212
4-Methylumbelliferone	188	862
Methylurea	103	333
Metycaine	173	769
Mezcaline sulfate	230–250	1106
Michler's hydrol (*p,p'*)	96	301
Monochloroacetic acid	62	137
Morphine	245–255	1113
Morphine hydrochloride	285–300	1178
Mucic acid	215–225	1049
Myristic acid	54	87
Naphthacene	325–350	1187
Naphthalene	80.5	231
1,2-Naphthalenediamine	98	310

TABLE I (*Continued*)

Compound	Melting point, °C	Code number
1,8-Naphthalenediamine	66	163
α-Naphthoflavone	157	674
α-Naphthoic acid	161	698
β-Naphthoic acid	184	836
α-Naphthol	96	300
β-Naphthol	122	460
β-Naphthol ethyl ether	35	11
β-Naphthol methyl ether	73	187
β-Naphthoquinoline	92	275
Naphthoresorcinol	124	475
β-Naphthoyl chloride	186	847
α-Naphthylacetic acid	131	523
α-Naphthylamine	49	56
β-Naphthylamine	112	396
α-Naphthylamine hydrobromide	285–293	1171
α-Naphthylamine hydrochloride	240–250	1102
β-Naphthylamine hydrochloride	213–225	1046
β-Naphthyl benzoate	107	362
β-Naphthyl cyanide	86	252
β-Naphthyl ethyl ether	35	11
β-Naphthyl salicylate	94	285
α-Naphthyl urethane	81	232
Narceine	155–165	718
Narceine hydrochloride	180–200	932
Narcotine	174	776
Narcotine hydrochloride	190–194	898
Neocinchophen	71–73	192
Neoergosterol	157	673
Neohexal	170–180	814
Neonal	126	486
Neothesin	173	769
Neo-Uliron	151	642
Neroline (ethyl)	35	11
Neroline (methyl)	73	187
Neuronal	66	157
Nicotinamide	129	503
Nicotinic acid	237	1077
Nipabenzyl	112	339
Nipagin A	116	419
Nipagin M	110	386
Nipasol	97	304
Nirvanol	199	927
4-Nitro-2-acetaminobenzoic acid	217–220	1033

(*Continued*)

TABLE I (*Continued*)

Compound	Melting point, °C	Code number
4-Nitro-2-aminobenzoic acid	262–272	1139
4-Nitro-2-aminophenol	143	589
3-Nitro-4-aminotoluene	117	428
4-Nitro-2-aminotoluene	107	361
m-Nitroaniline	114	411
o-Nitroaniline	72	185
p-Nitroaniline	148	617
p-Nitroanisole	54	91
5-Nitrobarbituric acid	185–190	879
m-Nitrobenzaldehyde	57	102
o-Nitrobenzaldehyde	42.5	30
p-Nitrobenzaldehyde	105.5	350
p-Nitrobenzamide	203	952
p-Nitrobenzenesulfonic chloride	80	227
p-Nitrobenzenesulfonyl chloride	80	227
N-[4-Nitrobenzenesulfonyl]-*p*-phenylenediamine	202	944
p-Nitrobenzhydrazide	200–208	975
m-Nitrobenzoic acid	142.5	582
o-Nitrobenzoic acid	147	609
p-Nitrobenzoic acid	241	1083
p-Nitrobenzonitrile	149	625
p-Nitrobenzoyl chloride	75	207
N-[*p*-Nitrobenzoyl]-piperidine	122	462
o-Nitrobenzyl chloride	49	61
p-Nitrobenzoyl cyanide	116	422
2-Nitro-4-bromoanisole	87	254
m-Nitrobromobenzene	55	94
o-Nitrobromobenzene	41	27
m-Nitrochlorobenzene	45	42
o-Nitrochlorobenzene	33	9
p-Nitrochlorobenzene	83	240
4-Nitro-2-chlorotoluene	65	150
m-Nitrocinnamic acid	203	951
p-Nitrocinnamic acid	286	1160
3-Nitro-*p*-cresol	32	7
4-Nitro-*m*-cresol	126	490
3-Nitro-4-hydroxytoluene	32	7
4-Nitro-3-hydroxytoluene	53	80
6-Nitro-3-hydroxytoluene	126	490
m-Nitroiodobenzene	36	14
4-Nitro-2-methylphenol	95	292
5-Nitro-2-methylphenol	117	429
Nitron	184	837
α-Nitronaphthalene	57	103

TABLE I (*Continued*)

Compound	Melting point, °C	Code number
p-Nitrophenetol	59	114
m-Nitrophenol	96.5	302
o-Nitrophenol	45	44
p-Nitrophenol	113	402
p-Nitrophenyl-acetdimethylamide	91	270
2-[*p*-Nitrophenyl]-1-bromoethane	70	178
p-Nitrophenylhydrazine	158	684
p-Nitrosodiethylaniline	84	244
p-Nitrosodimethylaniline	85	245
α-Nitroso-β-naphthol	106–110	385
β-Nitroso-α-naphthol	150–158	678
4-Nitrostilbene	157	676
m-Nitrotoluene	14	1
p-Nitrotoluene	52	75
Noctal	183.5	829
Nonadecanoic acid	68.5	171
Nonadioic acid	106.5	360
1,9-Nonanediol	43	34
Novalgine	224–226	1052
Novatophan	71–73	192
Novatophan K	59	117
Novocaine hydrochloride	156	668
Novocaine nitrate	103	331
Novonal	73	189
Numal	142	578
Octadecyl alcohol	59	115
Optochin base	125–129	510
Optochin hydrochloride	245	1093
Orcinol	110	382
Oreoselon	157–175	781
Orthoform new	143	584
Oxalic acid	188–191	886
Oxamic acid	210	990
Oxanilide	254	1111
Palmitic acid	63	142
Pantocaine	147	603
Pantocaine nitrate	132	527
Papaverine	146	595
Papaverine hydrochloride	215–220	1030
Parabanic acid	240–248	1099
Paracodeine bitartrate	188–190	866
Paracodeine hydrochloride	250–255	1114
Paracotoin	152	645
Parpanite	148.5	622

(*Continued*)

TABLE I (*Continued*)

Compound	Melting point, °C	Code number
Pellidol	74	198
Pentachlorophenol	190	882
Pentabromoacetone	74	201
Pentachloroaniline	232	1070
Pentachlorotoluene	220	1037
Pentadecanoic acid	52.5	78
Pentaerythritol	256	1117
Pentaerythritol tetranitrate	142	581
Pentamethylene tetrazole	59	110
α,α-Pentanedicarboxylic acid	105	348
Pentane-3,3-diethyl sulfone	89	262
Pentaphen	94	289
Pentobarbital	114	410
Percaine	99	314
Perchlorindone	148	615
Pernoston	132	525
Pervitin	174	778
Perylene	270–275	1143
Phanodorm	173	766
Phenacetin	135	546
Phenanthraquinone	210–211	993
Phenanthrene	99	311
9-Phenanthridine	105	345
Phenazone	157	675
p-Phenetidine citrate	167–179	808
p-Phenetylurea	173	768
Phenol	40	23
Phenol-α-*d*-galactoside	145	593
Phenol-β-*d*-galactoside	155	663
Phenol-α-*d*-glucoside	159	688
Phenol-β-*d*-glucoside	173	767
Phenolphthalein	263	1127
Phenoxyacetic acid	101	326
o-Phenoxyphenol	28.5	5
Phenylacetanilide	117	430
Phenylacetic acid	77	217
Phenyl-α-acetylacetonitrile	91	271
9-Phenylacridine	184	830
N-Phenyl-*o*-aminobenzoic acid	186	846
N-Phenylanthranilic acid	186	846
5-Phenylbarbituric acid	263	1126
Phenyl benzoate	69	173
2-[*N*-Phenyl-*N*-benzyl aminomethyl]-imidazoline hydrochloride	248	1100

TABLE I (*Continued*)

Compound	Melting point, °C	Code number
γ-Phenylbutyramide	85	248
γ-Phenylbutyric acid	50	69
1-Phenyl-3,5-dimethyl-1,2,4-triazole	46	46
Phenyldiphenyl carbamate	106	351
Phenyldiphenyl urethane	106	351
m-Phenylenediamine	63	140
o-Phenylenediamine	102	327
p-Phenylenediamine	142	579
5-Phenyl-5-ethylbarbituric acid	175	779
Phenylethyleneglycol	67	165
5-Phenyl-5-ethylhydantoin	199	927
Phenylglycine-*o*-carboxylic acid	202–208	977
Phenylhydrazine	16–19	3
Phenylhydrazine hydrochloride	240–250	1105
Phenylhydrazineoxalate	176–181	817
Phenylhydrazine-4-sulfonic acid	280–285	1156
α-Phenylhydrocinnamic acid	85–88	258
2-Phenyl-methylcinchoninate	59	117
1-Phenyl-3-methyl pyrazolone	129	507
N-Phenyl-α-naphthylamine	60	123
N-Phenyl-β-naphthylamine	109	373
N-Phenyl-*N*-ethyl-*N*'-acetylurea	147	608
N-Phenyl-*N*-ethylurea	66	159
Phenylpropiolic acid	136	553
Phenylisopropylmethylamine picrolonate	183	825
5-Phenyl-quinaldine-4-carboxylic acid	220	1034
2-Phenylquinoline-4-carboxylic acid	213	1001
Phenyl salicylate	42.5	31
1-Phenylsemicarbazide	172–174	771
Phenylthioacetamide	98	309
Phenylthiourea	154	655
Phenylurea	148	612
Phenylurethane	50	63
Phloridzin dihydrate	120–122	465
Phloroglucinol	205–220	1027
Phthalamide	218–220	1029
Phthalanil	209	986
o-Phthalic acid	220–222	1041
Phthalide	74.5	205
Phthalimide	235	1073
m-Phthalimidobenzonitrile	192	891
Physostigmine	106	352
Physostigmine salicylate	179	812

(*Continued*)

TABLE I (*Continued*)

Compound	Melting point, °C	Code number
Picramic acid	169–171	748
Picramide	190	883
Picric acid	122	461
Picrolonic acid	125	477
Picrotoxin	198–201	940
Picrylbromide	123	470
Picrylchloride	83	238
Pilocarpine hydrochloride	198–200	935
Pilocarpine nitrate	170–178	802
Pimelic acid	104	338
Pinacol	36–41	24
Piperic acid	215–221	1039
5-Piperidino-5-ethyl barbituric acid	217	1017
Piperine	129.5	513
Piperonal	36	16
Potassium bitartrate	260–268	1134
Potassium xanthate	210–213	999
Potassium xanthogenate	210–213	999
Procaine hydrochloride	156	668
Progesterone	129	504
l-Proline	200–220	1023
Prominol	179	810
Prontosil	223–230	1065
Propasin	74	200
Propionaldehyde-2,4-dinitrophenylhydrazone	155	662
Propionamide	79	225
β-Propionylphenylhydrazine	160	694
Proponal	148	618
m-Propyl-*p*-aminobenzoate	74	200
5-*n*-Propylbarbituric acid	205	967
n-Propyl carbamate	61	134
n-Propyl-3,5-dinitrobenzoate	74	203
Propyl-*p*-hydroxybenzoate	97	304
Proseptasine	178	803
Prostigmine	149	629
Prontalbin	166	730
Protocatechuic acid	203	950
Protocatechuic aldehyde	154	658
d-Pseudococaine bitartrate	149	626
Pseudocoprosterol	116	420
Pseudocumidine	66	162
d-Pseudoephedrine	118	438
Pseudoephedrine hydrochloride	184	835
rac-Pseudoephedrine hydrochloride	165	723
Psicaine	149	626

TABLE I (*Continued*)

Compound	Melting point, °C	Code number
Psicaine (new)	210–220	1028
Pyramidon	108	369
Pyramidon + butyrchloralhydrate	83	241
Pyramidon + voluntal	76	214
Pyrene	150	633
Pyridine-β-carboxylic acid	237	1077
Pyridine-β-carboxylic acid methyl ester	40	21
Pyridine-3-carboxylic amide	129	503
Pyridine mercuric chloride hydrochloride	177	799
Pyridine picrate	163	709
Pyridine-3-sulfonamide	111	391
Pyridoxin hydrochloride	207–214	1002
Pyrocatechol	104	339
Pyrocatechol diethyl ether	43	32
Pyrogallol	133.5	535
Pyrogallol-1,3-dimethyl ether	56	98
Pyrogallol triacetate	165	721
Pyromellitic anhydride	288	1163
Pyromucic acid	132	530
Quinaldinic acid	158	685
Quinalizarine	313–316	1183
Quinic acid	164–166	727
Quinidine	171	749
Quinidine acetate	110–122	459
Quinidine hydrochloride	257–262	1124
Quinidine sulfate	190–205	962
Quinine	176	790
Quinine bisulfate	153–158	681
Quinine cinnamylate	110–134	536
Quinine dihydrochloride	180–215	1006
Quinine hydrobromide	142–150	631
Quinine hydrochloride	145–148	613
Quinine salicylate	141	571
Quinine sulfate	219	1022
Quinine tartrate	205–208	980
Quininic acid	286–295	1175
Quinizarin	201	942
Quinoline-2-carboxylic acid	158	685
Quinoline picrate	204	959
Quinoline + salicylic acid	70–74	197
p-Quinone	113	404
Raffinose	132–135	542
Resorcinol	**110.5**	389

(*Continued*)

TABLE I (*Continued*)

Compound	Melting point, °C	Code number
Resorcylaldehyde	136	556
β-Resorcylic acid	204–208	981
Retene	98	308
Rivanol	230–245	1090
Rutonal	226	1051
Saccharine	228	1056
Salicin	200	937
Salicyl alcohol	85.5	251
Salicylaldehyde methyl ether	37	17
Salicylaldoxime	58	108
Salicylamide	140	568
Salicylic acid	158	682
Salicylic-*m*-cresol ether	76	215
Salicylic-*o*-cresol ether	33	8
Salicylic-*p*-cresol ether	39	19
Salicylic guaiacol ether	72	183
Salicylsalicylic acid	145–148	610
Saligenin	85.5	251
Salipyrine	92	274
Salol	42.5	31
Salophen	190	884
Sandoptal	139	561
Santonin	174	773
Sarcosine	210–211	992
Sarcosine anhydride	147	601
Scopolamine hydrate (inactive)	59	111
Scopolamine hydrobromide	194–197	918
Scopolamine hydrobromide trihydrate	90–100	319
Scopolamine hydrochloride	190–205	963
Scopolamine hydrochloride monohydrate	90–100	320
Sebacic acid	133	531
Sedormid	193	897
Semicarbazide hydrochloride	175	780
Semioxamazide	220–230	1069
Siaresinolic acid	283	1155
Sitosterol	136	555
Skatole	95	296
Skatole-ω-carboxylic acid	168–170	741
Sodium acetate	328	1185
Sonneryl	126	486
Soranil	296	1173
Sorbic acid	134	539
d-Sorbite	108–110	387
d-Sorbite hydrate	85–93	279

TABLE I (*Continued*)

Compound	Melting point °C	Code number
d-Sorbitol	108–110	387
Sparteine sulfate	103–105	343
Spasmine hydrochloride	195–216	1014
Stearic acid	70	179
Stigmasterol	167	736
Stilbene	125	480
G-Strophanthin	180–183	824
Strychnine	270–275	1144
Strychnine hydrochloride	275–295	1174
Strychnine nitrate	280–310	1182
Styphnic acid	177	798
Stypticin	182–188	856
Styracin	44	40
Suberic acid	141	572
Succinamide	268–270	1135
Succinic acid	188	861
Succinic anhydride	120	447
Succinimide	126	488
2-[*p*-Succinylaminobenzenesulfamino]-pyridine	296	1173
2-[*N*⁴-Succinylsulfanilamino]-thiazole monohydrate	188–193	893
Sucrol	173	768
Sucrose	185–190	870
Sudan I	132	529
Sulfadiazine	254–257	1120
Sulfaguanidine	190	872
Sulfamerazine	236–240	1082
Sulfamethyldiazine	236–240	1082
Sulfamethylthiazole	244	1089
p-Sulfamidobenzoic acid	284–286	1158
2-Sulfanilamidothiazole	201	943
2-Sulfanilylamino-3,5-dimethylpyrimidine	199	926
2-Sulfanilylaminopyridine	192	888
Sulfanilylurea	156–158	686
Sulfasuxidine	188–193	893
Sulfathiazole	201	943
o-Sulfobenzoic acid	135	534
o-Sulfobenzoic acid	90–100	318
o-Sulfobenzoic acid trihydrate	64–67	164
Sulfonal	126.5	491
5-Sulfosalicylic acid	224	1043
5-Sulfosalicylic acid hexamethylenetetramine	184	831
5-Sulfosalicylic acid-di-hexamethylenetetramine hydrate	170–180	814
Suprarenine	203–208	978

(*Continued*)

TABLE I (*Continued*)

Compound	Melting point, °C	Code number
Surfacaine	164	716
Sympatol	183–189	864
Synopen	172	759
d-Tartaric acid	170	747
dl-Tartaric acid	200–210	989
Tartronic acid	150–158	679
1,8-Terpin	106	358
cis-Terpin	106	358
Terpin hydrate	116–118	436
Testosterone	155	661
Testosterone propionate	123	469
3,′5′,3″,5″-Tetrabromophenolphthalein	270–290	1170
ω,ω,ω′,ω′-Tetrabromo-*m*-xylene	106	356
ω,ω,ω′,ω′-Tetrabromo-*o*-xylene	116	421
ω,ω,ω′,ω′-Tetrabromo-*p*-xylene	172	761
Tetracarbethoxyethane	74.5	204
Tetrachlorophthalic anhydride	257	1118
Tetrachloroquinone	280	1153
Tetradecane dicarboxylic acid	125	482
Tetrahydro-*β*-naphthylamine hydrochloride	246	1096
1,2,5,8-Tetrahydroxyanthraquinone	313–316	1183
Tetraiodoethylene	190	878
Tetramethyl-4,4′-diaminobenzophenone	172–174	772
1,2,4,5-Tetramethylbenzene	80	226
Tetramethyl-4,4′-diaminobenzhydrol	96	301
Tetramethyl-4,4′-diaminodiphenylmethane	92	276
1,1,2,2-Tetraphenylethane	212	997
Tetraphenylmethane	288	1164
Tetronal	89	262
Thebaine	193	896
Thebaine hydrochloride	180–193	895
Theobromine	320–340	1189
Theophylline	274	1141
Thiodiglycolic acid	132	528
Thioglycolic-*β*-aminonaphthalide	111	392
Thionalide	111	392
Thionaphthene	31	6
Thiosemicarbazide	181	820
Thiosinamine	71	180
Thiourea	176–180	815
Thymolphthalein	253	1107
Thymoquinone	47	48
Tolane	60	127
o-Tolidine	130	516
o-Toluenesulfonamide	156	671

TABLE I *(Continued)*

Compound	Melting point, °C	Code number
p-Toluenesulfonamide	139	563
4-Toluenesulfonyl-*β*-naphthylamide	127–129	511
o-Toluic acid	106	354
p-Toluidine	44	37
m-Toluylenediamine	99	312
m-*N*-Tolylacetamide	65	152
o-*N*-Tolylacetamide	110	379
p-*N*-Tolylacetamide	151	640
m-Tolylsemicarbazide	180–184	838
1,2,3-Triacetoxybenzene	165	721
Thymol	50	65
Tribenzoin	76.5	216
Tribenzylamine	95	294
2,4,6-Tribromoaniline	121	456
2,4,6-Tribromo-3-methoxytoluene	78	223
2,4,6-Tribromo-5-methylphenol	83	242
2,4,6-Tribromophenol	94	291
Tricarballylic acid	150–160	691
Trichloroacetic acid	56	95
Trichloroacetamide	142	580
β,β,β-Trichloro-*tert*-butyl alcohol	97	305
α,α,β-Trichlorobutyric acid	55–60	122
β,β,β-Trichloroethyl carbamate	59.5	120
β,β,β-Trichlorolactic acid	121	454
2,4,6-Trichlorophenol	66	156
Tridecanoic acid	41.5	28
Tridecylic acid	41.5	28
Trigemin	83	241
2,3,4-Trihydroxyacetophenone	171	750
1,2,3-Trihydroxybenzene	133.5	535
1,3,5-Trihydroxybenzene	205–220	1027
3,4,5-Trihydroxybenzoic acid	258–265	1129
4,5,7-Trihydroxy-2-methylanthraquinone	262	1123
3,4,5-Triiodonitrobenzene	167	734
3,4,5-Trimethoxy-*β*-phenylethylamine sulfate	230–250	1106
2,4,5-Trimethylaniline	66	162
Trimyristin	53–55	92
2,4,6-Trinitroaniline	190	883
2,4,6-Trinitroanisole	68.5	170
1,3,5-Trinitrobenzene	123.5	472
2,4,6-Trinitrobenzoic acid	190–210	987
2,4,6-Trinitrobromobenzene	123	470
2,4,6-Trinitro-5-*tert*-butyl-1,3-xylene	114	409
2,4,6-Trinitrochlorobenzene	83	238
1,3,8-Trinitronaphthalene	215	1005

(Continued)

TABLE I (*Concluded*)

Compound	Melting point, °C	Code number
2,4,6-Trinitrophenol	122	461
2,4,6-Trinitroresorcinol	177	798
2,4,6-Trinitrotoluene	81	234
Trional	76	212
Tripalmitin	62–65	153
Triphenylcarbinol	162.5	707
Triphenylene	198	920
1,1,2-Triphenylethane	56	97
2,4,5-Triphenyl-imidazole	277	1145
Triphenylmethane	94	284
Tropacocaine hydrochloride	285–288	1162
Tropine	48–52	77
Tropine mandelate	100	322
l-Tyrosine	260–270	1137
Uliron	195	910
Uliron C	112–134	537
Umbelliferone	228	1060
Ural	106	353
Uraline	106	353
Urea	135	544
Urea nitrate	142–152	647
Urethane	49	55
Uroxin	235–242	1084
d-Valine	300–310	1181
dl-Valine	299	1177
Vanillin	81.5	235
o-Vanillin	44	39
Veratric nitrile	115	417
Veratrine	145–153	649
Veronal	188–190	874
Vioform	180–181	818
Vitamin B_1	232–237	1078
Vitamin B_2	280–290	1167
Vitamin B_6	207–214	1002
Vitamin C	185–190	869
Voluntal	59.5	120
Xanthone	176	788
Xylene musk	107	364
p-Xylenol	75	210
m-Xylenol	64	145
o-Xylenol	62.5	139
p-Xylenolphthalein	280–285	1157
d-Xylose	143–147	598
Yohimbine	215–225	1048
Yohimbin hydrochloride	265–280	1150

TABLE II

Listing of Compounds by Code Numbers and Melting Points

Code number	Melting point, °C	Compound
1	14	m-Nitrotoluene
2	19	Benzylbenzoate
3	16–19	Phenylhydrazine
4	27	p-Bromotoluene
5	28.5	o-Phenoxyphenol (guaiacol)
6	31	Benzothiophene (thionaphthene)
7	32	3-Nitro-4-hydroxytoluene (3-nitro-p-cresol)
8	33	Salicylic-o-cresol ether
9	33	o-Nitrochlorobenzene
10	34	2-Methylnaphthalene
11	35	Ethyl-β-naphthyl ether (β-naphthyl ethyl ether)
12	36	2,4-Atoquinol (2-allylphenyl cinchonate)
13	36	Methyl cinnamate
14	36	m-Nitroiodobenzene
15	36	Benzylaniline
16	36	Piperonal (heliotropine)
17	37	o-Methoxybenzaldehyde (salicylaldehyde methyl ether)
18	38	Cinnamein (benzyl cinnamate)
19	39	Salicylic-p-cresol ether
20	40	Benzalacetone
21	40	Methyl nicotinate (pyridine-β-carboxylic acid methyl ester)
22	40	l-Ephedrine
23	40	Phenol
24	36–41	2,3-Dimethylbutanediol-2,3 (pinacol)
25	41	Ethyl-m-nitrobenzoate
26	41	1,6-Hexamethyleneglycol
27	41	o-Bromonitrobenzene
28	41.5	Tridecanoic acid (tridecylic acid)
29	42	l-Menthol
30	42.5	o-Nitrobenzaldehyde
31	42.5	Phenyl salicylate (salol)
32	43	o-Diethoxybenzene (pyrocatechin diethyl ether)
33	43	Methyl-p-chlorobenzoate
34	43	1,9-Nonanediol
35	43	3,4-Dimethoxybenzaldehyde
36	43	p-Chlorophenol
37	44	p-Aminotoluene (p-toluidine)
38	44	Lauric acid (dodecanoic acid)
39	44	2-Hydroxy-3-methoxybenzaldehyde (o-vanillin)
40	44	Styracin (cinnamyl cinnamate)

(*Continued*)

TABLE II (*Continued*)

Code number	Melting point, °C	Compound
41	44.5	Elaidic acid
42	45	*m*-Nitrochlorobenzene
43	45	*p*-Aminobenzylcyanide
44	45	*o*-Nitrophenol
45	45	Dianisylsulfide
46	46	1-Phenyl-3,5-dimethyl-1,2,4-triazole
47	47	*p,p'*-Diethylbenzophenone
48	47	Thymoquinone(2-methyl-5-isopropylbenzoquinone-1,4)
49	47	Dibenzyl succinate
50	48	*p*-Chlorobenzaldehyde
51	46–48	1,2-Dihydroxy-3-iodopropane (glyceryl-α-monoiodohydrin)
52	48	Methyl-*p*-hydroxybenzoate (methyl anisate)
53	48	Benzophenone
54	48	*m*-Cresol carbonate
55	49	Urethane (ethyl carbamate)
56	49	α-Naphthylamine
57	49	*o*-Aminodiphenyl
58	49	α-Bromoacetic acid
59	49	Formanilide
60	49	Hydrocinnamic acid
61	49	*o*-Nitrobenzyl chloride
62	49.5	Cetyl alcohol
63	50	Phenylurethane (Euphorin)
64	50	ω-Bromoacetophenone
65	50	Thymol
66	50	*N*-Benzoylpiperidine
67	50	β-Bromonaphthalene
68	50	2,5-Dichloroaniline
69	50	γ-Phenylbutyric acid
70	51	4-Chloro-1,3-dinitrobenzene
71	51	*p*-Cyanoethylbenzoate
72	52	Benzalaniline
73	52	Indole
74	52	2-Chlorophenyl salicylate
75	52	*p*-Nitrotoluene
76	52	*p*-Bromoacetophenone
77	48–52	Tropine
78	52.5	Pentadecanoic acid
79	53	Dibenzyl
80	53	4-Nitro-3-hydroxytoluene (3-hydroxy-4-nitrotoluene)
81	53	*N*-Ethylacetanilide

TABLE II (*Continued*)

Code number	Melting point, °C.	Compound
82	53	Maleic anhydride
83	53.5	Diphenylamine
84	54	m-Aminobenzonitrile
85	54	p-Dichlorobenzene
86	54	β,β-Dimethyl-γ-diethylaminopropyl-p-aminobenzoate
87	54	Myristic acid
88	54	p-Chloroiodobenzene
89	54	Hydroquinone monomethyl ether
90	54	Methyl carbamate
91	54	p-Nitroanisole
92	53–55	Trimyristin (glyceryl trimyristate)
93	55	o-Cresol carbonate
94	55	m-Nitrobromobenzene
95	56	Trichloroacetic acid
96	56	2-Aminopyridine
97	56	1,1,2-Triphenylethane
98	56	2,6-Dimethoxyphenol (pyrogallol-1,3-dimethyl ether)
99	56	Ethyl-p-nitrobenzoate
100	55–57	Chloral hydrate
101	57	m-Ethylaminophenol
102	57	m-Nitrobenzaldehyde
103	57	1-Nitronaphthalene
104	57	1,4-Dimethoxybenzene (hydroquinone dimethyl ether)
105	57	Benzalacetophenone
106	57	4-Aminoanisole (p-anisidine)
107	57	Benzoylacetone
108	58	Salicylaldoxime
109	59	5-Methylindole
110	59	Pentamethylene tetrazole (Cardiazole)
111	59	Scopolamine hydrate (inactive)
112	59	Acetophenonoxime
113	59	dl-α-Bromostearic acid
114	59	p-Nitrophenetol
115	59	Octadecyl alcohol
116	59	o-Hydroxydiphenyl
117	59	Novatophane k(2-phenylmethylcinchonate)
118	59	ω-Cyanobenzylbenzoate
119	55–59	Cocaine nitrate
120	59.5	Voluntal (β,β,β-trichloroethyl carbamate)
121	59.5	Ethyl hippurate
122	55–60	α,α,β-Trichlorobutyric acid

(*Continued*)

TABLE II (*Continued*)

Code number	Melting point, °C	Compound
123	60	*N*-Phenyl-α-naphthylamine
124	60	3,4-Dinitrotoluene
125	60	β-Chloronaphthalene
126	60	2,6-Dimethylquinoline
127	60	Diphenylacetylene (tolane)
128	60	Codeine hydrate
129	60	3,5-Dinitrobenzoic acid isoamyl ester
130	60	2-Methylindole
131	61	4-Chlorothymol
132	61	Guaiacol benzoate
133	61	Erythritol tetranitrate (1,2,3,4-butane tetranitrate)
134	61	*n*-Propyl carbamate
135	61	Acetoxime (acetoneoxime)
136	61.5	Heptadecanoic acid
137	62	Monochloracetic acid
138	62.5	*p*-Ethylbenzalacetophenone
139	62.5	3,4-Dimethylphenol (*o*-xylenol)
140	63	*m*-Phenylenediamine
141	63	1-Bromo-2-naphthylamine
142	63	Palmitic acid
143	63.5	2,6-Dinitrophenol
144	64	*p*-Bromoaniline
145	64	3,5-Dimethylphenol (*m*-xylenol)
146	64	Isoamyl carbamate
147	64	6-Chloro-*m*-cresol
148	64	2,4-Dichloroaniline
149	64	*N*-Methylphenylthioacetamide
150	64	4-Nitro-2-chlorotoluene
151	65	Cycloform (isobutyl-*p*-aminobenzoate)
152	65	*m*-*N*-Tolylacetamide (acet-*m*-toluidide)
153	62–65	Tripalmitin
154	65	3,4-Dimethoxybenzylcyanide
155	65	Exalton (cyclopentadecanone)
156	66	2,4,6-Trichlorophenol
157	66	Diethylbromoacetamide (Neuronal)
158	66	1,4-Dichloronaphthalene
159	66	*N*-Ethyl-*N*-phenylurea
160	66	Isobutyl carbamate
161	66	2,6-Dinitrotoluene
162	66	Pseudocumidine (2,4,5-trimethylaniline)
163	66	1,8-Naphthalenediamine
164	64–67	*o*-Sulfobenzoic acid trihydrate
165	67	Phenylethylene glycol
166	68	Azobenzene

TABLE II (*Continued*)

Code number	Melting point, °C	Compound
167	68	Diphenylnitrosamine
168	68	8,9-Diiodoricinstearolic acid
169	68	Benzoyl eugenol
170	68.5	2,4,6-Trinitroanisole
171	68.5	Nonadecanoic acid
172	69	Coumarin
173	69	Phenylbenzoate
174	69	Methyl-3,4-methylenoxyphenyl cyanoacetate
175	67–70	Alantolactone helenin
176	70	Diphenyl
177	70	α,α-Dipyridyl
178	70	β-Bromoethylnitrobenzene
179	70	Stearic acid
180	71	Allylthiourea (thiosinamine)
181	71	p-Chloroaniline
182	71	2,4-Dinitrotoluene
183	72	Salicylic guaiacol ether
184	72	4-Bromo-1,3-dinitrobenzene
185	72	o-Nitroaniline
186	72	Methyl-m-hydroxybenzoate
187	73	β-Naphthol methyl ether (Nerolin, methyl)
188	73	Diphenylurethane
189	73	Novonal (diethylallylacetamide)
190	73	1,10-Decamethylene glycol
191	73	p-Dimethylaminobenzaldehyde
192	71–73	Neocinchophen (ethyl-2-phenyl-6-methyl-cinchonate; Novatophan)
193	73	Glycol dibenzoate
194	73	4-Chlorophenyl salicylate
195	73	4-Bromo-1,2-dinitrobenzene
196	74	8-Hydroxyquinoline
197	70–74	Quinoline + salicylic acid
198	74	4-Diacetylamino-2,3'-dimethylazobenzene (Pellidol)
199	74	Formyldiphenylamine
200	74	n-Propyl-p-aminobenzoate (propasin)
201	74	Pentabromoacetone
202	74	p,p'-Dihydroxy-ditane decamethylene ether
203	74	n-Propyl-3,5-dinitrobenzoate
204	74.5	Tetracarbethoxyethane
205	74.5	Phthalide
206	75	1-[p-Methoxyphenyl]-1-phenylethylene
207	75	p-Nitrobenzoyl chloride
208	75	α-Dihydrophyllocladen (Iosen)

(*Continued*)

TABLE II (*Continued*)

Code number	Melting point, °C	Compound
209	75	Methyl-3,4-dimethoxyphenylcyanoacetate
210	75	p-Xylenol (2,4-dimethylphenol)
211	75.5	Eicosanoic acid (arachidic acid)
212	76	Methylsulfonal (trional)
213	76	3-Bromo-d-camphor
214	76	Pyramidon + Voluntal (Compral)
215	76	Salicylic-m-cresol ether
216	76.5	Tribenzoin (glyceryl tribenzoate)
217	77	Phenylacetic acid
218	77	Ethyl vanillin (bourbonal; 4-hydroxy-3-ethoxy benzaldehyde
219	77	Methyl benzoylmandelate
220	78	Lactamide
221	78	2-Carbmethoxy-1-naphthol (methyl-1-hydroxynaphthoate)
222	78	dl-Ethyl-α,β-dibromohydrocinnamate
223	78	2,4,6-Tribromo-3-methoxytoluene
224	78	Dibenzoylmethane
225	79	Propionamide
226	80	1,2,4,5-Tetramethylbenzene (durol)
227	80	p-Nitrobenzenesulfonyl chloride
228	80	Methyl-n-propyl carbinol urethane (Hedonal)
229	80	Acetamide
230	80	Diphenyl carbonate
231	80.5	Naphthalene
232	81	Ethyl-α-naphthyl carbamate (α-naphthylurethane)
233	81	Methyl-p-bromobenzoate
234	81	2,4,6-Trinitrotoluene (TNT)
235	81	Vanillin
236	83	N[β-Bromoethyl]-phthalimide
237	83	Fluorenone (diphenylene ketone)
238	83	2,4,6-Trinitrochlorobenzene (picryl chloride)
239	83	1,3-Diphenylbenzene
240	83	p-Nitrochlorobenzene
241	83	Trigemin (pyramidon + butyrchloralhydrate)
242	83	2,4,6-Tribromo-5-methyl phenol
243	84	Acetoacetanilide
244	84	p-Nitrosodiethylaniline
245	85	p-Nitrosodimethylaniline
246	85	7-Methylindole
247	85	Diphenylene oxide
248	85	γ-Phenylbutyramide
249	85.5	2,4-Dinitrophenetol
250	85	p-Methyldibenzoylmethane

TABLE II (*Continued*)

Code number	Melting point, °C	Compound
251	85.5	*o*-Hydroxybenzyl alcohol (saligenin; salicyl alcohol)
252	86	β-Naphthyl cyanide
253	87	*m*-Dimethylaminophenol
254	87	2-Nitro-4-bromoanisole
255	87	*p*-Aminobenzonitrile
256	87.5	*p*-Dibromobenzene
257	88	2,4-Dinitroanisole
258	85–88	α-Phenylhydrocinnamic acid
259	88	*p*-Chlorophenolbenzoate
260	88	Guaiacol carbonate
261	89	*p*-Bromodiphenyl
262	89	Pentane-3,3-diethylsulfone (tetronal)
263	90	*o*-Acetoxyacetophenone
264	90	Bromoacetamide
265	90	3,3'-Dimethoxydiphenylsulfone
266	90.5	Anesthesine (ethyl-*p*-aminobenzoate)
267	91	*m*-Dinitrobenzene
268	91	*p*-Bromoiodobenzene
269	91	Butyrchloral hydrate
270	91	*p*-Nitrophenylacetdimethylamide
271	91	Phenyl-α-acetylacetonitrile
272	92	Citraconic acid
273	92	Euchinin
274	92	Salipyrine (antipyrene salicylate)
275	92	5,6-benzoquinoline (β-naphthoquinoline)
276	92	Tetramethyl-4,4'-diaminodiphenylmethane
277	92	Ethyl-*dl*-tartaric acid
278	92	Ethylurea
279	85–93	*d*-Sorbite hydrate
280	93	Acenaphthalene
281	93	ω,ω'-Dibromo-*o*-xylene
282	93	Isopropyl carbamate
283	93	Ethyl-3,5-dinitrobenzoate
284	94	Triphenylmethane
285	94	β-Naphthyl salicylate (betol)
286	94	Benzalazine (dibenzalhydrazine)
287	94	3,3-Diethyl-2,4-dihydroxytetrahydropyridine
288	94	Acenaphthene
289	94	*p-tert*-Amylphenol (Pentaphen)
290	94	*p*-Methylphenylacetic acid
291	94	2,4,6-Tribromophenol
292	95	2-Methyl-4-nitrophenol
293	95	Benzil

(*Continued*)

TABLE II (*Continued*)

Code number	Melting point, °C	Compound
294	95	Tribenzylamine
295	95	Carbon tetrabromide
296	95	3-Methylindole (skatole)
297	95	4,6-Dichlororesorcinol
298	96	Methyl-*p*-nitrobenzoate
299	96	Methyl-isobutylketone-2,4-dinitrophenylhydrazone
300	96	*d*-Naphthol
301	96	Tetramethyl-4,4'-diaminobenzhydrol (Michler's hydrol)
302	96.5	*m*-Nitrophenol
303	97	2,7-Dimethylnaphthalene
304	97	Nipasol (Propyl-*p*-hydroxybenzoate)
305	97	β,β,β-Trichloro-*tert*-butyl alcohol (acetone-chloroform; chloretone)
306	98	Glycol diphenyl ether
307	98	Cocaine
308	98	1-Methyl-7-isopropyl phenanthrene (retene)
309	98	Phenylthioacetamide
310	98	1,2-Naphthalenediamine
311	99	Phenanthrene
312	99	*m*-Toluylenediamine (2,4-diaminotoluene)
313	99	Glutaric acid
314	99	Percaine (butoxy-cinchoninic acid diethylethylene diamide·hydrochloride)
315	99	*p*-Chlorobenzalacetophenone
316	99	Benzophenonehydrazone
317	99	Aminoazophenylene (benzotriazole)
318	90–100	*o*-Sulfobenzoic acid
319	90–100	Scopolamine hydrobromide trihydrate
320	90–100	Scopolamine hydrochloride trihydrate
321	100	Diphenylenesulfide
322	100	Homatropine (tropine mandelate)
323	100	Exalgine (*N*-methylacetanilide)
324	100	2,5-Dihydroxybenzaldehyde
325	100.5	α-Chlorocrotonic acid
326	101	Phenoxyacetic acid
327	102	*o*-Phenylenediamine
328	102	Adonite (adonitol)
329	102	3,3'-Diacetoxydiphenyl sulfone
330	102	Maleic anhydride adduct with 8,10-heptadecadiene-1-carboxylic acid
331	103	Novocaine nitrate
332	103	Acetyldiphenylamine
333	103	Methylurea

TABLE II (*Continued*)

Code number	Melting point, °C	Compound
334	103	4-Bromo-1-naphthylamine
335	103	Ethyl-*p*-nitrobenzoyl salicylate
336	103.5	4-Isopropyl antipyrene
337	100–104	Levulose (D-fructose)
338	104	Pimelic acid
339	104	Pyrocatechol (1,2-dihydroxybenzene)
340	104	*m*-Hydroxybenzaldehyde
341	104	Dianisylaldehyde
342	104	*p*-Bromophenolbenzoate
343	103–105	Sparteine bisulfate
344	105	*cis,cis,trans,trans*-Dihydrocholesterol (coprosterol)
345	105	9-Phenanthridine
346	105	Guajen (2,3-dimethylnaphthalene)
347	105	Benzyl-3,5-dinitrobenzoate
348	105	α,α-Pentane dicarboxylic acid (butylmalonic acid)
349	105	*p*-Bromobenzalacetophenone
350	105.5	*p*-Nitrobenzaldehyde
351	106	Phenyl diphenylurethane (phenyldiphenyl carbamate)
352	106	Physostigmine (eserine)
353	106	Uraline (Ural; chloral urethane)
354	106	2-Methylbenzoic acid (*o*-toluic acid)
355	106	2,5 Dinitrophenol
356	106	$\omega,\omega,\omega',\omega'$-Tetrabromo-*m*-xylene
357	106	*p*-Aminoacetophenone
358	106	*cis*-Terpin (1,8-terpin)
359	106	2-Methyl-1,4-naphthoquinone
360	106.5	Azelaic acid (nonanedioic acid)
361	107	4-Nitro-2-aminotoluene
362	107	β-Naphthyl benzoate (benzonaphthol)
363	107	3,5-Dinitroanisole
364	107,114	Xylene musk
365	107	Methyl-3,5-dinitrobenzoate
366	107	Hyoscyamine
367	108	*N*-Hydroxymethylbenzamide (*N*-methylolbenzamide)
368	108	Diethylstilbestrol dipropionate
369	108	Aminopyrene (pyramidon)
370	108	Benzoylperoxide
371	108	*N,N'*-Dimethylurea
372	108	2-Hydroxypyridine
373	109	Phenyl-β-naphthylamine
374	109	9,10-Dihydroanthracene

(*Continued*)

TABLE II (*Continued*)

Code number	Melting point, °C	Compound
375	109	*p*-Hydroxyacetophenone
376	109	Fluoranthene (idryl)
377	109	DDT (2,2-Bis(-*p*-chlorophenyl)-1,1,1-trichloroethane
378	110	Acridine
379	110	Acet-*o*-toluidide (*o*-*N*-tolylacetamide)
380	110	*o,o*-Diphenol (2,2'-dihydroxydiphenyl)
381	110	4,4'-Dimethoxybenzoin (anisoin)
382	110	3,5-Dihydroxy toluene (5-methyl resorcinol; orcinol)
383	110	Methyl-*n*-butyl ketone-2,4-dinitrophenylhydrazone
384	110	Bromohydroquinone
385	106–110	α-Nitroso-β-naphthol
386	110,127	Nipagin M (methyl-*p*-hydroxybenzoate)
387	108–110	*d*-Sorbitol
388	108–110	Abasin (*N*-acetyl-*N*'-diethylbromoacetylurea)
389	110.5	Resorcinol
390	111	2,6-Dimethylnaphthalene
391	111	Pyridine-3-sulfonamide
392	111	Thionalide (thioglycolic-β-aminonaphthalide)
393	111.5	Antipyrene
394	112	Dehydracetic acid
395	112	Ethylmalonic acid
396	112	β-Naphthylamine
397	112	Dibenzylidene acetone
398	112	*N,N*'-Diethylurea
399	112	Benzyl-*p*-hydroxybenzoate (Nipabenzyl)
400	110–113	Mannitol hexanitrate
401	113	2,4-Dinitrophenol
402	113	*p*-Nitrophenol
403	113	*p*-Cresol carbonate
404	113	1,4-Benzoquinone (*p*-quinone)
405	113	Di-α-naphthylamine
406	113	Benzhydrazide
407	113.5	γ-Hexachlorocyclohexane
408	114	Fluorene
409	114,107	Xylene musk (2,4,6-trinitro-5-*tert*-butyl-1,3-xylene)
410	114,129	Pentobarbital (5-ethyl-5-[-1-methylbutyl]-barbituric acid)
411	114	*m*-Nitroaniline
412	114	*p*-Ethylbenzoic acid
413	114	1-Cyclopentyl-*N*-methyl-2-propylamine (Clopane hydrochloride)
414	110–115	1-1-Amyltheobromine
415	115	Antifibrin

TABLE II (*Continued*)

Code number	Melting point, °C	Compound
416	115	Cholesteryl acetate
417	115	3,4-Dimethoxy benzoic nitrile (veratric acid nitrile)
418	116	Atropine
419	116	Ethyl-*p*-hydroxybenzoate (Nipagin A)
420	116	Pseudocoprosterol
421	116	ω,ω,ω',ω'-Tetrabromo-*o*-xylene
422	116	*p*-Nitrobenzylcyanide
423	116	*n*-Butyric amide
424	116	4,4'-Diacetoxy-2,2'-dimethyldiphenylsulfone
425	117	*p*-Dimethylaminoazobenzene
426	117	*p*-Hydroxybenzaldehyde
427	117	2-Diphenylacetyl triethylamine
428	117	3-Nitro-4-aminotoluene
429	117	5-Methyl-2-methylphenol
430	117	Phenylacetanilide
431	117	*N*-Ethyl-N-butyl-*N*'-acetylurea
432	117	Methylethylketone-2,4-dinitrophenylhydrazone
433	118	*N*-Methyl-*N*-ethyl-*N*,*N*'-diphenylurea
434	115–118	Thiobenzamide
435	118	*o*-Benzoylresorcinol
436	116–118	Terpin hydrate
437	118	Hordenine ([4-hydroxyphenylethyl]dimethylamine)
438	118	*d*-Pseudoephedrine
439	118	*o*-Dinitrobenzene
440	118	Acetoacetic ester-*p*-nitrophenylhydrazone
441	118	Lactophenetidine (lactophenin)
442	118,136	*p*,*p*'-Azoxyanisole
443	119	Chloroacetamide
444	119	*dl*-Mandelic acid
445	119	3-Bromo-4-acetaminotoluene
446	119.5	1,2,3,4-Butanetetrol (erythritol)
447	120	Succinic anhydride
448	120	Diethylstilboestrol diacetate
449	120	Acetylthiourea
450	120	Bromodiethylacetylurea
451	120	*d*-Camphoroxime
452	120	Cyanoacetamide
453	120	α-Cinnamylbenzylcyanide
454	120	β,β,β-Trichlorolactic acid
455	120	2,4'-Diacetoxy-3',5-dimethyldiphenylsulfone
456	121	2,4,6-Tribromoaniline
457	121	2,6-Diaminopyridine
458	121	3,5-Dinitroguaiacol (3,5-dinitro-1-hydroxy-2-methoxybenzene)

(*Continued*)

TABLE II *(Continued)*

Code number	Melting point, °C	Compound
459	110–122	Quinidine acetate
460	122	β-Naphthol
461	122	2,4,6-Trinitrophenol (picric acid)
462	122	N-[p-Nitrobenzoyl]-piperidine
463	122	m-Aminophenol
464	122	n-Butyraldehyde-2,4-dinitrophenylhydrazone
465	120–122	Phloridzin
466	122	Isopropyl-3,5-dinitrobenzoate
467	122.5	Benzoic acid
468	123	Iodoform
469	123	Testosterone propionate
470	123	2,4,6-Trinitrobromobenzene (picryl bromide)
471	123	N,N'-Dimethyl-N,N'-diphenylurea (dimethylcarbanilide)
472	123.5	s-Trinitrobenzene
473	124	Hebaral (5-hexyl-5-ethylbarbituric acid)
474	124	Chloramide (chloral formamide)
475	124	Naphthoresorcinol (1,3-dihydroxynaphthalene)
476	115–125	Lobeline
477	125	Picrolonic acid
478	120–125	Aludrin
479	125	p-Aminoazobenzene
480	125	Stilbene
481	125	Ethylidene diurethane
482	125	Tetradecane dicarboxylic acid
483	125	Methyl-4-amino-3-hydroxybenzoate
484	125	2,3'-Dimethoxydiphenylsulfone
485	126	Hydrazobenzene
486	126	Sonneryl (Neonal; 5,5-ethylbutyl barbituric acid)
487	126	ω-Isonitrosoacetophenone
488	126	Succinamide
489	126	Hexadecanedicarboxylic acid
490	126	6-Nitro-3-hydroxytoluene (4-nitro-m-cresol)
491	126.5	Bis[ethylsulfone]dimethylmethane (Sulfonal)
492	127	Diphenylsulfone
493	127	4,4'-Dimethoxydiphenylsulfone
494	127	Nipagin M (p-oxybenzoic acid methyl ester)
495	127	p-Bromonitrobenzene
496	127	o-Benzoylbenzoic acid
497	128	Acetone-2,4-dinitrophenylhydrazone
498	128	Benzamide
499	128	d-Camphor carbonic acid
500	129	5-Ethyl-5-[1-methylbutyl]barbituric acid (pentobarbital)
501	129	p-Diiodobenzene

TABLE II (*Continued*)

Code number	Melting point, °C	Compound
502	129	Benzidine (4,4'-diaminodiphenyl)
503	129	Nicotinamide (pyridine-3-carboxylic amide)
504	129	Progesterone
505	129	Idobutal (5-allyl-5-butylbarbituric acid)
506	129	*o'*,*m*-Dihydroxydiphenylsulfone
507	129	1-Phenyl-3-methylpyrazolone
508	129	Decamethylenedicarboxylic acid
509	129	Hexaethylbenzene
510	125–129	Optochin base
511	127–129	4-Toluenesulfonyl-β-naphthylamide
512	129.5	β-Acetylphenylhydrazine
513	129.5	Piperidine
514	130	5-Iodo-2-aminopyridine
515	130	*p*-Acetanisidine
516	130	3,3'-Dimethylbenzidine (*o*-tolidine)
517	130	Dihydroxy-4-methoxybenzophenone (cotoin)
518	131	3-[β,γ-Dibromopropyl]-5-diethylbarbituric acid
519	131	5-Allyl-5-*n*-propylbarbituric acid
520	131	*dl*-Malic acid
521	131	*N*-Isopropylbenzanilide
522	128–131	Bornyl chloride
523	131	α-Naphthylacetic acid
524	131	4,4'-Dimethoxybenzil (anisil)
525	132	5-*sec*-Butyl-5-[β-bromoallyl]-barbituric acid (**Pernoston**)
526	132	Hydrastine
527	132	Pantocaine nitrate
528	132	Thiodiglycolic acid
529	132	1-Benzeneazo-2-naphthol (Sudan I)
530	132	Pyromucic acid
531	133	Sebacic acid (decanedioic acid)
532	133	Glucose-β-pentacetate
533	133	Dibenzylsulfoxide
534	128–133	*d*-Mannose
535	135.5	1,2,3-Trihydroxybenzene
536	110–134	Quinine cinnamylate
537	112–134	Uliron C (4-[4'-aminophenylsulfonamido]phenylsulfonamide
538	134	Benzoin
539	134	Sorbic acid
540	134	Acetyl-β-naphthylamine (β-acetonaphthalide)
541	134	4,6-Dinitro-1,5-dimethyl-3-*tert*-butyl-2-acetylbenzene
542	132–135	Mellitose (Raffinose)

(*Continued*)

TABLE II (*Continued*)

Code number	Melting point, °C	Compound
543	135	o-Sulfobenzoic acid
544	135	Urea
545	135	*trans*-Cinnamic acid
546	135	Phenacetin
547	130–135, 146–148	p-Aminosalicylic acid
548	135	2,6-Dimethylyron
549	135.5	Cinnamic anhydride
550	136	Malonic acid
551	130–136	Acetylsalicylic acid (Aspirin)
552	136	Isobutyryl-p-phenetidide
553	136	Phenylpropiolic acid
554	136	d-Galactonic-γ-lactone
555	136	Sitosterol
556	136	Resorcylaldehyde(2,4-dihydroxybenzaldehyde)
557	136	p,p'-Azoxyanisol
558	137	1,6-Dihydroxynaphthalene
559	138	2,4-Dinitro-1-naphthol
560	138	8-Hexachlorocyclohexane
561	139	Sandoptal (5-isobutyl-5-allylbarbituric acid)
562	135–139	S-Benzyl thiouronium acetate
563	139	p-Toluenesulfonamide
564	135–139	5-Isoamyl-5-propylbarbituric acid
565	139	Ethyl-p-nitrocinnamate
566	140	o-Chlorobenzoic acid
567	140	β-Furyl-2-acrylic acid
568	140	Salicylamide
569	140	2-Methoxyphenyl-3,5-dinitrobenzoate
570	140	5-Cyclopentenyl-5-allylbarbituric acid
571	141	Quinine salicylate
572	141	Suberic acid
573	141	Dimethyl terephthalate
574	141	4,4'-Dimethoxy-3,3'-dimethyldiphenylsulfone
575	141	2,2'-Azoxydiphenyl (phenazone-N-oxide)
576	141	β-Benzoylaminoethanol
577	142	Benzoylaminoacetonitrile
578	142	5-Allyl-5-isopropylbarbituric acid (Numal)
579	142	p-Phenylenediamine
580	142	Trichloroacetamide
581	142	Pentaerythritol tetranitrate (PETN)
582	142.5	m-Nitrobenzoic acid
583	142.5	*trans,trans,trans,trans*-Dihydrocholesterol
584	143	Orthoform new (methyl-3-amino-4-hydroxybenzoate)

TABLE II (*Continued*)

Code number	Melting point, °C	Compound
585	135–143	Hydroxyurea
586	141–143	1-[*m*-Hydroxyphenyl]-2-methylaminoethanol (Adrianol)
587	143	*m*-Benzamino benzonitrile
588	141–143	Anthracene picrate
589	143	4-Nitro-2-aminophenol
590	144	Butolan (benzylphenyl carbamate)
591	144	Methylpropylketone-2,4-dinitrophenylhydrazone
592	145	*o*-Aminobenzoic acid
593	145	Phenol-*α*-*d*-galactoside
594	146	5-Ethyl-5-*n*-propylbarbituric acid
595	146	Papaverine
596	146	Evipan (*N*-methyl-5-methyl-5-cyclohexenylbarbituric acid)
597	141–147	Dithizone (diphenylthiocarbazone)
598	143–147	*d*-Xylose
599	144–147	Hematoxylin (hydroxybrasilin)
600	144–147	*S*-Benzyl thiouroniumformate
601	147	Sarcosine anhydride (*N*-methylglycine anhydride)
602	147	*ω,ω′*-Dibromo-*p*-xylene
603	147	2-Dimethylaminoethyl-4-butylaminobenzoate hydrochloride (Pantocaine)
604	147	Benzopyrazole (Indazole)
605	142–147	Diacetylphenolphthalein
606	147	*p*-Methylmandelic acid
607	147	2,2′-Dimethoxy-3,3′-dimethyldiphenylsulfone
608	147	*N*-Phenyl-*N*-ethyl-*N′*-acetylurea
609	147	*o*-Nitrobenzoic acid
610	145–148	Salicyl salicylic acid (diplosal)
611	145–148	Ammonium salicylate
612	148	Phenylurea
613	145–148	Quinine hydrochloride
614	146–148	*p*-Aminosalicylic acid
615	148	1,2-Hexachloroindene-3-one (perchloroindone)
616	148	Cholesterol
617	148	*p*-Nitroaniline
618	148	Proponal (5,5-dipropylbarbituric acid)
619	148	Ethylpropylketone-2,4-dinitrophenylhydrazone
620	148	*N,N′*-Diphenylguanidine
621	145–148	*d*-Glucose (dextrose)
622	148.5	2-Diethylaminoethyl-1-phenylcyclopentanecarboxylate (Parpanite)
623	149	*o*-Bromobenzoic acid

(*Continued*)

TABLE II (*Continued*)

Code number	Melting point, °C	Compound
624	147–149	Atropine hydrobromide (hyoscyamine hydrobromide)
625	149	*p*-Nitrobenzonitrile
626	149	Pseudococaine bitartrate (Psicaine)
627	149	Benzylurea
628	149	*o*-Hydroxyphenylacetic acid
629	149	Prostigmine
630	149	Cinnamic amide (cinnamide)
631	142–150	Quinine hydrobromide
632	145–150	Benzilic acid
633	150	Pyrene
634	150	4-Hydroxypyridine
635	150	Ethyl-4-benzaminobenzoic acid
636	140–150	Colchicine
637	148–150	Aesculin
638	148–150	Hydrastine hydrochloride
639	146–150	5,5'-Dimethyldihydroresorcinol
640	151	*p*-*N*-Tolylacetamide (acet-*p*-toluidide)
641	151	*p*-Chlorophenyl carbonate
642	151	4-[4'-Aminophenylsulfonamido]-phenylsulfone methylamide (Neo-Uliron)
643	152	Adipic acid
644	152	1,4-Diphenylbutadiene
645	152	Paracotoin
646	152	(α-Bromo-isovaleryl)urea (Bromural)
647	142–152	Urea nitrate
648	152	2-Hydroxy-5-methylbenzoic acid
649	145–153	Veratrine
650	151–153	α-Benzoinoxime
651	140–153	Gluconic-δ-lactone
652	153	*N*,*N*'-Diphenylthiourea
653	148–153	Benzylidenephenylhydrazine
654	148–154	Hyoscyamine hydrochloride
655	154	Phenylthiourea
656	154	5-Butyl-5-propylbarbituric acid
657	154	Dipropionamide
658	154	Protocatechuic aldehyde (3,4-dihydroxybenzaldehyde)
659	151–154	Citric acid
660	153–154	Isoamyl dihydrocupreine (Eucupine)
661	155	Testosterone
662	155	Propionaldehyde-2,4-dinitrophenylhydrazone
663	155	Phenol-β-*d*-galactoside
664	155	3,5-Dinitrobenzoic acid-1-menthyl ester

TABLE II (*Continued*)

Code number	Melting point, °C	Compound
665	140–155	Camphane
666	155.5	*m*-Bromobenzoic acid
667	149–156	Dionin (ethyl morphine hydrochloride)
668	156	Novocaine hydrochloride (procaine hydrochloride)
669	156	Codeine
670	156	Amytal (5-isoamyl-5-ethylbarbituric acid)
671	156	*o*-Toluenesulfonamide
672	150–157	Eupaverine
673	157	Neo ergosterol
674	157	α-Naphtholflavone (7,8-benzoflavone)
675	157	Phenazone
676	157	Nitrostilbene
677	155–158	Diphenylcarbazone
678	150–158	β-Nitroso-α-naphthol
679	150–158	Tartronic acid (hydroxymalonic acid)
680	151–158	Boldin (2,6-dihydroxy-3,5-dimethoxyaporphin)
681	153–158	Quinine bisulfate
682	158	Salicylic acid (*o*-hydroxybenzoic acid)
683	158	*N*-Allyl-*N*-butyl-*N* ′-acetylurea
684	158	*p*-Nitrophenylhydrazine
685	158	Quinaldinic acid (quinoline-2-carboxylic acid)
686	156–158	Sulfanilylurea
687	158	α-Hexachlorocyclohexane
688	159	Phenol-α-*d*-glucoside
689	159	*N*-Benzoyltetrahydropapaverine
690	159	5-Allyl-5-phenylbarbituric acid
691	150–160	Tricarballylic acid
692	150–160	Metaldehyde
693	160	5-Ethyl-5-allylbarbituric acid (Dormin)
694	160	β-Propionylphenylhydrazine
695	160	*N*,*N* ′-Dinitrosopiperazine
696	160	4-Iodoantipyrene
697	156–161	Hydroxylamine hydrochloride
698	161	α-Naphthoic acid
699	161	*dl*-Bromosuccinic acid
700	161	Cortin (Cortiron; desoxycorticosteroneacetate)
701	161	α-Acetnaphthalide (acetyl-α-naphthylamine)
702	161	Benzoyl-α-naphthylamine
703	159–162	Diphenylcarbazide
704	157–162	*l*-Arabinose
705	162	*tert*-Amylurea
706	162	*o*-Iodobenzoic acid
707	162.5	Triphenylcarbinol

(*Continued*)

TABLE II (*Continued*)

Code number	Melting point, °C	Compound
708	163	Arecoline hydrochloride
709	163	Pyridine picrate
710	163	p-Aminoacetanilide
711	163	2,3-Dihydroxynaphthalene
712	163	Benzanilide
713	163.5	Alypin nitrate (benzoyl-2-dimethylaminomethyl-1-methylaminobutane-2-nitrate)
714	155–164	Caffeine citrate
715	155–164	5-*sec*-Amyl-5-[β-bromoallyl]-barbituric acid
716	164	Surfacaine
717	164	Histadyl
718	155–165	Narceine
719	154–165	Gelsemine
720	165,200	Arbutin
721	165	1,2,3-Triacetoxybenzene(pyrogallol triacetate)
722	165	β-Cresotinic acid (2-hydroxy-1,3-toluic acid)
723	165	*rac*-Pseudoephedrine hydrochloride
724	165	1,2-Benzanthracene
725	165	Acetaldehyde-2,4-dinitrophenylhydrazone
726	165	p-Hydroxydiphenyl
727	164–166	Quinic acid
728	166	N,N'-Di-o-tolylthiourea
729	166	Hexamethylbenzene
730	166	Protalbin (p-aminobenzenesulfonamide)
731	166	d-Mannitol (mannite)
732	166	Malonamide
733	167	4,4'-Diacetoxy-3-nitrodiphenylsulfone
734	167	3,4,5-Triiodonitrobenzene
735	167	Formaldehyde-2,4-dinitrophenylhydrazone
736	167	Stigmasterol
737	168	Diethylstilboestrol (4,4'-dihydroxy-α,β-diethylstilbene)
738	169	2-Methoxy-4-methyl-5-bromobenzenesulfonamide
739	169	p-Benzaminobenzonitrile
740	169	p-Bromoacetanilide
741	168–170	Skatole-ω-carboxylic acid (indolylacetic acid)
742	165–170	Codeine hydrochloride dihydrate
743	170	Alypin hydrochloride
744	170	Atropine hydrochloride
745	170	4-Acetaminodiphenyl
746	170	Bis-[p-methoxyphenyl]-azimethylene (anisaldazine)
747	170	d-Tartaric acid
748	169–171	Picramic acid
749	171	Quinidine

TABLE II (*Continued*)

Code number	Melting point, °C	Compound
750	171	Gallactophenone (2,3,4-trihydroxyacetophenone)
751	171	Di-β-naphthylamine
752	171	1,8-Dinitroresorcinol
753	171	3,3'-Diaminodiphenylsulfone
754	171	Ferulic acid (*m*-methoxy-*p*-hydroxycinnamic acid)
755	165–171	2-Hydroxy-1,5-toluic acid
756	152–172	*N*,*N*'-Di-*o*-tolylguanidine
757	170–172	Heroin (diacetylmorphine)
758	169–172	Helmitol
759	172	Synopen
760	172	Benzanthrone
761	172	$\omega,\omega,\omega',\omega'$-Tetrabromo-*p*-xylene
762	172	5-Furfuryl-5-isopropylbarbituric acid (Dormovit)
763	172	3,5-Dinitrosalicylic acid
764	172.5	Hydroquinone (1,4-dihydroxybenzene)
765	171–173	Chloramine T
766	173	5-Cyclohexenyl-5-ethylbarbituric acid (Phanodorm)
767	173	Phenol-β-*d*-glucoside
768	173	*p*-Phenetylurea (sucrol; dulcin; *p*-ethoxyphenyl-urea)
769	173	γ-[2-Methylpiperidino]-propanol hydrochloride (Metycaine; Neothesin)
770	173	Benzimidazole
771	172–174	1-Phenylsemicarbazide
772	172–174	Tetramethyl-4,4'-diaminobenzophenone
773	174	Santonin
774	174	5-Cycloheptenyl-5-ethylbarbituric acid (Medomine)
775	174	*p*-Dinitrobenzene
776	174	Narcotine
777	174	5,5-Diallyl barbituric acid (Dial)
778	174	N-Methyl-α-methyl-β-phenylethylamine hydrochloride (Pervitin)
779	174	5-Phenyl-5-ethylbarbituric acid (Luminal)
780	175	Semicarbazide hydrochloride
781	157–175	Oreoselon
782	165–175	Hydroquinine
783	175	Estradiol
784	175	5-Isopropyl-5-*n*-propylbarbituric acid
785	175	*o*-Aminophenol
786	175	Di-isobutyramide
787	174–176	Camphor
788	176	Benzophenone oxide (xanthone)
789	176	Methylarbutin

(*Continued*)

TABLE II (*Continued*)

Code number	Melting point, °C	Compound
790	176	Quinine
791	176	4-Benzalamino antipyrene
792	176	4,4'-Dibromoazoxybenzene
793	172–177	Marbadal
794	160–177	Genatropine hydrochloride
795	174–177	Guanicaine (dianisylphenetylguanidine hydrochloride; acoin)
796	177	Arecoline hydrobromide
797	177	3-Hydroxy-1,4-toluic acid (γ-cresotinic acid)
798	177	2,4,6-Trinitroresorcinol (styphnic acid)
799	177	Pyridine mercuric chloride hydrochloride
800	170–178	Brucine
801	174–178	Acetone thiosemicarbazone
802	170–178	Pilocarpine nitrate
803	178	Proseptasine (N^4-benzylsulfanilamide)
804	178	Isobutylamine hydrochloride
805	178	m-Aminoazobenzene
806	172–178	N,N'-Di-o-tolylthiourea
807	178	Aldomedonanhydride
808	167–179	Citrophen (p-phenetidine citate)
809	179	4-Hydroxy-1,2-toluic acid
810	179	3-Methyl-5-ethyl-5-phenylbarbituric acid (Prominal)
811	179	2,4-Dinitroaniline
812	179	Physostigmine salicylate
813	179	2-Mercaptobenzothiazole
814	170–180	5-Sulfosalicylic acid dihexamethylenetetramine hydrate (Neohexal)
815	176–180	Thiourea
816	177–180	N-Acetyl-5-ethyl-5-phenylhydantoin (Acetylnirvanol)
817	176–181	Phenylhydrazine oxalate
818	180–181	7-Iodo-5-chloro-8-hydroxyquinoline (Vioform)
819	181	Anthralin (cignolin; 1,8-Dihydroxy-x-anthranol)
820	181	Thiosemicarbazide
821	181	p-Aminobenzenesulfonamide-β,β-dimethyl-acrylamide
822	181	2,4'-Dimethoxy-3,5'-dimethyldiphenylsulfone
823	183	N-[α-Bromoisovaleryl]-piperazine
824	180–183	G-Strophanthin
825	183	Phenylisopropylmethylamine picrolonate
826	183	2,4'-Dihydroxy-3',5-dimethyldiphenylsulfone
827	183	α-Iodoisovaleryl urea
828	183,176	Veronal

TABLE II (*Continued*)

Code number	Melting point, °C	Compound
829	183.5	5-Isopropyl-5-[β-bromallyl]-barbituric acid (Noctal)
830	184	9-Phenylacridine
831	184	5-Sulfosalicylic acid hexamethylenetetramine (Hexal)
832	184	Androsterone
833	184	*p*-Aminobenzenesulfoneacetamide (Albucid)
834	184	Isobutyraldehyde-2,4-dinitrophenylhydrazone
835	184	Pseudoephedrine hydrochloride
836	184	β-Naphthoic acid
837	184	Nitron
838	180–184	*m*-Tolylsemicarbazide
839	178–185	Guanidine hydrochloride
840	175–185	Dikodid hydrochloride
841	175–185	Lobeline hydrochloride
842	180–185	Inulin
843	185	*p*-Methoxybenzoic acid (anisic acid)
844	185	*o,p′*-Dihydroxydiphenylsulfone
845	185	*p*-Aminophenol
846	186	*N*-Phenylanthranilic acid (*N*-phenyl-*o*-aminobenzoic acid)
847	186	β-Naphthoyl chloride
848	186	[4-Acetaminobenzyl]-benzoylamine
849	186	*p*-Iodoacetanilide
850	186	α-Chlorolose
851	187	*p*-Aminobenzoic acid
852	187	Ethyl-1-methyl-4-phenylpiperidine-4-carboxylate
853	187	β,β′-Dinaphthyl
854	187	4,4′-Dichloroazobenzene
855	187	Diquinine carbonate (aristoquin)
856	182–188	Stypticin (cotarnine hydrochloride)
857	182–188	Berberine hydrochloride
858	186–188	Aconitine nitrate
859	188	Cholein acid (desoxycholic acid + palmitic or stearic acid)
860	188	*cis,trans,trans,trans*-Epidihydrocholesterol
861	188	Succinic acid
862	188	4-Methylumbelliferone (7-hydroxy-4-methylcoumarin)
863	188	2-[*p*-Aminobenzenesulfamino]-5-ethylthiadiazole
864	183–189	1-[*p*-hydroxyphenyl]-2-methylaminoethanol tartrate (Sympatol)
865	189	Dulcit
866	188–190	Paracodeinebitartrate (dihydrocodeinebitartrate)
867	188–190	1,5-Dinaphthylenediamine

(*Continued*)

TABLE II (*Continued*)

Code number	Melting point, °C.	Compound
868	184–190	*N,N'*-Di-*p*-tolylthiourea
869	185–190	*l*-Ascorbic acid (vitamin C)
870	185–190	Sucrose (cane sugar)
871	190	*p*-Acetaminobenzenesulfonaminoacetonitrile
872	190	Sulfaguanidine (*p*-Aminobenzenesulfonylguanidine monohydrate)
873	190	Ephetonin (*rac*-ephedrine hydrochloride)
874	188–190,183	5,5-Diethylbarbituric acid (Veronal)
875	190	*N*-Benzoylaminoacetic acid (hippuric acid)
876	190	Lithocholic acid
877	190	*d*-Camphoric acid
878	190	Tetraiodoethylene (ethylene periodide; diiodoform)
879	185–190	5-Nitrobarbituric acid (dilituric acid)
880	190	2,7-Dihydroxynaphthalene
881	180–190	Hexachloroethane
882	190	Pentachlorophenol
883	190	2,4,6-Trinitroaniline (picramide)
884	190	Salophen
885	189–191	Cocaine hydrochloride
886	188–191	Oxalic acid
887	191	*N*-Acetyl-4-bromo-1-naphthylamine
888	192	2-Sulfanilylaminopyridine
889	190–192	Atropine sulfate
890	192	2,2'-Diacetoxydiphenylsulfone
891	192	*m*-Phthalimidobenzonitrile
892	192	Formaldomedon
893	188–193	2-[*N*⁴-Succinylsulfanilamino]thiazole monohydrate (Sulfasuxidine)
894	193	6-Hydroxyquinoline
895	180–193	Thebaine hydrochloride
896	193	Thebaine
897	193	*N*-Allyl-*N*-isopropyl-*N'*-acetylurea (Sedormid)
898	190–194	Narcotine hydrochloride
899	190–194	Lysidine bitartrate
900	194	*o,o'*-Dihydroxydiphenylsulfone
901	190–194	*p*-Acetaminobenzenesulfothiourea (Acetbadional)
902	194	1,8-Dihydroxyanthraquinone (chrysazin)
903	192–194	*S*-Benzylthiuronium-3,5-diiodo-4-hydroxybenzenesulfonate
904	180–195	Hyoscyamine sulfate
905	180–195	Aconitine
906	195	1,8-Dihydroxy-3-methylanthraquinone
907	195	*m,m'*-Dihydroxyphenylsulfone
908	190–195, 270–275	Cinnamoyl-*p*-hydroxyphenylurea (Elbon)

TABLE II (*Continued*)

Code number	Melting point, °C	Compound
909	190–195	5-Iodo-2-hydroxypyridine
910	195	4-[4′-Aminophenylsulfonamido]phenylsulfondimethylamide (Uliron)
911	185–195	Anhydromethylene citric acid
912	190–196	o-Acetylsalicyltheobromine
913	192–196	1-Hydroxy-2-naphthoic acid
914	196	Phenylisopropylaminepicrolonate
915	196	Hemimellitic acid (1,2,3-benzenetricarboxylic acid)
916	194–196	2,2′-Dimethoxy-4,4′-dimethyldiphenylsulfone
917	197	2,2′-Dihydroxy-4,4′-dimethyldiphenylsulfone
918	194–197	Scopolamine hydrobromide
919	197	Aniline hydrochloride
920	198	Triphenylene
921	195–198	4-Hydroxyquinoline
922	196–198	2,4-Dinitrophenylhydrazine
923	198	2,2′-Dimethoxydiphenylsulfone
924	198	5,7-Dibromo-8-hydroxyquinoline
925	199	2,2′-Diacetoxy-4,4′-dimethyldiphenylsulfone
926	199	2-Sulfanilylamino-3,5-dimethylpyrimidine
927	199	5-Phenyl-5-ethylhydantoin (Nirvanol)
928	199	2,2′-Dinitrostilbene
929	197–199	Benzoyl-2,2-dimethyl-3-diethylaminopropanol hydrochloride (Larocain)
930	196–200	Cholic acid
931	198–200	p-Phenoxyacetophenoneazine
932	180–200	Narceine hydrochloride
933	198–200	S-Benzylthiuronium-4-sulfosalicylate
934	195–200	Glutamic acid
935	198–200	Pilocarpine hydrochloride
936	200	Arbutin
937	200	Salicin
938	about 200	N,N′-Dimethyloxamide
939	201	3,3′-Dinitrodiphenylsulfone
940	198–201	Picrotoxin
941	199–201	Gluconic phenylhydrazide
942	201	1,4-Dihydroxyanthraquinone (quinizarin)
943	201	2-Sulfanilamidothiazole (sulfathiazole)
944	202	N-[4-Nitrobenzenesulfonyl]-p-phenylenediamine
945	202	5-Ethyl-5-cyclohexylbarbituric acid
946	202	m-Hydroxybenzoic acid
947	200–202	α,β-Dibromohydrocinnamic acid
948	202	Mesaconic acid
949	200–203	Benzoyl-1-ecgonine

(*Continued*)

TABLE II (*Continued*)

Code number	Melting point, °C	Compound
950	203	Protocatechuic acid (3,4-dihydroxybenzoic acid)
951	203	*m*-Nitrocinnamic acid
952	203	*p*-Nitrobenzamide
953	195–204	Carbamylcholine chloride (Doryl)
954	204	Cinchonidine
955	204	Benzbromoanilide
956	204	Isatin
957	204	5-Ethyl-5-isopropylbarbituric acid (Ipral)
958	199–204	Ferropyrine
959	204	Quinoline picrate
960	204	Iodogorgonic acid (3,5-diiodotyrosine)
961	200–204	Artemisine
962	190–205	Quinidine sulfate
963	190–205	Scopolamine hydrochloride
964	190–205	Brucine hydrochloride
965	200–205	Hydroxynaphthyl-*o*-hydroxy-*m*-toluic acid (epicarin)
966	205	*p*-Acetaminobenzonitrile
967	205	5-*n*-Propylbarbituric acid
968	206	2,2'-Dihydroxy-5,5'-dimethyldiphenylsulfone
969	206	2-Methylanthracene
970	206.5	3,5-Dinitrobenzoic acid
971	195–207	Cevadine
972	195–207	Ethylnarceine hydrochloride
973	198–207	*p*-Aminophenylacetic acid
974	195–208	Cinchonidine sulfate
975	200–208	*p*-Nitrobenzhydrazide
976	200–208	5-Butylbarbituric acid
977	202–208	Phenylglycine-*o*-carboxylic acid
978	203–208	Adrenaline (suprarenine)
979	204–208	Aspidospermine
980	205–208	Quinine tartrate
981	204–208	β-Resorcylic acid (2,4-dihydroxybenzoic acid)
982	208	*N,N*-Diethyl-*N'*-acetylurea
983	208	9,10-Dihydronaphthacene
984	208	Borneol
985	208	2,3-Benzdiphenyleneoxide (2,3,5,6-dibenzocoumarone)
986	209	Phthalanil
987	190–210	2,4,6-Trinitrobenzoic acid
988	190–210	Camphoric acid imide
989	200–210	*dl*-Tartaric acid
990	210	Oxamic acid
991	210	5-Benzyl-5-propylbarbituric acid
992	210–211	*N*-Methylglycine (sarcosine)

TABLE II (*Continued*)

Code number	Melting point, °C	Compound
993	210–211	Phenanthraquinone
994	210–212	Dicyandiamide
995	200–212	Hordenine sulfate
996	212	2,3-Benzofluorene
997	212	1,1,2,2-Tetraphenylethane
998	212	Coniine hydrobromide
999	210–213	Potassium xanthate
1000	213	5-Isopropylbarbituric acid
1001	213	2-Phenylquinoline-4-carboxylic acid (atophane)
1002	207–214	Vitamin B_6 (pyridoxin hydrochloride; 2-methyl 3-hydroxy-4,5-di(hydroxymethyl)-pyridine hydrochloride
1003	214	*p*-Hydroxybenzoic acid
1004	214	Guanidine nitrate
1005	215	1,3,8-Trinitronaphthalene
1006	180–215	Quinine dihydrochloride
1007	190–215	Caffeic acid (3,4-dihydroxycinnamic acid)
1008	205–215	Emetine hydrochloride
1009	206–215	*trans*-4-Coumarinic acid (*trans*-4-hydroxycinnamic acid)
1010	215	Isoborneol
1011	215	Diacetyl tetrabromopyrocatechin
1012	215	Anthracene
1013	206–216	Lactose
1014	195–216	Dibenzylsuccinate hydrochloride (spasmine hydrochloride)
1015	216	N^4-Ethylsulfanilamide
1016	215–217	Homatropine hydrobromide
1017	217	S-Piperidino-5-ethylbarbituric acid (Eldoral)
1018	208–218	Cinchonine hydrochloride
1019	215–218	Coniine hydrochloride
1020	218	Cantharidine
1021	218	*p*-Bromobenzoic anhydride
1022	219	Quinine sulfate
1023	200–220	*l*-Proline
1024	205–220	*p*-Aminosalicylic acid hydrochloride
1025	216–220	*o*-Aminobenzaldehyde phenylhydrazone
1026	215–220	2,6-Dihydroxynaphthalene
1027	205–220	1,3,5-Trihydroxybenzene (phloroglucinol)
1028	210–220	Psicaine (new)
1029	218–220	Phthalamide
1030	215–220	Papaverine hydrochloride
1031	215–220	*trans*-Coumarinic acid (*trans*-2-hydroxycinnamic acid)

(*Continued*)

TABLE II (*Continued*)

Code number	Melting point, °C	Compound
1032	215–220	3,4-Dimethylbenzoyl-*p*-aminobenzenesulfonamide
1033	217–220	4-Nitro-2-acetaminobenzoic acid
1034	220	5-Phenyl-quinaldine-4-carboxylic acid
1035	220	Diphenylmaleic imide
1036	220	Ephedrine hydrochloride
1037	220	Pentachlorotoluene
1038	220	1-Acetylaminoanthraquinone
1039	215–221	Piperic acid
1040	dec. 200	*p*-Bromobenzoic acid
1041	220–222	*o*-Phthalic acid
1042	222	3-Hydroxy-2-naphthoic acid
1043	224	5-Sulfosalicylic acid
1044	220–224	Conteben
1045	224	Diethylmalonamide
1046	213–225	β-Naphthylamine hydrochloride
1047	222–225	*meso*-Inositol
1048	215–225	Yohimbine
1049	215–225	Mucic acid
1050	225	2,4-Diamino-6-phenyl-1,3,5-triazine
1051	226	5-Methyl-5-phenylbarbituric acid (Rutonal)
1052	224–226	Novalgine
1053	225–227	Ergotinine
1054	227	Adipic amide
1055	226–228	5-Amylbarbituric acid
1056	228	*o*-Benzylsulfimide (saccharine)
1057	228	2-[N^4-Acetylsulfanilamino]pyridine
1058	228	2,2'-Dimethoxy-5,5'-dimethyldiphenylsulfone
1059	228	2,2'-Diphenic acid
1060	228	Umbelliferone
1061	228	Hexachlorobenzene
1062	230	Bulbocapnine hydrochloride
1063	225–230	Allantoin
1064	225–230	Homatropine hydrochloride
1065	223–230	2,4-Diaminoazobenzene-4'-sulfonamide (Prontosil)
1066	215–230	Kryptopine
1067	228–230	Atropinebromoethylate
1068	220–230	*d*-Arginine
1069	220–230	Semioxamazide
1070	232	Pentachloroaniline
1071	234	Dehydrocholic acid
1072	200–235	Hydrastinine hydrochloride
1073	235	Phthalimide
1074	235	*N*-[4-Acetaminobenzenesulfonyl]-*p*-phenylenediamine

TABLE II (*Continued*)

Code number	Melting point, °C	Compound
1075	220–235	Codeine phosphate
1076	236	Caffeine
1077	237	Pyridine-β-carboxylic acid (nicotinic acid)
1078	232–237	Vitamin B_1 (Aneurin hydrochloride)
1079	237	3-[4-Acetaminobenzenesulfamino]benzonitrile
1080	238	Dimethylglyoxime
1081	238–240	Apoatropine hydrochloride
1082	236–240	Sulfamethyldiazine (sulfamerazine)
1083	241	*p*-Nitrobenzoic acid
1084	238–242	Uroxin (alloxantin)
1085	242	α-Benzildioxime
1086	243	*p*-Chlorobenzoic acid
1087	240–244	Hydrazine sulfate
1088	220–244	Brucine nitrate
1089	244	Sulfamethylthiazole
1090	230–245	Rivanol
1091	240–245	Digitonin
1092	245	Diphenylimide (carbazole)
1093	245	Optochin hydrochloride
1094	246	α,β-Bis-diphenylenethane (difluorenyl)
1095	240–246	Diacetyldioxyphenylisatin
1096	246	Tetrahydro-β-naphthylamine hydrochloride
1097	247	*p,p'*-Dihydroxydiphenylsulfone
1098	247	*N,N'*-Diphenylurea (carbanilide)
1099	240–248	Parabanic acid
1100	248	2-[*N*-Phenyl-*N*-benzylaminomethyl]imidazoline hydrochloride (Antistin)
1101	249	α-Diphenylglyoxime
1102	240–250	α-Naphthylamine hydrochloride
1103	250	Hexamethylenetetramine
1104	246–250	2,4,6,2',4',6'-Hexanitrodiphenylamine
1105	240–250	Phenylhydrazine hydrochloride
1106	230–250	Mezcaline sulfate (3,4,5-trimethoxy-β-phenylethylamine sulfate)
1107	253	Thymolphthalein
1108	250–253	4,4'-Dicyandiphenylsulfone
1109	252–254	Malonylurea (barbituric acid)
1110	254	Chrysene
1111	254	Oxanilide
1112	245–255	Marfanil (4-aminomethylbenzene sulfonamide hydrochloride)
1113	245–255	Morphine
1114	250–255	Paracodeine hydrochloride

(*Continued*)

TABLE II (*Continued*)

Code number	Melting point, °C	Compound
1115	255	α-Aminoanthraquinone
1116	250–255	4,4'-Dimethoxydiphenylsulfone-2,2'-dicarboxylic acid
1117	256	Pentaerythritol
1118	257	Tetrachlorophthalic anhydride
1119	247–257	Aminoacetic acid (glycine)
1120	254–257	2-[*p*-Aminobenzenesulfonamino]-pyrimidine
1121	235–260	Eucodal (sulfadiazine)
1122	261	Acenaphthenequinone
1123	262	4,5,7-Trihydroxy-2-methylanthraquinone (Emodin)
1124	257–262	Quinidine hydrochloride
1125	262	*p*-Acetaminobenzoic acid
1126	263	5-Phenylbarbituric acid
1127	263	Phenolphthalein
1128	264	Cinchonine
1129	258–265	3,4,5-Trihydroxybenzoic acid (gallic acid)
1130	about 265	Dibenzylamine hydrochloride
1131	250–265	Benzedrine hydrochloride (amphetamine)
1132	263–266	*p*-Acetylaminobenzenesulfonylguanidine
1133	258–268	Creatine
1134	260–268	Potassium bitartrate
1135	268–270	Succinamide
1136	220–270	Apomorphine hydrochloride
1137	260–270	β-[*p*-Hydroxyphenyl]-α-aminopropionic acid (*l*-tyrosine)
1138	260–270	Codeine hydrochloride
1139	262–272	4-Nitro-2-aminobenzoic acid
1140	262–272	*p*-Dimethylaminobenzylidenerhodanine
1141	274	Theophyllin
1142	270–275	Cinnamoyl-*p*-hydroxyphenylurea
1143	270–275	Perylene
1144	270–275	Strychnine
1145	277	Triphenylimidazole (Lophine)
1146	278	*peri*-Dinaphthalenethiophene
1147	275–278	β-Eucaine
1148	275–280	Berberine sulfate
1149	260–280	Meconic acid
1150	265–280	Yohimbine hydrochloride
1151	280	1,5-Dihydroxyanthraquinone
1152	270–280	2-[4-Hydroxy-3-carboxyphenyl]-quinoline-4-carboxylic acid (Hexophen)
1153	280	Tetrachloroquinone (chloranil)
1154	278–280	Dipropylamine hydrochloride
1155	283	Siaresinolic acid

TABLE II (*Concluded*)

Code number	Melting point, °C	Compound
1156	280–285	Phenylhydrazine-4-sulfonic acid
1157	280–285	*p*-Xylenolphthalein
1158	284–286	Benzoic-*p*-sulfonamide (*p*-sulfamidobenzoic acid)
1159	286	Anthraquinone
1160	286	*p*-Nitrocinnamic acid
1161	280–288	Guanidine sulfate
1162	285–288	Tropacocaine hydrochloride
1163	288	Pyromellitic anhydride
1164	288	Tetraphenylmethane
1165	289	1,2-Dihydroxyanthraquinone (alizarin)
1166	about 290	Fumaric acid
1167	280–290	Vitamin B_2 (lactoflavin)
1168	280–290	α-Amino-β-methylvaleric acid (*l*-isoleucine)
1169	280–290	β-Dextrine
1170	270–290	3′,5′,3″,5″-Tetrabromophenolphthalein
1171	285–293	α-Naphthylamine hydrobromide
1172	293	4,4′-Bis-acetaminodiphenylsulfone
1173	296	2-[*p*-Succinylaminobenzenesulfamino]pyridine (Soranil)
1174	275–295	Strychnine hydrochloride
1175	286–295	6-Methoxyquinoline-4-carboxylic acid (quininic acid)
1176	298	5,5-Diphenylhydantoin
1177	299	*dl*-Valine
1178	285–300	Morphine hydrochloride
1179	290–300	α-Dextrin
1180	260–300	β-Hexachlorocyclohexane
1181	300–310	*d*-Valine
1182	280–310	Strychnine nitrate
1183	313–316	1,2,5,8-Tetrahydroxyanthraquinone (quinalizarine)
1184	300–320	Diisobutylamine hydrobromide
1185	328	Sodium acetate
1186	300–330	Ethylenediamine hydrochloride
1187	325–350	Naphthacene
1188	300–330	Dilaudid hydrochloride
1189	320–340	Theobromine

TABLE III
Eutectic Melting Points with Standard Compounds

Melting point, °C	Code number	Melting point, °C	Code number
	Benzene		β-Naphthol ethyl ether
−18	1	−3	1
−16	2	+3	2
−4	3	8	3

Azobenzene

Melting point, °C	Code number	Melting point, °C	Code number
Liquid	8,36,46,95,122		199,223,231,299
12	12	43	79,84,100,143,152,163,173,
13	4		198,227,247,296
15	21	44	87,93,151,172,188,249,256,
16	6,10		267,283,294
18	5	45	92,96,101,157,187,206,215,
19	7		221,238,246
20	9,14,155	46	82,120,137,193,226,233,239,
21	13		254,268,311
22	11,18	47	121,146,149,154,196,197,210,
23	17,19,66		216,222,236,242,257,273,275,
24	20,80		276,284,288,289,307
25	15,23,27,48	48	170,208,281,286,291
26	16,25,31,32,33,67	49	212,217,230,245,250,259,285
27	57,73	50	90,115,134,174,185,200,205,
28	35,37,45,47,50,52,54,71		219,244,293,297,300
29	53,75,125,156	51	136,160,204,214,234,258,262,
30	39,40,42,68,69,74,85,88,116		298,303
31	22,30,44,65,70,76,81,129	52	142,153,186,189,218,274
32	29,60,61,126,207	53	127,228,232,237,260
33	28,56,83,91,94,114,131,150,	54	209,265,295,315,316
	305	55	128,164,168,224,235,252,306
34	24,49,64,97,103,104,109,110,	56	171,241,253,266
	112,113,117,123	57	133,165,179,270,290,302
35	38,63,124,280,292	58	255,261,263
36	58,98,107,108,195	59	140,304
37	105,111,147,201,203	60	211,271
38	34,41,43,59,72,77,102,130,132,	61	269,282,310
	141,176,177	62	251,287,309,312
39	26,86,89,119,138,144,159,175,	63	243,248,314
	182,213,240	64	190
40	118,158,167,194	65	264
41	55,99,135,145,161,162,169,	66	180,220,225,229,313
	178,183,192,202,308	67	272,277,278,279,317
42	51,62,78,106,139,181,184,191,	68	166

TABLE III (*Continued*)

Melting point, °C	Code number	Melting point, °C	Code number

Benzil

Liquid	8,36,46,95,122	50	87,90,135,166,183,185,194,
17	5,12		203,232
18	6	51	154,169,188,238
19	23	52	133,134,146,187,198,231,429
20	4	53	158,186,267,268
21		54	196,200,205,257
22	7,9,10	55	128,140,160,174,192,193,202,
23	15		212,215,237,245,247,249
24	80	56	153,197,214,230,233,291
25	14,73	57	115,204,206,217,219,221,224,
26	13,16		244,327
27	11,18,19,27,37	58	216,218,222,236,254,275,281,
28	20,25,56		283,289,292,310
29	31,35,39,68	59	136,209,239,302,308
30	21,65,66	60	142,164,165,189,250,255,261,
31	24,30,33,42,54,116,147		276,299,311
32	32,50,57,109,124	61	223,253,256,258,262,284,339
33	22,48,52,58	62	285,307,401
34	17,40,45,53,70,75,83,131	63	168,228,252,259,266,270,273,
35	47,61,67,69,71,155,156,305		286,288,298,321,323,334,376
36	43,63,64,81,110,195	64	180,226,235,241,260,294,384,
37	29,74,76,89,91,123,125,144		402,407
38	26,49,60,88,94,98,108,130,141	65	171,265,303,346,373,380,397
39	28,34,44,59,72,93,111	66	243,312,365,377,389,394,396,
40	38,85,99,103,113,126,145,148,		414,421
	163,295	67	179,190,251,274,316,332,336,
41	77,79,84,100,137		351,355,361,378,382,404,428
42	41,55,104,105,106,112,114,	68	208,263,271,290,325,350,356,
	129,161,175,181,207		363,405,408,432
43	82,86,96,97,107,117,127,132,	69	306,315,324,345,369
	139	70	242,248,269,342,347,374,422
44	51,143,150,296	71	225,287,359,368,403,433
45	118,120,151,246	72	304,309,326,329,335,341,349,
46	62,101,119,159,162,167,177,		352,362,364,390,393,412,439
	182,297	73	211,220,282,322,383,385,411,
47	152,172,199,201,234,280,300		424
48	121,138,170,173,176,178	74	314,317,330,340,357,417,434
49	78,92,102,149,157,184,191,	75	353,370
	210,213,227,240	76	264,354,388,392,399,419,425,
			445

(*Continued*)

TABLE III (*Continued*)

Benzil (*Continued*)

Melting point, °C	Code number	Melting point, °C	Code number
77	229,348,366,379,427,430,435,	86	395
	440	87	443
78	375,381,400,415	88	367,423
79	371,372,442	89	
80	301,343,344,416	90	360,391
81	277,398,406,413	91	
82	333,338,358,418,426,438	92	279
83	272,278,420,441	93	331,446
84	313,437,444	94	328,337
85	431	95	293

Acetanilide

Melting point, °C	Code number	Melting point, °C	Code number
25	382	74	379,459,494
27	454	75	330,355,397,412,434,483
30	402,413	76	354,357,428,467,510,536,560
32	543	77	360,388,414,462,487,528
33	389	78	358,392,423,445
37	339	79	322,327,334,361,401,422,472,
44	384		474,533,549
46	348,380	80	345,351,404,486,537
47	343,475	81	365,391,430,525,551
50	395,558	82	329,350,396,406,441,463,465,
51	325,393,427		498,507,513
53	400,553	83	359,378,440,470,563
55	326,336,433	84	366,457,458,471,473,511,545
56	444	85	347,363,373,376,385,479,500,
58	323,324,490		505,519,520,527,539,552
59	460,535	86	335,349,368,424,439,464,481,
60	369,371		515
61	340,394	87	356,383,417,443,447,451,540
62	550	88	321,342,344,381,407,432,449,
63	398		476,477,485,502,512
64	496	89	341,418,450,492,503,564
65	353,375	90	346,370,403,431,455,514,546
66	429	91	362,491,493,495,516,531
68	332,506,548	92	374,405,421,438,466,497,522,
69	338,372,530		561
70	399,426,469,499,556	93	364,377,408,437,521,526,559
71	352,461,517,523	94	367,435,448,484,518,524,541
72	333,411	95	390,508
73	331,419,504,566	96	510,532,538

TABLE III (*Continued*)

Melting point, °C	Code number	Melting point, °C	Code number
		Acetanilide (*Continued*)	
97	337,425,452,453,456,480,482, 488,565	97	458,479,551,622
98	442	98	457,464,498,502,511,545,592, 658,722,726
99	489,501	99	465,471,472,477,486,505,533,
100	328,416		563,578,638,706
101	468	100	470,601,708
102	529,544	101	451,485,513,514,525,588,604,
103	478		634,649
104	562	102	450,453,473,500,512,519,539,
105	555		540,567,568,599,610,679
108	446	103	447,629,666,713,741
109	420,554	104	448,449,455,481,492,516,520,
110	509		527,552,587
114	534,542	105	466,488,495,497,584,603,612,
115	415		617,654,698,717
		Phenacetin	
48	454	106	484,493,503,526,531,624
56	475	107	491,508,561,564,576,577,661,
64	558		671,696
69	460	108	480,518,521,570,578,585,594,
71	535,553		620,653,659,681,690,691
72	490	109	456,541,559,572,579,618,627,
75	459,711		639,640,642
76	510	110	476,482,538,586,605,625,630,
79	536		685
81	506	111	522,524,565,646,655,678,700
82	496	112	452,489,501,510,515,532,569,
83	583,609		574,656,665,670,675,718
84	499,550,556	113	607,633,643,650,701,719,738
85	611	114	468,529,596,647,662,668,684,
86	517,523,589		705,712
87	461,494,530	115	555,591,645,657,693,694,715,
88	467,487,699		716
89	483	116	595,635,652,674,680,723,739,
90	469,566,623		740
91	548,590,682	117	573,593,608,615,669,677,695,
92	474,560		703,707,709
93	528	118	478,619,714,724,730
94	463,504,628,632	119	562,602,641,710
95	462,507,537,636,648	120	597,600,614,683,725,735
96	549,580,606,613,631,667		

(*Continued*)

TABLE III (*Continued*)

Melting point, °C	Code number	Melting point, °C	Code number

Phenacetin (*Continued*)

Melting point, °C	Code number	Melting point, °C	Code number
121	571,583,626,676,687	128	554,697,736
122	616,644,660,663,664,673,689,733,734	129	651
		130	542,598
123	637,686,737	131	727,732
124	581,721	133	621,692,731
125	544	134	704
127	509,534,543,688,729	135	546,728

Benzanilide

Melting point, °C	Code number	Melting point, °C	Code number
91	570	129	583,633,656,657,668,678,702,724,738,740,772,789,796
94	787		
104	744	130	576,614,635,641,680,684,690,694,741,813
105	622,636		
106	601,667,795	131	608,681,725,745,776,788,791,844
107	575,743		
108	582,763	132	593,597,660,676,677,705,715,735,775,778,807,823
109	611,711,747		
110	609,665	133	581,616,650,652,655,707,716,733,739,785,797,804,809,832
111	589,613,638,649		
112		134	626,643,644,664,687,689,693,703,710,748,760,811
113	580,852		
114	588	135	586,600,673,720,734,757,783,825,849
115	603,623,629,632,696,700,713		
116	605,654,708,769	136	714,723,750,766,816,826,841,857
117	568,590,631,661,717		
118	569,604,634,759,856	137	683,721,762,779,822,830,834
119	574	138	691,737,761,802,810,812,862
120	584,617,674,698,726,781,794	139	753,754,837
121	577,587,591,640,645,675,682,831,840	140	598,637,679,749,768,819,821,848,851,858
122	592,595,607,624,628,648,662,699,752,773,798	141	647,651,751,803,805,827,836,846
123	567,578,579,596,618,620,625,630,701	142	663,746,771,777,790,801,829,833
124	594,606,610,612,619,627,653,658	143	730,774,784,843
125	706,719,764	144	729,818,835
126	573,599,642,646,666,669,685,718,770	145	621,838,850,863,867
127	585,615,671,695,722,756,800	146	659,697,792,824,845,855
128	571,572,602,639,670,709,755	147	736,847
		148	688

TABLE III (*Continued*)

Melting point, °C	Code number	Melting point, °C	Code number

Benzanilide (*Continued*)

Melting point, °C	Code number	Melting point, °C	Code number
149	854	157	820
150	686,799,861	158	704,732,758,808,866
152	765,853,859	159	727,869
153	728,782,815	160	814,839,842
154	767,860	161	731
155	817	162	780,865
156	692,793,864	163	712,870

Salophen

Melting point, °C	Code number	Melting point, °C	Code number
95	918,963	152	776,805,807,823,834,889,894,
115	763		1006,1008
119	743,756,787,901	153	749,760,768,779,789,826,935
120	744	154	747,762,767,825.832,984,998,
122	757		1028
124	795	155	761,790,816,849,862,885,947,
125	898		1019,1021,1026
126	794,1043	156	751,771,777,819,835,836,900,
127	857		925,929,946,961,964,1003,
128	1072		1017,1113
129	895	157	746,803,810,812,822,843,847,
130	769		956,972,1088
131	781	158	786,821,829,846,848,858,887,
132	765,798,886,1018		917,962,1083
133	852,882	159	774,801,845,913,993,1027,
134	759		1033
135	752,881	160	784,867,877,891,902,915,921,
137	856		948,981,1042,1052,1060,1117
139	764	161	758,833,838,850,861,879,909,
140	770		914,940,965
141	748,755	162	792,799,827,873,906,922,951,
142	970		966,1093,1154
143	773,802,804,987	163	817,818,859,874,905,910,914,
144	796,949,999		1005,1076,1106
145	778,797,813,841,988	164	793,863,952,959,976,986,1068,
146	750,754,775,809,904,1138		1097,1184
147	745,840,907,1121	165	782,896,957,973,978,979,1009,
148	788,811,844,1010		1030,1056,1114
149	772,785,800,871,883,950	166	780,936,954,958,975,1067,
150	791,830,837,880,968		1070
151	766,783,1023	167	854,855,926,927,930,944,955.

(*Continued*)

TABLE III (*Continued*)

Melting point, °C	Code number	Melting point, °C	Code number

Salophen (*Continued*)

Melting point, °C	Code number	Melting point, °C	Code number
	1031,1059,1081	179	1015,1047,1061,1080,1156,
168	808,853,890,892,903,919,938,		1161,1165,1171
	945,1007,1014,1034,1162,	180	831,960,990,1053,1065,1077,
	1174		1079,1096,1099,1101,1102,
169	824,872,876,888,897,911,967,		1128,1136,1141,1144,1146,
	991,1011,1064,1100,1142		1148,1151
170	814,815,866,920,923,928,971,	181	989,1045,1089,1125,1163,
	1024,1071,1073,1090		1170,1180
171	924,977,1001,1035,1041,1104,	182	842,899,1153,1160,1166,1175,
	1149		1176,1177,1185
172	933,939,943,985,1016,1039	183	851,875,1002,1004,1054,1057,
173	870,893,937,953,969,1000,		1150,1159,1164,1168
	1020,1032,1086,1118	184	1074,1078,1095,1110,1112,
174	839,865,869,931,983,1046,		1116,1120,1137,1158
	1066,1082,1107,1123,1127	185	868,1091,1105,1108,1111,
175	820,860,980,982,994,996,1012,		1140,1145,1157,1181,1188,
	1025,1040,1048,1050,1051,		1189
	1092,1130,1182	186	942,1069,1075,1094,1126,
176	997,1036,1038,1055,1058,		1173,1178,1187
	1103,1115,1124	187	934,1013,1044,1084,1109,
177	864,941,995,1022,1029,1037,		1132,1172
	1062,1098,1122,1139,1147	188	1133,1134,1155,1179,1183
178	878,974,992,1085,1129	189	1063,1152,1167

Dicyandiamide

Melting point, °C	Code number	Melting point, °C	Code number
90	963	128	1067
92	918	130	948,1008,1088,1106
95	1072	131	895,1114
100	889	132	915,999
101	935	133	899,911,970,1188
103	1151	134	998,1171
105	904,1023	135	987,989,1028
106	898,953	136	992
114	1024,1154	138	885,1033
119	1018	139	1087,1148
121	1138	140	893,1052
122	1006,1019	141	875,933,990,1105,1162
123	919	142	972,1078
125	929	143	1046
126	964	144	1075
127	1064,1124	145	1041,1102

TABLE III (*Continued*)

Melting point, °C	Code number	Melting point, °C	Code number

Dicyandiamide (*Continued*)

Melting point, °C	Code number	Melting point, °C	Code number
146	962	180	879,890,957,978,1060,1104, 1139,1185
147	1016,1081,1093	181	1029,1037,1129,1161
148	946,1011,1059,1121	182	993,1032,1073,1141
149	977	183	1021,1051,1125,1158
150	950,1036,1077	184	1040,1069,1116,1118
151	981,1002,1100,1112	185	894,1010,1089,1126
152	1004,1009,1166	186	878,882,892,896,897,974, 1057,1135,1168
153	913,973,1042	187	965,1063,1080
154	907,1003,1184	188	923,945,991,1085,1177
155	947,976,1083	189	982,1017,1119
156	936,1027	190	891,971,1091,1101,1181
158	872,932	191	902,1074,1133,1167,1169
159	903,995,1007,1031	192	906,1095,1132
160	880,937,951,1043,1096,1174, 1182	193	954,1044,1065,1086,1122, 1150,1160
161	956,1056	194	1134
162	909,958,1014,1090	195	928,968,1053,1079,1153
163	877,881,930,1013,1156	196	924,939,955,1020,1048,1108, 1137,1173,1175
164	949,975	197	920,931,983,1005,1189
165	873,925,959,967	198	1022,1120,1179
166	988,1130	199	
167	912,943,1026,1068,1136,1186	200	986,1035,1127,1165
168	914,921,940,941,980	201	942,1038,1098,1123,1144
169	871,934,961,1039,1147	202	1050,1066,1149
170	876,901,960	203	979,1164,1176
171	1049,1054,1131	204	1058,1084,1092,1107,1140, 1172
172	874,917,926,952,1152	205	969,996,1012,1109,1110,1187
173	883,888,1047,1062,1076	206	997,1025,1111,1128,1145, 1146,1159
174	922,938,1015,1030,1071,1113, 1117	207	985,1115,1170,1183
175	927,1000,1001,1103,1142, 1163,1178	208	1070,1094,1099,1157,1180
176	884,910,1034	209	1155
177	886,900,905,1045,1097	210	994,1143
178	966		
179	887,916,944,1055,1082		

(*Continued*)

TABLE III (*Concluded*)

Melting point, °C	Code number	Melting point, °C	Code number
		Phenolphthalein	
138	1154	228	1131,1135,1153
142	1185	229	1163
155	1106	230	1105,1145
162	1100	231	1111
165	1138,1162	232	1126,1139,1160,1188
175	1128	233	1118
180	1121	234	1123,1125
185	1093	235	1099,1104
186	1142	236	1101,1178
188	1090,1117	237	1110
190	1084,1124,1130,1174,1184	238	1094,1129,1159
192	1088	239	1085
193	1103	240	1109,1175
194	1147	242	1165
205	1148	244	1157,1186
208	1144,1182	245	1119,1137,1149,1189
210	1102	246	1140,1143,1150,1151,1158
212	1133,1136	248	1167,1168,1170,1177
214	1098	249	1180
216	1089	250	1166
217	1122	252	1146,1181
218	1097	255	1113,1152
220	1087	256	1161,1164
222	1083,1091,1092,1115,1141	257	1187
225	1086,1107,1108,1112,1155,	258	1179,1183
	1156,1171	260	1134,1169
227	1120		

TABLE IV
Refractive Indices and Temperature Coefficients of Index for Melts

Compounds with Refractive Indices Less than 1.4339
at Their Melting Point

55	228	431	550	861
90	269	447	572	897
134	272	481	643	938
135	282	482	657	982
146	348	489	683	984
160	395	508	705	988
204	398	531	786	1020
225	423	532	787	1080

Temperatures at Which Melt Has Same Refractive Indices
as Glass Standard 1.4339

Temperature, °C	$\Delta n/\Delta T \times 10^4$	Code number	Temperature, °C	$\Delta n/\Delta T \times 10^4$	Code number
40–41	—	24	118–119	—	371
45	—	28	135–140	—	305
53	—	87	69–70	—	115
55–56	—	137	69–70	—	179
57	—	78	73	—	171
58	—	229	77	—	211
62	—	142	80–90	—	26
65	—	136	86–90	—	277
68–70	—	62	87–88	—	29
88–90	—	41	144–145	4.3	358
94–96	—	92	150–151	3.4	278
95–98	—	153	152–153	5.6	353
98–100	—	313	179–181	—	721
101–103	—	190	200–204	3.1	491
105–108	4.1	82	207–209	—	877
106–107	—	338	220–225	—	948

Compounds with Refractive Indices between 1.4339 and 1.4584
at Their Melting Points

34	452	691	804	1054
443	522	736	1045	1055

(*Continued*)

TABLE IV (*Continued*)

Temperatures at Which Melt Has Same Refractive Indices
as Glass Standard 1.4584

Temperature, °C	$\Delta n/\Delta T \times 10^4$	Code number	Temperature, °C	$\Delta n/\Delta T \times 10^4$	Code number
46–48	4.1	82	143–144	—	656
62–63	—	95	144	4.7	670
69	—	220	153	6.2	486
76–77	—	189	153–155	—	618
77–78	3.4	278	154–156	4.7	454
78–80	—	155	155–157	2.9	413
88	4.3	358	161–162	4.0	500
90	4.1	122	164–165	4.3	594
99	4.1	58	165–168	4.5	509
106–108	3.2	333	167–168	—	784
108–110	5.6	353	169	4.3	505
110–115	—	499	169–170	2.9	446
114–115	—	520	170–173	—	659
118	—	581	171–173	3.8	416
120–122	3.8	330	179–182	—	1019
122–124	3.1	491	181	4.0	601
131–132	—	564	182–184	—	874
134–136	—	473	196–198	—	807
135	—	451	197–198	—	860
140–142	3.4	262	219	—	967

Compounds with Refractive Indices between 1.4584 and 1.4683
at Their Melting Points

892   911   976   1004

TABLE IV (*Continued*)

Temperatures at Which Melt Has Same Refractive Indices
as Glass Standard 1.4683

Temperature, °C	$\Delta n/\Delta T \times 10^4$	Code number	Temperature, °C	$\Delta n/\Delta T \times 10^4$	Code number
60–63	—	133	144–147	3.8	416
67	4.1	122	146	4.3	505
75	4.1	58	146–147	—	548
75–76	3.2	333	148–150	—	747
94–95	3.8	330	148–151	—	573
99	4.4	157	156	—	544
103–105	3.6	212	156	4.0	601
108–110	5.3	226	162	4.2	420
112	3.4	262	165–167	—	646
121–123	2.9	413	167–168	3.8	583
133–134	4.7	454	175–178	—	693
135–136	2.9	446	175–180	—	729
135–138	—	580	190–195	—	934
136–137	6.2	486	191–192	—	664
136–138	4.0	500	215	—	945
139–140	4.3	488	221	—	998
140–143	4.3	594	228	—	991
144–146	4.7	388	239	3.1	865
144–146	4.5	509			

Compounds with Refractive Indices between 1.4683 and 1.4840
at Their Melting Points

100   530   850   1041

(*Continued*)

TABLE IV (*Continued*)

Temperatures at Which Melt Has Same Refractive Indices
as Glass Standard 1.4840

Temperature, °C	$\Delta n/\Delta T \times 10^4$	Code number	Temperature, °C	$\Delta n/\Delta T \times 10^4$	Code number
51–54	—	120	134–136	—	578
58–62	3.6	212	145–146	2.9	328
63	4.4	157	145–147	—	616
78–80	5.3	226	146–148	—	555
91–93	3.1	110	153–155	4.5	541
96–98	3.8	213	155–156	3.1	528
102–104	4.3	488	155–160	—	992
109–112	—	561	158–162	—	777
110–111	4.7	388	177–179	4.0	629
113–114	4.7	289	182–185	—	732
116–118	—	474	187	3.2	762
117–119	—	450	187	—	832
123–124	3.1	344	188	3.1	865
124	4.2	420	190	2.8	731
124–126	—	438	200–202	4.1	876
125–126	3.8	583	201–203	3.8	774
125–130	—	639	204–205	—	1017
126–127	4.1	290	206–208	—	859
130–131	5.1	323	210–213	3.6	971
134–136	—	539			

Compounds with Refractive Indices between 1.4840 and 1.4936
at Their Melting Points

551	743	899	1023	1049
713	802	953	1028	1071

TABLE IV (*Continued*)

Temperatures at Which Melt Has Same Refractive Indices as
Glass Standard 1.4936

Temperature, °C	$\Delta n/\Delta T \times 10^4$	Code number	Temperature, °C	$\Delta n/\Delta T \times 10^4$	Code number
50–60	—	77	153–154	—	704
60–63	3.1	110	156–157	2.8	731
69–71	4.8	21	156–158	3.6	596
71–72	3.8	213	157–159	3.2	762
82–84	4.9	104	158–162	—	727
86–87	8.4	263	165–166	3.0	651
93–94	3.1	344	166–168	3.2	606
93–95	4.7	289	167	3.8	715
95	3.4	208	170–172	4.8	608
97–98	4.9	209	175–177	—	622
103–104	4.1	290	176–177	3.8	695
110–112	4.3	217	176–178	3.8	774
111–112	2.9	328	177–178	4.1	876
113	5.1	323	182–183	1.8	708
121–123	3.6	307	182–185	3.6	971
121–123	—	404	188	3.3	673
125–126	—	466	189–191	3.2	766
125–126	3.1	528	193–194	3.8	773
129–131	4.2	368	193–195	2.4	716
129–131	4.5	552	195–196	3.9	816
133	4.5	541	197–198	3.7	829
137–139	4.0	364	217–220	4.7	670
139–141	4.0	629	233–236	2.8	935
144–146	3.4	554	240–241	—	1077
148–149	4.6	467	263–264	—	1076
150–152	2.7	598	275–278	—	1040

Compound with Refractive Indices between 1.4936 and 1.5000

at its Melting Point

823

(*Continued*)

TABLE IV (*Continued*)

Temperatures at Which Melt Has Same Refractive Indices
as Glass Standard 1.5000

Temperature, °C	$\Delta n/\Delta T \times 10^4$	Code number	Temperature, °C	$\Delta n/\Delta T \times 10^4$	Code number
53–54	—	48	150	3.8	715
65–70	—	989	151–152	3.7	379
67–69	4.4	65	153–155	5.1	525
69–71	4.9	104	156	4.4	441
70–71	4.4	69	156–157	4.6	546
72–73	4.6	81	157–159	4.8	608
76	3.4	208	159–160	3.8	695
95–96	4.3	217	166–167	—	700
96–97	4.8	174	167	2.9	518
84–86	4.9	209	167	3.7	519
102–104	4.2	121	167	2.4	716
103–105	3.9	175	167–168	4.2	640
103–105	3.6	307	169	3.3	673
109–110	5.9	271	170	3.2	766
114–115	5.3	326	172–174	3.3	626
114–116	4.2	368	176–177	3.8	773
116–117	4.4	469	179–180	4.6	694
121–123	4.0	364	179–181	3.9	816
122–123	4.2	304	180–182	3.7	829
124–128	3.4	554	184–186	—	769
125	—	403	188–190	—	809
127	2.7	598	189	5.1	757
128–130	5.3	412	191–192	4.4	641
130	5.6	298	192–194	2.9	778
134–135	4.6	467	195–197	—	797
134–136	4.4	418	197–199	—	843
135–137	3.7	337	200–225	—	961
136–137	5.3	354	205	5.4	925
136–137	4.6	448	205–208	3.0	870
137–138	4.0	414	210–211	4.4	890
138–140	3.6	596	210–211	—	930
139–140	4.6	419	211–213	2.8	935
145	3.0	651	219–221	3.7	767
146–148	3.2	606	231–233	3.6	927
147–148	1.8	708	240–241	4.8	1058

Compounds with Refractive Indices between 1.5000 and 1.5101
at Their Melting Points

628   722   808   858   905   1013

TABLE IV (*Continued*)

Temperatures at Which Melt Has Same Refractive Indices as Glass
Standard 1.5101

Temperature, °C	$\Delta n/\Delta T \times 10^4$	Code number	Temperature, °C	$\Delta n/\Delta T \times 10^4$	Code number
44–45	4.4	65	116–117	4.3	322
47–48	4.4	69	117–118	5.3	354
50–51	4.6	81	117–118	4.6	419
53–54	—	60	118–120	—	437
63	5.2	22	123–125	—	394
65–66	4.5	71	124–126	3.7	379
71–72	8.6	25	130–133	4.7	260
74–76	4.5	99	132	2.9	518
75–76	4.8	174	132–133	4.4	441
77–78	3.9	175	134–135	4.6	546
78–79	4.2	121	136–139	—	534
78–80	5.3	210	137–138	3.1	444
79–80	—	145	138–140	5.1	525
79–81	4.4	52	139–141	4.9	222
80	3.1	129	140	3.7	519
82–83	4.1	63	142	3.3	626
88–91	—	279	142–145	2.9	621
88–91	4.7	131	143–144	4.2	640
90–95	—	164	146–148	3.2	714
92–94	5.9	271	151	—	687
93–95	4.3	86	151–152	3.6	570
93–95	—	287	152–154	3.4	504
94	4.4	469	153–154	6.4	483
95–96	4.1	154	156–158	4.3	494
96	5.3	326	157	—	560
96–98	3.7	49	157–159	4.6	694
97–98	3.9	139	157–159	2.9	778
97–98	4.1	203	159–160	4.3	422
98–100	—	264	161–163	—	471
98–100	4.2	304	161–163	2.9	649
107–109	—	241	162–164	—	648
108–110	3.7	337	163–164	4.3	577
109–110	4.3	412	165–168	—	755
110–111	4.5	248	166–169	4.9	566
110–112	4.0	414	168–169	4.4	641
111–112	5.6	298	168–170	5.1	757
111–112	4.4	418	171	—	407
114–115	4.6	448	171–173	3.7	563
114–118	—	366	172–174	3.0	870

(*Continued*)

TABLE IV (*Continued*)

Temperatures at Which Melt Has Same Refractive Indices as Glass
Standard 1.5101 (*Continued*)

Temperature, °C	$\Delta n/\Delta T \times 10^4$	Code number	Temperature, °C	$\Delta n/\Delta T \times 10^4$	Code number
173–174	—	810	192–194	3.7	767
173–175	4.7	625	194–196	3.4	593
174–176	—	609	198	—	949
175–177	5.2	682	200	—	875
177–178	5.2	733	203–205	3.7	663
185–186	3.4	661	203–205	3.6	927
185–186	5.4	925	212–214	2.6	835
185–187	5.2	688	214–217	2.6	873
186–188	—	775	219–221	4.8	1058
187–188	4.4	890	233–235	3.1	937
187–189	—	789	258–259	4.1	1051
189–192	3.8	671	275	3.3	1056

Compounds with Refractive Indices between 1.5101 and 1.5204
at Their Melting Points

869	889	946	987	1069
885	904	979	1064	

Temperatures at Which Melt Has Same Refractive Indices as Glass
Standard 1.5204

42–43	4.5	71	77–78	3.5	54
43	5.2	22	83	5.0	75
47	3.1	129	87–88	4.5	248
51–52	4.5	99	88–89	4.5	98
55–56	4.5	33	92–93	4.3	322
56–57	4.4	52	92–93	4.0	230
57–58	4.1	63	93–94	3.5	214
62–64	4.4	5	93–94	—	283
67–68	4.7	131	99–100	4.1	165
68–70	3.7	49	99–100	4.5	219
69–70	4.3	86	101–102	3.5	159
69–72	4.5	85	103	4.0	186
70–71	—	93	103–105	4.3	193
70–71	4.1	154	103–106	3.1	444
71–72	3.9	139	105–106	4.8	233
73	4.1	203	105–107	4.5	168
76–77	—	119	109–110	3.2	202

TABLE IV (*Continued*)

Temperatures at Which Melt Has Same Refractive Indices as Glass
Standard 1.5204 (*Continued*)

Temperature, °C	$\Delta n/\Delta T \times 10^4$	Code number	Temperature, °C	$\Delta n/\Delta T \times 10^4$	Code number
106–110	4.7	260	163–165	3.8	671
114–116	3.2	714	164–166	3.4	593
117–119	8.6	147	165–167	5.2	688
118–120	4.9	222	166–168	2.6	542
122–123	3.4	504	170	3.3	660
122–123	3.6	570	172–174	2.7	627
123–125	5.0	343	173–175	2.6	835
125–128	4.7	439	175–177	3.7	663
126–128	2.9	649	175–178	—	723
127–128	—	365	178–180	2.6	873
132–133	4.3	494	179–180	2.4	796
133–135	2.5	852	181–182	—	768
135–136	4.3	422	182–184	—	839
136–137	3.5	415	197–198	—	764
136–138	6.4	483	197–199	4.1	666
137–140	4.5	515	199–202	3.1	937
139–140	3.8	455	208–210	4.3	822
139–140	4.3	577	209–211	4.0	916
143–145	3.7	563	212–216	—	995
146–148	4.9	566	218–221	—	1047
151–153	4.7	625	221–222	—	966
155–156	3.4	661	222–224	3.8	923
155–157	5.2	682	228–230	4.4	968
157–159	5.2	733	234	4.1	1051
158–159	2.9	543	242–244	—	1073
162–164	3.8	462	244	3.3	1056
162–164	4.1	521			

Compounds with Refractive Indices between 1.5204 and 1.5299
at Their Melting Points

794   963   1037

(*Continued*)

TABLE IV (*Continued*)

Temperatures at Which Melt Has Same Refractive Indices
as Glass Standard 1.5299

Temperature, °C	$\Delta n / \Delta T \times 10^4$	Code number	Temperature, °C	$\Delta n / \Delta T \times 10^4$	Code number
34–35	4.5	33	118–119	4.1	329
41	4.4	5	120	4.3	251
48–49	8.6	25	125–127	6.1	258
49–51	4.5	85	125–126	5.8	433
50–52	6.9	4	125–126	—	437
51	3.5	54	125–127	2.9	543
60–65	—	111	126–127	5.0	341
64	5.0	75	128–129	6.5	339
67	3.5	214	129	5.2	424
67–68	4.5	98	129–131	2.6	542
68–69	4.0	230	132–133	5.5	363
70–73	4.0	89	134–136	4.2	335
74–75	3.5	159	137–138	3.8	462
76–77	4.1	165	137–139	4.5	476
77–78	—	162	138–139	6.1	350
78–79	4.5	219	138–140	5.2	369
79	4.0	186	139–140	4.1	521
79–81	3.2	202	139–140	2.4	796
80–82	4.5	66	141	3.3	660
81–82	4.3	193	142	—	512
82–84	2.2	23	143	—	527
84–86	4.5	168	144–146	5.0	445
85–87	4.8	233	150–151	—	654
88–89	4.5	151	152–153	4.3	498
96–98	2.5	852	157–158	5.5	582
98–99	5.0	114	157–159	4.7	607
101–103	6.1	205	158	4.7	565
105	5.0	343	174–176	4.1	666
106–108	8.6	147	176–179	3.9	779
107–109	3.8	306	177–179	5.0	623
108–110	4.7	243	181–183	4.5	690
109–111	3.5	415	185–188	—	737
111–112	3.6	352	186	4.0	916
114–115	4.7	169	186–187	4.3	822
114–116	3.8	455	192–194	—	915
115–116	4.3	270	194–196	5.5	669
116–117	4.7	336	196–198	3.7	936
118	4.5	515	197	5.5	740

TABLE IV (*Continued*)

Temperature at Which Melt Has Same Refractive Indices as Glass Standard 1.5299 (*Continued*)

Temperature, °C	$\Delta n/\Delta T \times 10^4$	Code number	Temperature, °C	$\Delta n/\Delta T \times 10^4$	Code number
198	3.8	923	220–223	—	1003
207	4.4	968	234–235	4.3	952
212–213	3.5	929	237–240	5.2	997
213	4.7	917	250–255	—	1061
218–220	—	824			

Compounds with Refractive Indices between 1.5299 and 1.5403 at Their Melting Points

382   812   941   947   1031   1081

Temperatures at Which Melt Has Same Refractive Indices as Glass Standard 1.5403

Temp	$\Delta n/\Delta T$	Code	Temp	$\Delta n/\Delta T$	Code
28–30	5.2	1	93–94	4.1	329
35–36	2.2	23	94–95	4.7	336
35–37	6.9	4	95–97	4.3	251
44–47	4.0	89	98–100	4.7	112
57–58	4.5	66	101–102	4.5	173
60	4.3	17	101–103	5.0	240
65–66	5.2	9	105–106	—	273
65–66	5.2	37	105–107	3.8	132
65–66	4.0	46	105–107	5.0	341
65–66	4.5	151	106–108	4.7	182
71–72	—	152	107–108	5.8	433
73–74	4.1	124	108–109	6.1	258
76–78	5.2	42	108–109	5.2	424
77–79	5.0	114	109–110	4.2	335
79–81	4.3	161	112–114	6.5	339
80–82	4.5	118	113–115	5.5	363
81–83	4.0	36	114–115	4.1	249
83	3.6	352	114–116	4.5	476
84	5.0	150	115–116	4.7	267
84–86	6.1	205	117–120	5.2	369
85–89	4.7	243	119	5.0	266
87–88	4.5	188	120–122	3.4	427
90–92	4.1	216	122	6.1	350
92	4.3	270	122–123	3.7	367
92–93	4.7	169	123–124	5.0	445

(*Continued*)

TABLE IV (*Continued*)

Temperatures at Which Melt Has Same Refractive Indices
as Glass Standard 1.5403 (*Continued*)

Temperature, °C	$\Delta n/\Delta T \times 10^4$	Code number	Temperature, °C	$\Delta n/\Delta T \times 10^4$	Code number
124	3.3	391	172–173	4.7	568
125–127	4.3	259	172–173	—	838
129	4.3	498	175–177	5.5	669
131–132	3.3	314	177–179	5.5	740
134–135	4.3	294	178–180	—	824
134–137	4.7	607	182–183	4.7	738
136	4.7	565	182–189	3.3	783
138–139	5.5	582	182–183	3.5	929
139–141	6.2	417	184	—	871
142–146	—	553	185	—	970
145–146	4.7	429	190–192	3.4	912
145–147	4.5	302	191	4.7	917
149–151	3.5	389	194–196	3.4	782
151–152	3.9	779	211	4.3	952
155–157	—	567	212–214	4.1	855
156	3.8	503	215–216	3.7	884
156–157	5.0	623	218–220	5.2	997
158–160	4.5	690	219–221	—	1066
159–160	5.0	495	221–222	4.0	900
159–160	—	624	226–227	4.7	882
161–162	—	569	237	—	1011
161–163	3.5	603	239–241	—	1021
165–169	—	776	241–243	4.0	986
168–169	3.7	936	244–246	3.7	1059
169–170	3.5	605			

Compounds with Refractive Indices between 1.5403 and 1.5502
at Their Melting Points

487	841	896	954	1016	1033	1052
590	866	919	972	1022	1043	1067

TABLE IV (*Continued*)

Temperatures at Which Melt Has Same Refractive Indices as Glass
Standard 1.5502

Temperature, °C	$\Delta n/\Delta T \times 10^4$	Code number	Temperature, °C	$\Delta n/\Delta T \times 10^4$	Code number
9–10	5.2	1	107–110	5.7	181
37	4.3	17	108–110	4.7	253
40	—	32	112	4.3	294
40–41	4.0	46	113–115	—	331
46–47	5.2	9	114–115	4.7	234
47	5.2	37	120–125	—	611
49–50	4.1	124	121–123	3.5	389
51	—	79	123	7.3	347
55–58	4.3	161	123–124	6.2	417
56–58	4.0	36	124	4.5	302
56–58	5.2	42	124–125	4.5	340
58–60	4.5	118	124–125	4.7	429
63–64	5.0	13	125–126	4.2	274
64	5.0	150	126	5.5	303
65–66	4.5	188	127–128	3.9	332
66–68	4.1	216	129	5.2	459
69–70	4.5	61	130	3.8	503
70–71	5.0	106	133–135	3.5	603
73–74	4.7	30	134–135	5.5	375
77–79	4.7	112	136–137	4.2	399
79–80	4.5	173	137–138	4.7	372
80	3.2	132	139–140	4.4	484
81–82	5.0	240	139–140	5.0	495
84–87	4.7	76	139–140	6.1	507
85–86	4.7	182	140–142	5.2	342
89–90	5.0	43	142	3.5	605
90–91	5.0	215	142–143	4.7	492
90–91	4.1	249	144–147	4.4	393
90–92	4.7	102	145–146	4.5	574
91–93	3.4	427	147–148	4.2	406
92	4.7	91	148–150	4.2	435
93–95	3.3	391	149–150	5.2	472
94–95	4.7	267	151–152	4.7	568
96	5.2	218	154–156	3.3	783
96	4.7	227	155–156	4.2	1079
99	5.0	266	156–157	4.7	535
100–102	5.0	183	156–157	5.2	545
101–102	3.3	314	159–162	3.9	526
102–103	4.3	259	161–162	3.6	612

(*Continued*)

TABLE IV (*Continued*)

Temperatures at Which Melt Has Same Refractive Indices as Glass
Standard 1.5502 (*Continued*)

Temperature, °C	$\Delta n/\Delta T \times 10^4$	Code number	Temperature, °C	$\Delta n/\Delta T \times 10^4$	Code number
161–162	4.7	738	192–193	4.5	790
161–162	3.4	912	192–195	3.2	668
165–167	3.4	782	193–194	4.0	821
168–171	4.2	689	193–194	4.5	826
169–171	5.2	584	193–195	4.7	707
172–176	—	918	194–196	—	994
173–175	4.7	602	195–196	3.7	759
174–176	—	728	196–197	4.0	900
175–178	—	785	205–206	4.7	882
176	2.9	610	206–208	—	1015
176–177	5.5	635	210–211	4.5	848
180–181	4.5	604	212–214	—	951
183–187	3.9	771	216–218	4.0	986
186–188	4.2	749	217–219	3.7	1059
188–190	4.1	855	223–224	4.4	939
189	3.7	884	244–246	—	1070

Compounds with Refractive Indices between 1.5502 and 1.5611
at Their Melting Points

50	632	833	974	980	1082
207	718	962	975	1075	

TABLE IV (*Continued*)

Temperatures at Which Melt Has Same Refractive Indices as Glass

Standard 1.5611

Temperature, °C	$\Delta n/\Delta T \times 10^4$	Code number	Temperature, °C	$\Delta n/\Delta T \times 10^4$	Code number
35	4.2	2	106	—	390
41–42	5.0	13	107–109	4.2	148
45–46	4.5	61	107–108	7.3	347
48–49	5.0	106	108	5.2	459
50–51	4.7	30	109	4.9	381
62–63	4.0	8	109–111	3.4	265
62–64	4.0	35	109–112	—	510
62–64	4.7	76	110–112	4.2	399
64–65	4.0	39	113–114	3.3	257
66–67	4.0	19	114	5.2	235
67–68	4.7	102	114	4.9	256
67–68	5.0	43	114–115	4.7	372
68–69	4.2	47	114–115	5.5	375
68–70	4.7	91	114–115	4.4	484
68–70	5.0	215	114–116	4.2	236
72	4.7	80	116–118	4.5	206
72–73	4.7	227	117–118	4.2	293
73–74	—	51	119–121	5.2	342
75	5.2	218	119–121	4.7	492
76–78	4.0	64	120–122	4.4	393
77–78	4.5	44	121	4.2	296
79	5.0	183	121–122	6.1	507
79–81	4.0	59	121–122	4.5	574
80–81	4.0	31	122	4.2	406
80–81	4.7	107	122–124	4.2	435
84–86	4.5	96	123	5.6	346
85	4.9	156	128–130	5.2	472
85–86	4.7	253	129–130	—	576
88–89	4.7	178	130	4.5	359
89–90	5.7	181	130	4.2	1079
91–93	4.7	234	130–132	2.1	586
94	3.9	170	131–132	3.6	612
98–100	4.7	254	131–134	3.9	526
99–100	4.2	274	133	4.0	430
100	3.9	332	133	4.0	351
100–101	4.5	340	133–135	4.7	535
105–108	—	478	136	5.2	545
106	5.5	303	136–138	4.0	374

(*Continued*)

TABLE IV (*Continued*)

Temperatures at Which Melt Has Same Refractive Indices as Glass Standard 1.5611 (*Continued*)

Temperature, °C	$\Delta n/\Delta T \times 10^4$	Code number	Temperature, °C	$\Delta n/\Delta T \times 10^4$	Code number
139	2.9	610	167–169	3.3	571
139–140	4.2	493	168–169	4.5	790
140	5.2	490	169–170	4.5	826
143–145	4.2	689	170–172	4.7	707
147–149	—	650	171–173	—	717
148–149	5.2	584	174–175	4.0	710
150–152	4.7	602	175–178	—	805
150–160	—	814	177–178	4.2	595
156–158	4.5	604	186–188	4.0	630
156–158	5.5	635	186–188	4.5	848
157–158	3.9	771	190–192	4.0	712
159–160	3.9	496	197	3.3	770
159–161	3.2	668	198–199	4.4	939
160–162	4.2	749	214–215	—	931
165–168	4.2	592	215	3.6	844
166–167	3.7	759	217–219	4.5	891
166–168	4.0	821	243–244	2.8	907

Compounds with Refractive Indices between 1.5611 and 1.5700 at Their Melting Points

840   1018   1027   1048   1074

Temperatures at Which Melt Has Same Refractive Indices as Glass Standard 1.5700

Temperature	$\Delta n/\Delta T \times 10^4$	Code number	Temperature	$\Delta n/\Delta T \times 10^4$	Code number
14	4.2	2	61–63	4.7	107
38–40	—	7	64–65	5.0	20
40–42	4.0	35	64–65	4.5	96
41	4.0	8	66–68	4.9	156
42–44	4.0	39	67–68	4.1	16
44–45	4.0	19	69–70	4.7	178
47–49	4 2	47	70–71	3.9	170
53	4.7	80	72–73	5.2	94
54–55	4.0	64	77	4.3	74
57–58	4.5	44	79–80	4.3	84
57–59	4.0	59	79–81	4.7	254
57–60	4.0	31	81–84	—	370
60–61	3.7	101	83–85	4.5	70
60–62	5.3	27	84	3.4	265

TABLE IV (*Continued*)

Temperatures at Which Melt Has Same Refractive Indices
as Glass Standard 1.5700 (*Continued*)

Temperature, °C	$\Delta n/\Delta T \times 10^4$	Code number	Temperature, °C	$\Delta n/\Delta T \times 10^4$	Code number
85–88	4.3	126	140–145	—	681
85–88	3.3	257	142	4.3	426
86–88	4.2	148	145–147	4.2	592
87–88	4.1	194	147–148	4.0	463
87–89	4.5	68	153	4.0	710
88–90	2.1	586	153–155	4.8	470
92–94	4.0	108	154–156	4.8	524
93–94	4.2	236	155–156	4.3	523
94–98	5.2	235	156–157	4.2	595
95–97	—	297	162–163	—	756
96–98	4.5	206	164–166	4.0	630
96–98	4.2	293	164–167	3.5	634
100	4.2	296	168–169	4.0	712
104–106	4.8	232	169–171	3.3	770
107	5.6	346	172–173	3.7	506
109–110	4.5	359	175–177	—	726
110	5.6	276	177–179	4.1	703
110–111	4.8	199	185–188	—	868
110–111	4.0	351	186–187	4.3	926
110–111	4.0	430	189–190	4.8	706
114–115	4.1	238	189–191	4.1	701
114–116	4.0	374	190	3.6	844
118–120	4.2	493	190–191	4.5	763
119–120	—	355	197–199	4.5	891
122–123	8.6	377	198–199	4.5	745
122–123	5.2	490	200–202	5.6	849
127	4.9	381	200–203	3.5	910
134	4.5	361	207–209	3.7	795
135–138	3.9	496	211–212	2.8	907
136	5.0	411	213	5.0	847
136–137	4.5	281	220–221	5.0	955
139–140	3.8	317	228–229	4.0	956
approx.			241	4.5	1035
140	—	533	241–242	3.8	1057
140–141	3.3	571			

Compounds with Refractive Indices between 1.5700 and 1.5795
at Their Melting Points

800	801	1009	1032	1042

(*Continued*)

TABLE IV (*Continued*)

Temperatures at Which Melt Has Same Refractive
Indices as Glass Standard 1.5795

Temperature, °C	$\Delta n/\Delta T \times 10^4$	Code number	Temperature, °C	$\Delta n/\Delta T \times 10^4$	Code number
34–36	3.7	101	133–134	4.3	523
42–44	5.3	27	133–135	4.8	470
44–45	4.1	16	134–136	4.8	524
45–46	5.0	20	137–138	5.1	402
54–55	5.2	94	137–138	3.4	536
55	4.3	74	137–140	3.5	634
57–58	4.3	84	141–144	—	667
62–63	4.5	70	143–144	5.4	380
64–65	4.1	194	146–147	3.7	506
64–66	4.3	126	147–149	2.8	301
66–68	4.8	68	154–156	—	579
67–68	4.7	11	154–156	4.1	703
68–69	6.4	53	159–160	4.9	587
68–70	4.0	108	162–165	—	781
69–70	4.4	18	164–165	4.4	549
76	—	754	165	4.3	926
84	4.3	109	166–167	4.1	701
84–85	—	176	169–170	4.8	706
84–85	4.8	232	169–170	4.5	763
90–91	4.8	199	173–176	3.5	910
91–92	4.1	238	174–176	—	613
92–93	5.6	276	176–177	6.4	685
100–101	4.3	246	177–178	4.5	745
100–101	4.3	252	178–180	3.2	730
100–102	4.6	231	179–181	—	698
101–102	4.6	187	181–182	3.7	795
102–103	4.3	167	183–184	5.6	849
111–112	8.6	377	188–189	4.9	619
113	4.5	361	193	—	851
113–116	4.4	184	194	5.0	847
114–115	3.8	317	195–198	—	836
115–116	4.9	292	197–199	4.1	739
115–117	4.5	281	200–202	3.5	803
116–117	5.0	411	201–203	5.0	955
119–121	4.3	426	204–206	4.0	956
122–125	—	458	216–217	3.8	1057
122–125	4.0	463	220	4.5	1035
125	4.3	255	222–223	3.8	928
125–127	5.1	401	231–233	4.4	887
126–127	4.6	312			

TABLE IV (*Continued*)

Compounds with Refractive Indices between 1.5795 and 1.5897
at Their Melting Points

913   944

Temperatures at Which Melt Has Same Refractive Indices
as Glass Standard 1.5897

Temperature, °C	$\Delta n/\Delta T \times 10^4$	Code number	Temperature, °C	$\Delta n/\Delta T \times 10^4$	Code number
45–46	4.7	11	121–122	5.7	288
46–47	4.4	18	124–125	5.4	380
53	6.4	53	127–129	5.0	316
59	—	10	130–131	4.4	362
60	4.3	109	133	—	408
76–77	4.3	246	135–136	6.3	357
76–78	4.3	252	135–137	3.7	485
77–78	4.8	177	139	4.9	587
78–79	4.3	167	141–142	4.4	549
79	4.6	231	145–146	4.4	461
79–80	4.6	187	146–147	3.2	730
80	2.5	130	155	4.1	383
82–83	5.0	143	159	5.2	517
83	4.8	40	159–160	4.8	460
84–85	5.4	116	160–161	6.4	685
84–85	—	284	160–162	4.8	449
85–86	4.2	45	167–169	4.9	619
90–92	4.8	144	170–172	4.8	540
91–93	4.4	184	170–173	4.6	620
93	5.0	195	171–172	3.5	803
94–95	4.9	292	173–174	4.1	739
97–98	3.9	180	174–176	4.8	696
99–101	5.0	223	177–180	2.9	631
99–102	4.6	149	181–182	—	788
100–101	4.3	255	183–184	—	846
100–105	—	324	185–187	3.1	637
104–105	4.6	312	187–188	3.1	642
105–106	5.1	401	189	—	834
107–109	3.4	536	191–192	4.1	752
108–109	4.2	221	195–196	3.8	928
110–112	2.8	301	207–208	3.8	761
111–112	4.4	198	208–210	4.4	887
111–113	—	295	214–215	5.4	862
112	—	384	220–223	8.8	983
115–118	—	327	227–229	5.2	854
117–119	5.1	402	239	5.0	1005

(*Continued*)

TABLE IV (*Continued*)

Compounds with Refractive Indices between 1.5897 and 1.6011
at Their Melting Points

197   556   1002

Temperatures at Which Melt Has Same Refractive Indices
as Glass Standard 1.6011

Temperature, °C	$\Delta n/\Delta T \times 10^4$	Code number	Temperature, °C	$\Delta n/\Delta T \times 10^4$	Code number
35	2.5	130	136–137	4.8	449
43–44	—	15	137	5.2	517
54	4.8	177	137–140	2.9	631
58–59	4.8	40	139	5.0	480
58–59	4.2	45	143–144	3.6	511
59–61	5.0	143	144–145	4.6	457
63–64	5.4	116	146–147	4.8	540
63–64	—	172	146–148	4.6	620
66–68	4.8	144	148–150	3.1	637
68–69	3.9	180	148–152	—	658
69–70	5.0	195	150–151	3.1	642
71–72	—	125	150–151	4.8	696
75–77	4.6	149	161	—	591
76	5.5	88	163–164	4.1	752
76–77	5.0	223	167	9.6	652
81–83	4.2	221	173	—	798
85–86	4.4	198	177–178	3.8	761
98–100	4.8	138	180–185	—	964
101–102	5.7	288	183–185	—	901
102–106	4.4	362	185–190	—	711
104–105	3.7	485	188–189	—	893
104–106	5.0	316	192–195	5.4	862
105	4.4	247	200–203	3.0	825
112–115	4.8	261	201–202	3.7	888
117–118	6.3	357	205–207	5.2	854
120	4.4	461	206–207	5.7	746
124–126	4.3	285	208–210	8.8	983
127	4.1	383	216	5.0	1005
129–131	5.2	309	223–224	4.3	702
135–136	4.8	460			

TABLE IV *(Continued)*

Compounds with Refractive Indices between 1.6011 and 1.6126
at Their Melting Points

1026   1039

Temperatures at Which Melt Has Same Refractive Indices
as Glass Standard 1.6126

Temperature, °C	$\Delta n/\Delta T \times 10^4$	Code number	Temperature, °C	$\Delta n/\Delta T \times 10^4$	Code number
55	5.5	88	115	—	428
65–66	5.3	6	116	5.0	480
70	—	201	119–120	4.6	457
70–71	5.0	57	127–128	5.0	315
74–75	4.8	138	128–131	5.8	291
79	4.4	247	129–130	5.9	250
82–83	5.5	83	155	9.6	652
82–84	—	196	163–164	3.0	825
87–89	4.6	158	170–171	3.7	888
87–88	5.3	192	170–173	3 1	537
88	5.3	72	171–173	—	872
88–89	6.1	67	172–175	6.2	442
88–91	5.8	127	178–179	3.7	753
89–91	4.8	261	179–181	4.6	645
93–94	4.4	103	179–181	5.0	791
97–98	4.3	285	185–186	5.7	746
105	3.8	140	192–196	—	894
105–108	5.2	309	196–198	4.3	702
107–109	5.0	300	198–202	—	880
108–109	—	440	205–208	—	914
111	—	299	225–228	—	969
111	5.0	268	240–242	4.8	1012
111–113	3.6	511			

(Continued)

TABLE IV (*Continued*)

Compounds with Refractive Indices between 1.6126 and 1.6231
at Their Melting Points

686   895   1038

Temperatures at Which Melt Has Same Refractive Indices
as Glass Standard 1.6231

Temperature, °C	$\Delta n/\Delta T \times 10^4$	Code number	Temperature, °C	$\Delta n/\Delta T \times 10^4$	Code number
46	5.3	6	129	5.5	513
49–50	5.0	57	119–121	5.1	237
63–64	5.5	83	134	5.1	421
64–66	4.6	158	137–139	3.1	537
66–67	5.3	14	139–141	6.1	349
67–68	5.3	72	146–147	5.3	432
67–68	5.3	192	147–148	5.1	397
70	4.4	103	150–151	3.7	753
71–73	6.1	67	151	6.1	456
72	5.8	127	154–158	6.2	442
76–77	3.8	140	155–160	—	653
82–84	—	191	156–158	4.6	645
85–88	7.6	105	160–162	5.1	516
86–87	5.0	300	165–170	—	748
87	6.1	113	172	6.1	662
90	5.0	268	172–174	4.7	615
102–104	4.9	239	179	5.3	497
106–108	5.0	315	184–186	10.2	644
111–113	5.8	291	185–188	—	819
112–114	5.9	250	205–208	—	924
112–114	—	308	206–208	4.7	772
113–114	5.8	185	218–220	4.8	1012
116–118	6.8	286	218–220	—	1034
118	5.8	356	242–244	5.1	1001

Compounds with Refractive Indices between 1.6231 and 1.6353
at Their Melting Points

655   993   1025   1030

TABLE IV (*Continued*)

Temperatures at Which Melt Has Same Refractive Indices
as Glass Standard 1.6353

Temperature, °C	$\Delta n/\Delta T \times 10^4$	Code number	Temperature, °C	$\Delta n/\Delta T \times 10^4$	Code number
43–44	5.3	14	125–126	5.5	396
55–57	4.8	12	125–126	5.1	397
65–75	7.6	105	131	6.1	456
67	6.1	113	135–138	5.1	516
76	5.2	166	140–143	—	589
77–79	4.9	239	142–143	3.7	392
82	—	242	145–148	4.7	615
91–93	4.6	117	152	6.1	662
92–94	5.8	185	156	5.3	497
93–97	5.1	237	172–173	10.2	644
97	5.8	356	180–181	4.7	772
98–99	6.8	286	185	5.4	725
99–100	—	224	196–199	4.1	676
104–105	5.4	280	205–207	4.8	792
110	5.1	421	211–212	—	996
117	—	464	218–219	5.1	1001
119–121	6.1	349	224–226	4.6	830
124	5.3	432	225–228	—	985

Compounds with Refractive Indices between 1.6353 and 1.6483
at Their Melting Points

867   943   965

Temperatures at Which Melt Has Same Refractive Indices
as Glass Standard 1.6483

Temperature, °C	$\Delta n/\Delta T \times 10^4$	Code number	Temperature, °C	$\Delta n/\Delta T \times 10^4$	Code number
28–29	4.8	12	160–162	—	675
51	5.2	166	161	5.4	725
63–64	4.6	117	165–167	4.1	676
81	5.4	280	171–173	4.0	502
106–108	—	475	178–180	4.6	617
107–108	3.7	392	178–180	4.8	792
110–113	—	558	188–189	—	883
124–125	4.4	514	190	—	735
125	4.5	321	190–192	5.0	674
128–129	5.0	345	196–197	4.6	830
131–132	—	434	198	5.2	811
137–138	—	815	211–212	—	799
143–145	—	501	218	—	959
146–147	5.0	373	219–221	4.6	853

(*Continued*)

TABLE IV *(Continued)*

Temperatures at Which Melt Has Same Refractive Indices
as Glass Standard 1.6598

Temperature, °C	$\Delta n/\Delta T \times 10^4$	Code number	Temperature. °C	$\Delta n/\Delta T \times 10^4$	Code number
63–64	—	56	155–158	5.3	378
91	5.3	123	167–168	5.0	674
98	4.1	311	175–177	4.9	405
98–99	4.4	514	176	5.2	811
99	4.5	321	182–185	—	818
105–106	5.0	345	184–188	—	906
119–121	4.9	141	188–192	—	837
123–124	5.0	373	194–195	4.6	853
138–142	—	559	217	—	902
143	4.0	502	224–226	4.9	751
152–153	6.9	453	224–226	4.7	920
153–155	4.6	617			

Compounds with Refractive Indices between 1.6598 and 1.6715
at Their Melting Points

820   922   1044

Temperatures at Which Melt Has Same Refractive Indices
as Glass Standard 1.6715

135–136	6.9	453	197–200	4.7	920
149	—	376	200–202	4.9	751
151–152	4.9	405			

Temperatures at Which Melt Has Same Refractive Indices
as Glass Standard 1.6877

76–80	—	163	188–199	—	479
170–172	—	575	198–200	—	760
175–178	—	633	Ca 200	—	425

Compounds with Refractive Indices Greater than 1.6877
at Their Melting Points

244   245   684   734   813   827   878

TABLE IV (*Concluded*)

Compounds that Decompose Badly at Their Melting Points

310	636	709	817	898	1007	1065
385	638	719	831	950	1008	1068
400	647	741	842	977	1014	1072
468	677	744	845	978	1046	1078
477	678	758	856	981	1050	
585	680	765	857	990	1053	
599	697	780	879	999	1062	
614	699	793	886	1006	1063	

Compounds that Sublime Completely at Their Melting Points

881   1029

INDEX

Absorption purification, 118
Accessories for fusion methods, 15
Acenaphthene (94°C; 288)*
 -acetamide, 174
 -azobenzene, 166
 -azobenzene-benzil, 166
 -benzil, 177
 -TNF, 109
Acetaldehyde-2,4-dinitrophenylhydra-
 zone (165°C; 725), 94
Acetamide (80°C; 229)
 -acenaphthene, 174
 -benzil, 153
Acetanilide (115°C; 415)
 -benzil, 166, 179
 -benzil-dinitrophenol, 179
 crystal front, 67
 -2,4-dinitrophenol, 180
 eutectic melting points, 112
 -phloroglucinol, 112
 polymorphism, 72
 refractive index of the melt, 58
 solubility of air in melt, 73
Acet-p-bromoanilide
 -propion-p-bromoanilide, 94, 129,
 130
Acetylsalicylic acid (130–136°C; 551)
 crystal front, 66
 decomposition, 111
Acridine (110°C; 378)
 -TNF, 109
Addition compounds, 159
 composition diagram, 144
 eutectics observed, 111, 148
 TNF-aromatics, 105
Adipic acid (152°C; 643)
 -anthranilic acid, 155
 crystal habit, effect of succinic acid
 on, 126
Adsorption sublimation, 120
β-Alanine, 189

Alypine hydrochloride (170°C; 743)
 -narcotine hydrochloride, 132
Amatol
 areal analysis, 124
 composition diagram, 144
p-Aminoazobenzene (125°C; 479)
 -TNF, 106, 109
Aminoguanidine bicarbonate, 189
3-Aminoquinoline
 -TNF, 109
Ammonium nitrate
 polymorphism, 51, 71, 138, 139
 shrinkage cracks, 73, 74
 -TNT, 124, 144
Ammonium picrate
 anomalous polarization colors, 78
 dispersion of the optic axes, 91
 pleochroism, 73
 polymorphism, 101, 139
Analysis of mixtures, 123
 areal, 124
 counting, 125
 critical solution temperature, 61
 crystal habit change, 126
 crystallization velocity, 126
 freezing point depression, 129
 refractive index of the melt, 130
 solid solutions, 94, 126
Anesthesine
 -TNT, 178
Aniline-phenol, 62
Annealing of crystals, 72, 192
Anomalous polarization colors, 77, 79,
 83–94
Anthracene (215°C; 1012)
 -2,4-dinitrophenol, 178
 supercooling, 66
 -TNF, 109
 2,4,6-trinitrotoluene, 153
Anthranilic acid (145°C; 592)

* For greater convenience the melting point and code number are given for
all compounds covered in the Identification Tables, Chapter V.